Envision

Envision
A history
of the
GE healthcare
business
1893–2008

Leon Janssen and Gene Medford

Copyright © 2009 by Meadow Brook Farm
Publishing LLC

First Edition
2009

Meadow Brook Farm Publishing LLC, Waukesha, Wisconsin

Publisher Leon P. Janssen
Editor Gene Medford
Editorial Support Karen A. Kuhla Ph.D.
Designer Jena Sher
Project Advisor Doug Frohmader
Project Advisor–GE Brian S. Johnson
Image Archive Technical Advisor John C. Jacobson
Printer The Fox Company

Printed in the United States of America

Mixed Sources
Product group from well-managed
forests, controlled sources and
recycled wood or fibre
www.fsc.org Cert no. SW-COC-002680
© 1996 Forest Stewardship Council

ISBN: 978-0-9822431-2-1

MEADOW BROOK FARM PUBLISHING LLC

Dedication

This work is dedicated to the men and women of General Electric through the years who committed their professional lives to improving the health of people around the world.

It is dedicated to those whose passion, enthusiasm, intellect, and integrity made working in the business a privilege.

It is dedicated to those inspirational leaders who brought out the best in us and enabled us to become world leaders.

It is dedicated to the CEOs who brought their abundant skills and special leadership styles that served the unique needs of their eras.

Finally, it is dedicated to the memory of a valued colleague, mentor, and friend, Robert L. Stocking (1934–2004).

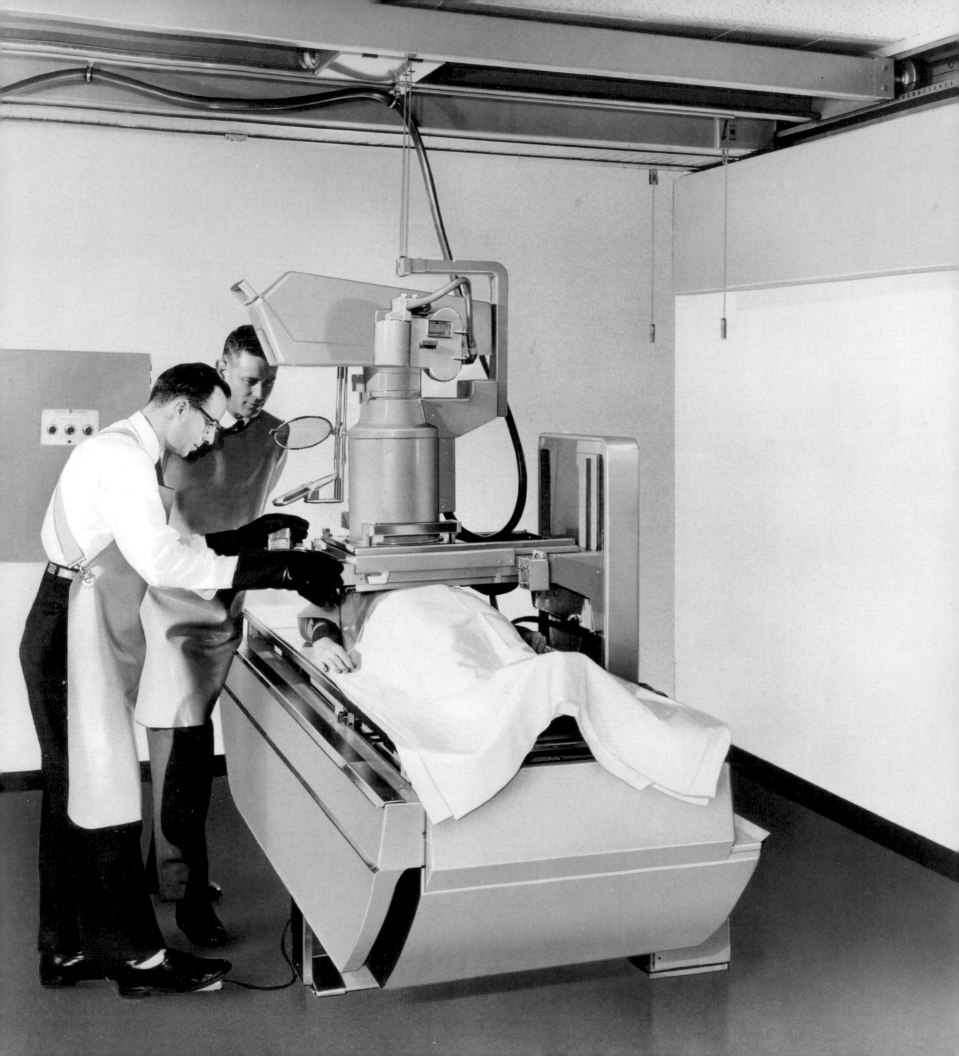

Contents

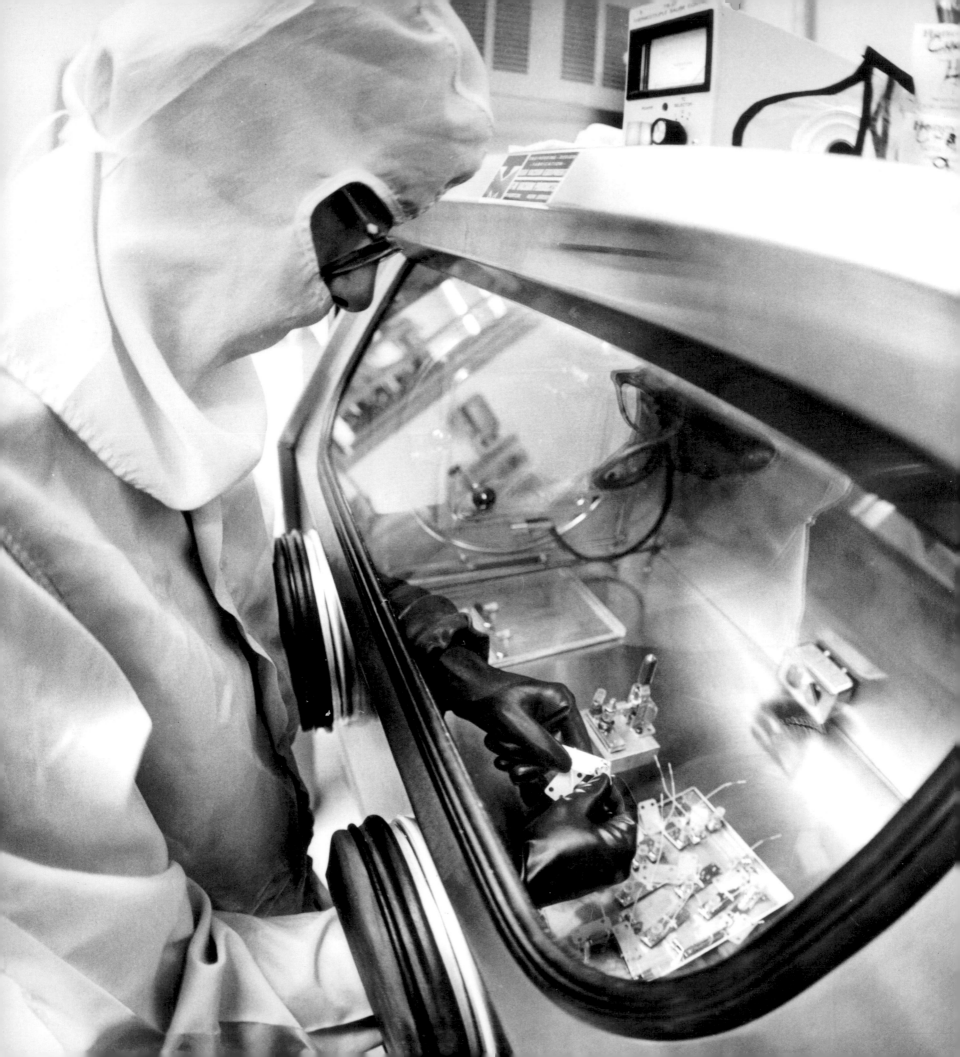

Foreword

Our long tenure at GE has given us great respect for the enormous accomplishments of dedicated GE individuals and teams around the world over GE's long history. We believed there were stories of many of these individuals and teams that needed to be told, and when we discussed the need, we said to each other "if not us, then who?" That launched us into the project late in 2007. Early on we decided to treat the full 100 plus year history and include many of the businesses that eventually became part of GE Healthcare. We also decided to build the story around the eras of each of the CEOs. The early CEOs were grouped into two eras called the "The Early Years" and "The Middle Years." Starting with Jim "Walt" Nelson, each CEO's era is treated individually and has had the CEO's personal engagement in creating the story of his era. Jim "Walt" Nelson was an enthusiastic contributor to the book. Unfortunately, while he saw and approved the final draft of the Nelson Era section, he passed away in March 2009 in Milwaukee and, thus, was unable to see the final work.

For each era we started with the perspective of the CEO. We asked them to identify the top five defining events in their era and the people who most impacted those events. We then went to the individuals identified by the CEO to learn more of the story. While this approach helped us focus on the most important events as viewed by each CEO, it also necessarily excluded many important events, contributions, and people.

Common across the imaginative inventors and business leaders throughout the years was the capacity to "envision". It has been the capacity to envision a technology development that would dramatically change how GE customers carried out their missions, or the capacity to envision a business strategy that would enable GE to serve more customers around the world. Today, these dedicated GE people are envisioning ways to reduce healthcare costs and improve quality while increasing access with lower cost products.

It is entitled "Envision–A history of the GE healthcare business." It is called "a" history rather than "the" history because we fully recognize this work is neither comprehensive nor the definitive view. It is our hope that this work will inspire others to record their perspectives on this special business and its people.

While significant effort has been given to ensuring that we have the facts and names right, we apologize for any errors that may have crept into this work.

Leon Janssen   Gene Medford

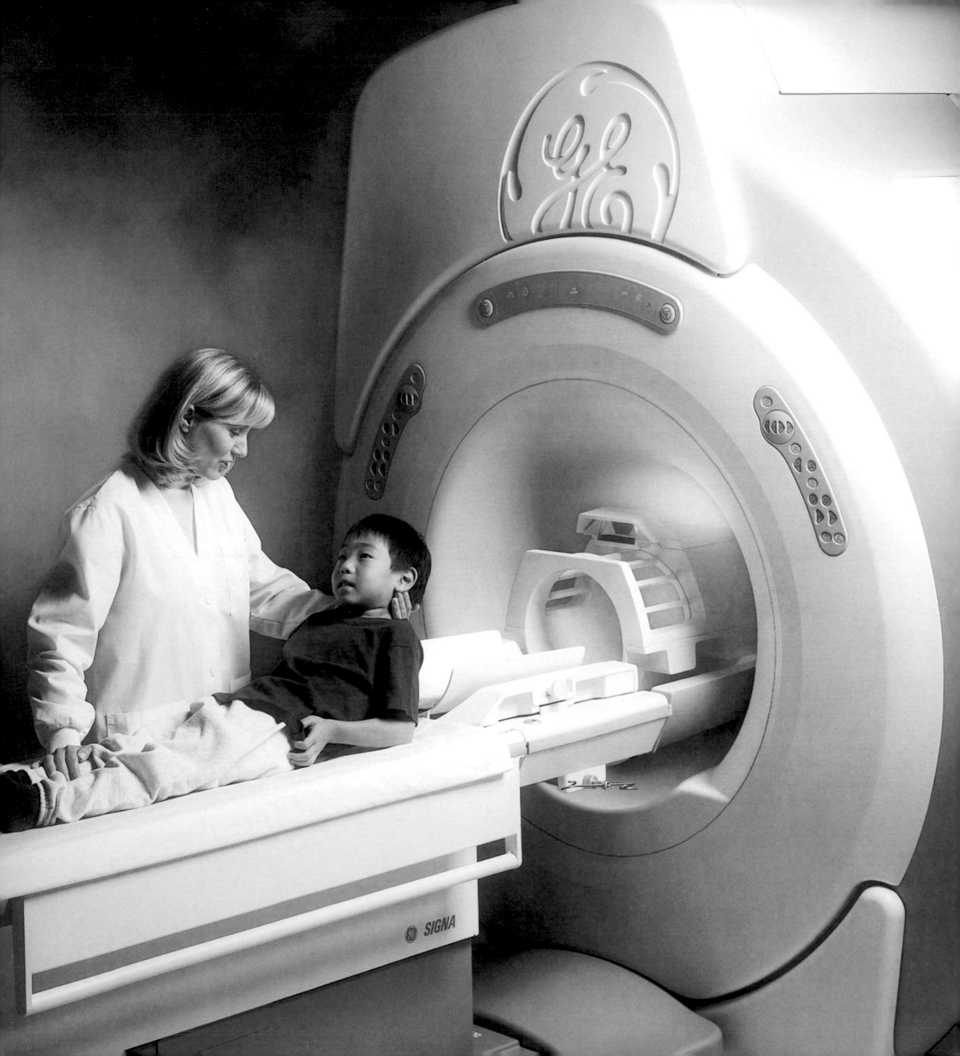

Acknowledgments

We are grateful to Jeff Immelt, who lent his considerable influence in opening doors and memories to our research; to Joe Hogan, with whose support this effort was launched; to Brian Johnson, GE Healthcare's Global Marketing Communications manager, who eased access to important sources of information and helped us achieve the appropriate "GE look"; to Karen Kuhla, Leadership Development Program Manager at the John F. Welch Leadership Centre, who graciously volunteered her amazing proofreading and editorial skills; and to Communicor Inc. for their generous assistance in providing access to GE product image archives.

Our sincere thanks also to the many people, both within General Electric and without, who contributed materially to telling the story of GE's healthcare business. Without their active interest and help, this effort would have been the poorer. Many of them are mentioned below.

Finally, we appreciate the scores of other people who assisted our efforts in small but important ways. Though your names may not be included, you deserve to share in the credit, too.

Sholom Ackelsberg
Marie-Claire Andrieu-Breitwiller
Mike Barber
Agnes Barrett
Geraldine Barry
Kathleen Beebe
Mark Bellamy
Bill Berezowitz
Tom Bird
Morry Blumenfeld
Paul Bottomley
Ginny Bowen
Mike Brickey
Patricia Brigman
Bill Buchholtz
Jean-Yves Burel
Sir Wiliam Castell
Ram Charan
Art Chen
Chih Chen
Caroline Claie
John Clifford
Mike Cudahy
Jim Del Mauro
Ken Denison
Richard di Benedetto
Burt Drayer
Brian Duchinsky
Tom Dunham
Lonnie Edelheit
Philip Farrell
Bruce Fetter
Bob Filip
Jim Fitzgerald
Steve Flax
Stan Fox
Tommy Frist Jr.
Rick Frowein
Yoshiaki Fujimori
Sam Gambhir
Reinaldo Garcia

Gary Glazer
Art Glenn
Gary Glover
Charlene Grabowski
Tom Grist
Angela Grundey
Haiyan Ma
Buzz Hardy
Bill Hawes
John Heinrich
Barbara Herrmann
Dan Hoffman
Hedi Hricak
Joan Hunt
Serge Huot
Omar Ishrak
Bob Jarr
Mike Jones
Patti Kaeding
Mac Kaiser
John Kese
Bob King
Jan Kloeffler
Y. Kukita
Roxanne Kupfer
Esa Kupiainen
Al LeBlang
Julia Lorenc
Jean-Michel Malbrancq
Gören Malm
Alex Margulis
Joe Marion
Mary Ellen Maroszek
Scott Mathews
Pete McCabe
Dee Mellor
Nancy Miller
Paul Mirabella
Vincenzo Morelli
Keith Morgan
Bob Mueller

Rob Newman
Ron O'Keefe
Marc Onetto
Ted Opie
Phil Peck
Jeff Peiffer
Marc Pelon
Phyllis Piano
Jane Polin
Jim Potchen
Carl Ravin
Katri Reijonen
Nobuko Schlough
Jim Schumacher
Jeffrey Schwab
Bob Senzig
Rich Stevens
Claire Stocking
Gary Strong
Takashi Sugiyama
Norio Tanaka
Mona Theobald
Jean-Lynne Thompson
Noel Tichy
John Truscott
Mark Vachon
Ed Voboril
Kobi Vortman
Pete Walchli
Vishal Wanchoo
Don White
Alan Williams
Shaoija Xiong
Keiki Yamaguchi
Chrystal Ye
Orlin Yenerich
Bill Zabriskie

The Early Years
1893-1930

top
Professor Roentgen's laboratory
at the University of Würzburg.

bottom, left to right
Exterior view of Roentgen's laboratory with plaque commemorating
his discovery.

A Crookes gas tube similar to the
one used by Professor Roentgen.

Professor Wilhelm Conrad Roentgen,
discoverer of the x-ray.

The discovery of x-rays in 1895 was as important a contribution to modern medicine as anesthesia and antibiotics. It is impossible to imagine health care today without the x-ray image, the fluoro screen, the mammography scanner, even those contemporary technologies that took their imaging cues from the loyal Radiographic & Fluoroscopic machine—such as ultrasound, nuclear medicine, computed tomography, magnetic resonance, positron emission tomography, and so on. However the x-ray didn't earn its key role without effort . . . and some controversy.

When Wilhelm Conrad Roentgen decided to conduct some experiments in his modest laboratory at the University of Würzberg in Bavaria, he had no reason to expect a life altering result. A physics professor, Dr. Roentgen was using a so-called Hittorf-Crookes gas tube to study cathode rays. He carefully covered the tube with black paper so no light could escape and connected it to a high-voltage generating coil. By chance, a barium-platinocyanate screen was lying on the table where the apparatus was positioned. After darkening the room, he sent a current through the Hittorf-Crookes tube. To his complete surprise, the cardboard screen began to glow, though there was no visible light either leaking into the room or from the tube. He recognized an unknown phenomenon at play. A classic scientist, he decided to investigate.

Dr. Roentgen turned the Hittorf-Crookes tube on and off; the screen responded. He placed a heavy book between the tube and the screen; still the glow appeared. He shielded the screen with his hand; the glow persisted. As one writer later described the event, "The flash of the fluorescent cardboard had to be answered with a flash of genius, and the rest was merely a matter of detail."

The date was November 8, 1895, and in that brief instant, Wilhelm Conrad Roentgen had opened an entirely new field of scientific exploration to both serious researchers and charlatans. Before the century was out, medicine would recognize the x-ray as a vital new weapon in improving the health and welfare of mankind.

Footsteps of Pioneers

Wilhelm Conrad Roentgen was born in Lennep, Germany, on March 27, 1845 and died in Munich, Bavaria, on February 10, 1923. Surprisingly, he did not enjoy an auspicious educational career, having been expelled from high school in Holland, then failing his college entrance exams. Nonetheless, he was permitted to audit classes at the University of Utrecht for 2 years without credit, then won admission to the University of Zürich (Switzerland). Though he was never recognized as an outstanding scholar, he graduated in engineering and received his Ph.D. in physics at age 24 in 1869. He worked his way up the academic ladder at a series of minor posts at smaller German universities until being invited in 1888, at age 43, to head the University of Würzburg's new Physics Institute. In 1901, he won the Nobel Prize in physics.

In 1895, President Grover Cleveland had one of those "newfangled contraptions"—the telephone—installed for the first time in the White House. Electric illumination had replaced gaslights on the streets of New York City, Chicago, Boston, and several European cities. A thriving young company called General Electric (GE) had just completed the first major conversion of a steam railroad to electricity on the Baltimore & Ohio's New York City–Washington line. The GE-equipped Niagara Falls Power Station No. 1 had just opened as a low cost, reliable source of electricity.

Though the age of electricity had clearly arrived even before Dr. Roentgen conducted his famous experiment, he recognized that nothing like this mysterious ray, which he named after the mathematical symbol "X" for the unknown quantity, had ever been described in the scientific literature. He was intrigued, because he appeared to have discovered a phenomenon that had no rational explanation. To be certain he could duplicate these findings, he experimented another 7 weeks before confidently announcing his results to an astonished world on December 28, 1895.

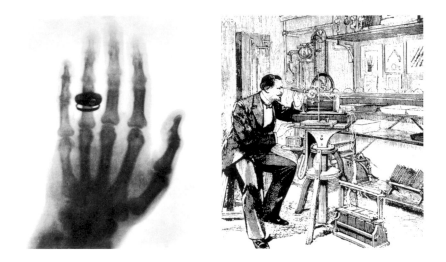

Almost immediately after the announcement, hysterical front-page headlines spread the news of the wonder rays. A London firm capitalized on the ignorance of the public by advertising "X-ray proof" underclothing. An American legislator reacted to the sensational news by introducing a law to bar the use of x-rays in opera glasses.

Fabulous powers were attributed to this invisible light by headline-hunting reporters. One conjectured on the possibility of photographing the soul. Another claimed the mystery ray was being used to teach medical students anatomy by "reflecting anatomic diagrams directly into their minds." Pictures of the bones inside a living human body seized the fancy of the public and were soon on display in almost every bookshop and drugstore. Even Thomas A. Edison, the famous American experimenter and GE founder, made a well-publicized attempt to photograph the brain.

As Phillipp Lenard, a contemporary and rival of Roentgen's declared, "Almost everywhere a great hubbub had broken out over Roentgen's discovery."

It was all utter nonsense, of course, but it sounded plausible to a generation immersed in the Industrial Revolution and steeped in the speculative fiction of H. G. Wells and Jules Verne.

Dr. Roentgen gave his first and only formal lecture on the x-ray before the Würzberg Physical Medical Society on January 23, 1896. During the presentation, he invited a colleague, anatomist Geheimer Rat Prof. Albert von Koellilker, to allow his hand to be photographed by x-rays, then displayed this picture before the group. Von Koelliker declared these new rays should henceforth be called "Roentgen Rays."

Birth of an industry

The speed with which the x-ray found its role in medical imaging and therapy is astonishing. Literally within weeks of Roentgen's announcement, entrepreneurs around Europe and across the United States were already offering devices for both x-ray imaging and treatment. The first advertisement for x-ray equipment appeared in a Viennese newspaper in late January 1896. And the "Wizard of Menlo Park," Thomas Edison, claimed to have reproduced Roentgen's apparatus within 24 hours of receiving word of the discovery.

Of particular interest was an article that appeared in the August 22, 1896 issue of *Electrical World,* one of the leading technical journals of the day:

> Investigators and others practically interested in Roentgen-ray work will without doubt be greatly interested in noting the appearance of the General Electric Company as manufacturer of all kinds of Roentgen-ray apparatus. The name of this concern is a guarantee of the completeness and efficiency of any apparatus that it may put out.

That endorsement from the 19th century remains just as true today in the 21st century.

Private x-ray offices had opened as early as February 1896. Of course, this was at a time when anyone with a functional x-ray apparatus was considered a legitimate practitioner. Such rapid dispersion was, in part, driven by Dr. Roentgen's refusal to patent any aspect of his discovery and his adamant rejection of all proposals for commercial cooperation. Rather, he chose to give his discovery freely to the benefit of mankind.

top left
An early x-ray image believed to be of Mrs. Roentgen's hand.

top right
Professor Roentgen in his laboratory at the University of Würzburg.

middle
This statue of Roentgen at Berlin's Potsdamer Bridge was melted down for its metal during World War II.

bottom
An early x-ray laboratory. The hand-cranked coil powered the gas tube.

One of those early entrants was a small firm in Chicago called Victor Electric Company, which became the principal predecessor firm to today's GE Healthcare.

Two ambitious young men, C. F. (Charles Francis) Samms and J. B. (Julius Benjamin) Wantz, were at work in the basement shop of the Wantz home at 887 Washington Street in early 1895, when they were faced with a difficult decision. Should they dismantle the nearby coal bin or move their growing electric shop to a second floor bedroom? The two had begun working together in 1893, when Samms, who was in the electric wiring and repair business, was faced with the challenge of hooking a "dental device" to an electric motor. He called on Wantz, a mechanic with an interest in electromechanical gadgets, to help, and the two decided to go into businesses developing similar equipment for dentists. Executive offices were under Samms' hat. He was the sales department; Wantz constituted the factory staff.

Lessons in Leadership

Charles Francis Samms (1868–1934) co-founded Victor Electric Company in 1895 and led the company as president through its evolution into Victor X-Ray Corporation in 1915 and, following several merger agreements, General Electric X-Ray Corporation in 1930. He served as president until his retirement in 1933 and was chairman of the board at the time of his death on Sept. 7, 1934. He was survived by his widow, Adela, a daughter, Gladys and three sons, Louis, Larry and Frank.

Samms and Wantz were an extremely effective pair even from the beginning. First, they decided to incorporate their new business as the Victor Electric Company in October 1895. Next, their progress had been so swift they decided to neither dismantle the coal bin nor move into a bedroom. Rather, they rented two rooms—300 square feet—in a loft at 218 Washington Street and hired six men to help them operate their new shop. Their product line also expanded into light brackets, therapy lamps, sterilizers, air compressors, dental lathes, bone surgery engines, eye magnets, illuminators, massage apparatus, vibrators, electrodes, and even beer pump motors.

Lessons in Leadership

Julius Benjamin Wantz (1874–1952) was known as the "grand old man of x-ray," both for the 53 years he devoted to Victor and GE X-Ray and over 50 patents he held in the x-ray and electro-medical fields. Around 1890, Wantz gave up a $3.00 a week job to take one with Chicago's Knapp Electric Company at $2.50 a week in order to work with electro-medical gadgets. Within a year, at age 18, he was head of the firm's experimental department. Wantz was honored in 1940 as one of 59 "modern pioneers" at a celebration of the 105th anniversary of the U.S. patent system. Later, he was one of nine GE engineers selected from among the nation's leading inventors to join the National

top to bottom, left to right

C. F. Samms, co-founder and President of Victor Electric, Victor X-Ray, and GE X-Ray Corp. He retired in 1933.

J. B. Wantz (1939 photo), co-founder of Victor Electric Company and, for 53 years, the technical and engineering genius behind Victor X-Ray and GE X-Ray Corp.

Static x-ray generator.

Original model of the Wantz high-frequency apparatus to power x-ray tubes.

Association of Manufacturers' Hall of Fame. His brother and son also worked for the business, the latter retiring in the mid-1960s as GE X-Ray's exhibits manager.

So Victor Electric was well positioned to respond when news of Roentgen's discovery came to their attention. As 1896 went by, Victor Electric began producing electric motors to power static therapeutic and x-ray machines. That same year, the company also tripled its space by shifting to new headquarters. This was followed by several additional moves by 1899, eventually landing them in a spacious new shop at 418 Dearborn Street.

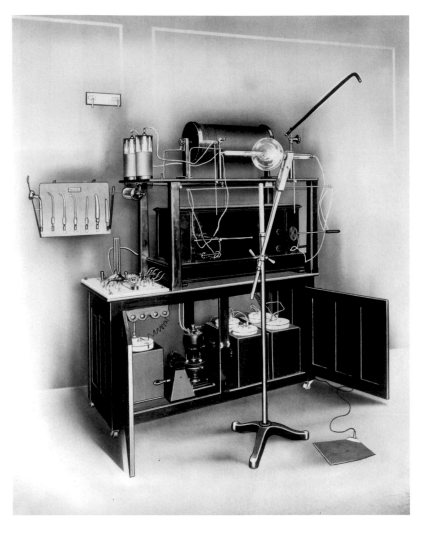

top to bottom
Scheidel-Western hi-rad induction coil.

William David Coolidge

opposite
Dr. Coolidge explains his process for producing ductile tungsten to the famed inventor and GE founder, Thomas Edison.

Meanwhile, in Paris, also in 1896, a young engineer by the name of Georges Gaiffe had built a generator that could produce x-rays from a gas tube. He had succeeded his father, Adolph, just a few years before in running the family's optics and mechanics business. Like so many others, he was intrigued by the sensational new ray and decided to make his fortune in this new field.

In fact, new competitors were springing up on all sides. Swett & Lewis, an x-ray device manufacturer, purchased the gas tube business of rival, Frye. Herman Lemp developed an "automatic wave selector" (mechanical high-voltage rectifier) at GE's Lynn (Massachusetts) Laboratory, Western X-ray Coil Company was organized in 1901, Macalaster & Wiggin purchased the x-ray tube business of Swett & Lewis in 1902, and Radio Electric Company (later called Snook-Roentgen Manufacturing Company) was incorporated in 1903. General Electric got deeper into the game during this period by starting to manufacture gas tubes at a small factory in Cambridge, Massachusetts. Not to be outdone, Victor Electric acquired two huge floors of new space at 55–61 Market Street in 1903 and moved its operations there.

As more and more companies crowded into the competitive fray (for example, W. Scheidel Coil Company in 1905 and Macalaster-Wiggin Company in 1906), it was inevitable the x-ray industry would have to consolidate eventually. That process first became apparent in 1907, when Scheidel absorbed Western to become Scheidel-Western X-ray Coil Company. But it still took almost 10 more years for the largest mergers to be completed. More on that in a moment.

Triumph in the lab

In the annals of x-ray lore, no achievement could ever match Dr. Roentgen's initial discovery, of course. The one that came the closest occurred in 1908 at GE's new (1900) Research Laboratory in Schenectady, New York, when a brilliant young research scientist named William D. Coolidge discovered the method for making tungsten, a notoriously brittle metal, ductile. Two more years were to pass before he and his colleagues found a practical method for producing ductile tungsten in quantity. This development did more to capture the elusive x-ray for the service of mankind than probably any other single technical advance in the long history of the industry. It had enormous consequences for the development and diffusion of reliable, economical incandescent lighting, as well.

Why is ductile tungsten so important? And so hard to achieve?

First, as the *Encyclopedia Britannica* enthuses, tungsten excels all other metals, because it has the highest melting point, the greatest tensile strength, the lowest coefficient of expansion, and can be drawn into the finest wire. Unfortunately, tungsten in its basic form is also extremely brittle and impractical to use. What Dr. Coolidge did was find a method of making tungsten ductile so scientists and engineers could more readily explore the full range of its possible applications.

As Herman A. Liebhafsky explained in his 1974 eponymous tribute to Dr. Coolidge, "Making tungsten ductile is not easy even today, and it is still done by the complex Coolidge process essentially unchanged." That process involves a complicated series of steps to work the tungsten into smaller and smaller wire, slowly changing its microstructure to yield a ductile material of tremendous tensile strength and superior fineness.

By the time Dr. Coolidge had completed his quest for ductile tungsten, the GE Research Laboratory had invested approximately $116,000 in the project—a mere trifle today but an enormous sum then. The first major application of ductile tungsten was as filament wire in incandescent light bulbs. It provided a long-lasting and inexpensive solution (one pound of tungsten drawn into a wire 8.5 miles long providing filaments for 23,000 60-watt lamps) that helped make electrical lighting an economical option for tens of thousands, then tens and hundreds of millions, around the world. In fact, it

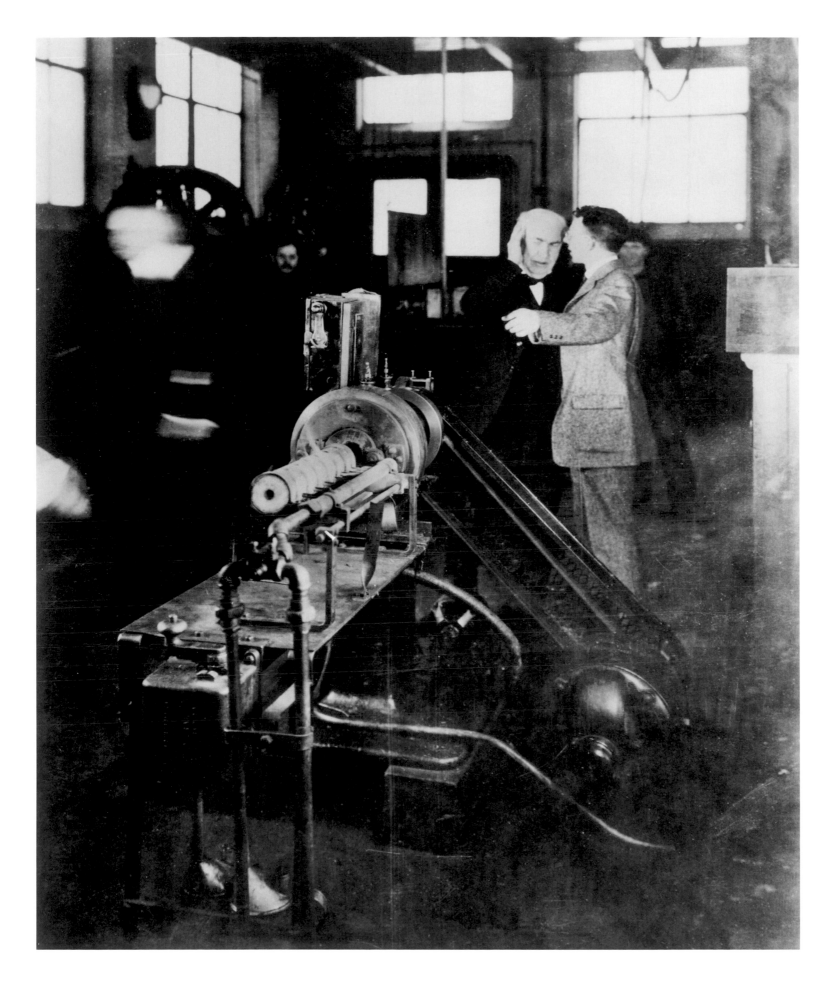

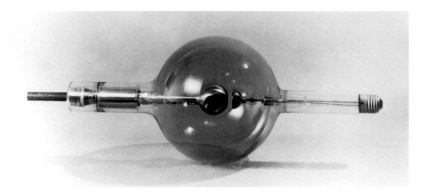

was estimated at the time that efficient, reliable ductile tungsten filaments were producing $200 million in annual aggregate savings in the cost of electric illumination.

Dr. Coolidge's second signal achievement during his distinguished career is of greater interest here, though it, too, sprang directly from his ductile tungsten success.

The summer after Roentgen announced his discovery, Coolidge was at home in rural Massachusetts, having just graduated from Massachusetts Institute of Technology as an electrical engineer. While waiting to enter the University of Leipzig that autumn, he amused himself by building a large electrostatic machine to produce high voltages for the generation of x-rays. In fact, he later sold the device to a local doctor for x-ray work.

Footsteps of Pioneers

William David Coolidge was born in Hudson, Massachusetts, October 23, 1873, and died in Schenectady, New York, February 3, 1975. His scholastic record and mechanical and electrical skills won him a state scholarship to attend Massachusetts Institute of Technology (then called Boston Tech), where he graduated as an electrical engineer in 1896. With his growing interest in science and research, he obtained a grant to study at the University of Leipzig (Germany), where he received his Ph.D. summa cum laude in 1899 (and had occasion to actually talk with Prof. Roentgen). Following several years as a physics teacher and physical chemist at MIT, he was persuaded to join the GE Research Laboratory. Among his many awards, he holds the Rumford Medal of the American Academy of Arts and Science, the Gold Medal of the American College of Radiology, and the Hughes Medal of the Royal Society of London. He was the first person elected in his lifetime to the National Inventor's Hall of Fame.

Coolidge never forgot this early interest in the x-ray. So when he had completed his work on ductile tungsten, his thoughts turned to what role this newly tamed metal might play in helping tame this elusive ray. With the encouragement of Dr. Willis R. Whitney, the first director of the GE Research Laboratory, he turned his attention toward solving this latest puzzle.

Taming the gas tube

The early gas tubes used to produce x-rays, including those manufactured by GE, were filled with gas to provide a source for the positive ions that bombarded the cathode and generated electrons which, in turn, bombarded the anode to release x-rays. Because of this gas, these tubes were highly erratic and difficult to use, even in the hands of experts. One moment they would operate perfectly; the next, not at all.

Coolidge and his GE colleague, Irving Langmuir, soon found it was possible to get controllable electron emission from a hot tungsten filament in a complete vacuum. So Coolidge immediately installed a heated tungsten filament in an x-ray tube, along with a tungsten disk anode. After evacuating all gas from the tube, he found he had created the first completely stable and controllable x-ray producer. To change the power and intensity of the x-ray beam was a simple matter of adjusting the tube voltage and filament temperature.

GE patented the "Coolidge" hot cathode, high vacuum x-ray tube in 1913, forever supplanting the art of the radiographer with the science of the radiologist.

Dr. Coolidge contributed many other x-ray advances, including the hooded anode x-ray tube (1915), a self-rectifying x-ray tube (1917), a portable x-ray unit tube (1918), a shockproof dental x-ray unit (1919), and many more. He succeeded Dr. Whitney as GE's Director of Research in 1932 and served in this prestigious position until January 1, 1945, when the successful conclusion of World War II could be anticipated.

Coolidge's Research Laboratory colleagues were also active in this growing field.

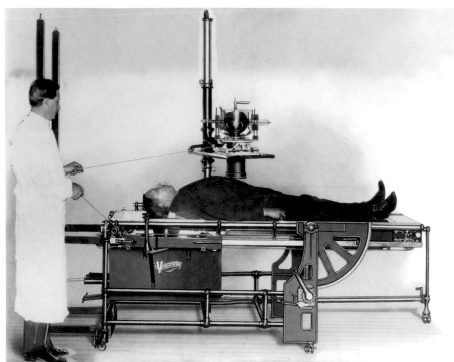

In 1914 alone, for example, Saul Dushman developed a hot-cathode, high-voltage valve tube (kenotron), and Elihu Thomson demonstrated a rotating anode x-ray tube. The level of commitment and success that Dr. Coolidge and his colleagues brought to medical technology research would have profound consequences for General Electric and its customers in future years.

Victor marches on

Even while GE was earning a commanding position in the market for x-ray imaging and therapy tubes, Victor Electric was making similar strides in the x-ray apparatus market. In 1911, Victor transferred its factory to a larger facility at Jackson Boulevard & Robey Street (now Damen Avenue), which was to remain its home location for the next 35 years. Then, 5 years later, Victor Electric, Scheidel-Western, Snook, and Maca laster-Wiggin combined in a blockbuster merger to form the Victor Electric Corporation. C. F. Samms was elected president of the new company, which was capitalized for $2.5 million.

Similar business machinations were afoot in Paris, where G. Gaiffe Cie was succeeded by Gallot & Cie. Just 5 years later, in 1919, H. Pilon Cie merged with Gallot & Cie to form Gaiffe Gallot & Pilon, one of the leading French x-ray equipment producers of the era.

General Electric officials certainly were impressed by what they saw going on in Chicago. So, in 1920, they acquired a substantial interest in Victor Electric, which immediately reincorporated as the Victor X-Ray Corporation. At the same time, GE named Victor X-Ray the sole distributor of the Coolidge x-ray tube in the U.S. and ceased all production of gas tubes at its plant in Cambridge, Massachusetts.

Samms and Wantz retained their previous positions of president and vice president, respectively, while W. S. Kendrick, who had been associated with Coolidge x-ray tube sales through the GE Special Products Section, became Victor X-Ray's new vice president in charge of sales.

Things also were astir in the Far East that would eventually have major consequences in the medical imaging marketplace. In 1920, Yokogawa Electric Works was founded in Japan.

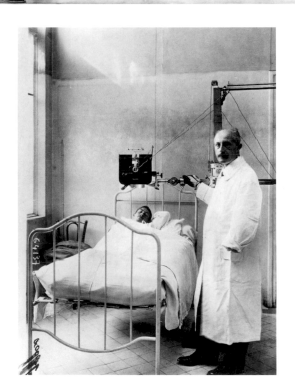

opposite, left
Experimental Coolidge "hot cathode" x-ray tube from about 1912, one of the first to use a tungsten target.

The "Coolidge tube" (1913) revolutionized radiography.

opposite, right
Dr. Coolidge adjusts the tube on his portable x-ray unit (1918).

top, left to right
Charles Proteus Steinmetz (1865–1923) was one of the founding geniuses behind GE's Research Lab. He was an early researcher into the mathematics of alternating current and experimented with ultra-high voltage phenomena.

The Model 7 table was a best-seller for Victor X-Ray.

bottom
During WWI, Dr. Vaillant, a radiologist at Lariboisiere Hospital in Paris, positions a bedside x-ray unit to image the pelvis of a wounded soldier.

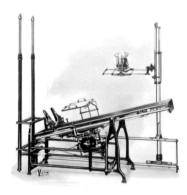

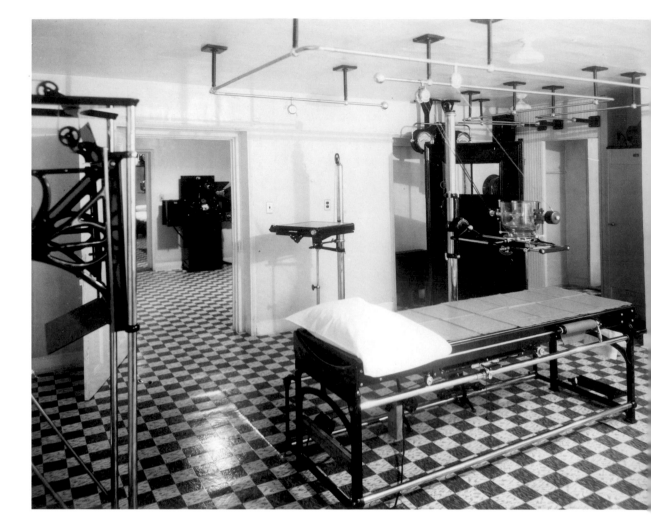

The following year, recognizing that its network of dealers could not always maintain the high level of technical service expertise required by more powerful and more complex x-ray equipment, Victor X-Ray established one of the first direct, factory-operated field sales and service organizations in the industry. That was the same year a Victor 200-kVp x-ray machine was installed at the Watertown (New York) Arsenal for pioneering industrial x-ray purposes. In 1924, GE discontinued the manufacture of Coolidge x-ray tubes in Schenectady and transferred production to the Victor X-Ray plant in Chicago.

opposite, left to right, top to bottom
The Victor Model 9 Table with tubestand.

Victor equipped rad room at Roper Hospital, Charleston, South Carolina.

Victor x-ray room at Alexian Brothers Hospital, St. Louis (1925).

Not all was business at Victor X-Ray. The New York office held an elegant dinner-dance at the McAlpin Hotel on February 20, 1922.

left to right, top to bottom
This site adjoining the Victor X-Ray factory in Chicago was selected for the 1925 addition.

Following demolition of the old buildings, real steam shovels began the excavation.

As late summer approached, the new Victor X-Ray factory was rapidly taking shape. The original factory is in the background.

By November 1925, moving-in day was almost at hand. All that was lacking was the rooftop water tank.

Recognizing a good thing when they saw it, GE decided it would be a good idea to make Victor X-Ray a full member of the team. So, on July 28, 1926, a deal was closed making Victor a wholly owned affiliate company. However, the cast of characters remained unchanged with C. F. Samms continuing as president, W. S. Kendrick as vice president, J. B. Wantz as vice president and production manager, R. L. Frederick as treasurer, and F. E. Scheven as production superintendent. From that moment on, Victor and GE's fates were inextricably linked.

Chicago's Reputation As A Tough Town *gained another colorful chapter when, on a Friday afternoon in late November 1926, three armed bandits burst into the lobby of Victor X-Ray's Robey St. factory. In front of the crowd of employees queuing up for their weekly pay, the crooks grabbed a portion of the payroll and escaped in a waiting auto. Fortunately, the box they stole contained only a very small portion of the total payroll. Nonetheless, Victor had learned its lesson and, thereafter, paid its employees by check.*

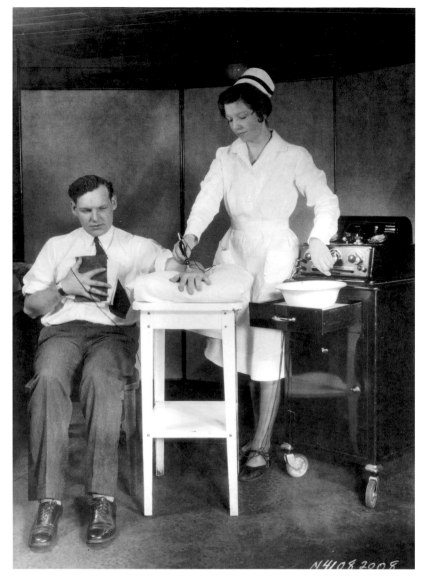

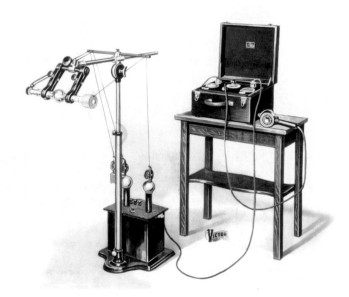

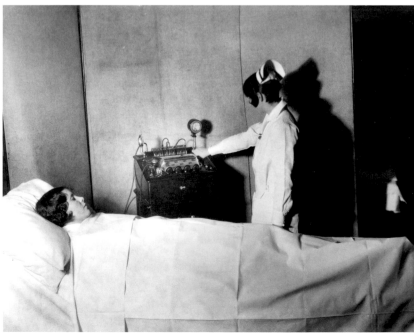

top, left to right
Victor office portable x-ray unit (1927).

Wantz multiwave generator used to test for degenerative ionization due to ulcers, coagulation, etc. (1928).

bottom, left to right
Snook (Victor) transformer and rectifier.

Diathermy devices, such as this variable-frequency unit being used to treat a pneumonia patient, were a staple in Victor's product catalog.

Technological innovation continued apace. J. J. Grobe of Victor X-Ray patented an over/under-table tube mount in 1926, a 1-mEv therapy tube for deep tumor radiation therapy appeared in 1928, and J. B. Wantz, himself, got credit for an oil-immersed x-ray unit in 1929.

A new die is cast

Finally, on January 18, 1930, the courtly dance between General Electric and Victor X-Ray culminated in the creation of the General Electric X-Ray Corporation, one of the most respected names in the industry for more than two decades until it, too, yielded to yet another organizational rechristening.

SOME ACTUAL MUD THROWING HERE

F. C. Slemmer of the St. Louis Organization sends in the accompanying picture with the following comments:

"Am sending this as my official road report

for northern Missouri, and shows the 'Covered Wagon' at work and at play. I didn't think the old saying about Missouri mud meant anything until now. The road on which the car is parked for the picture is paved."

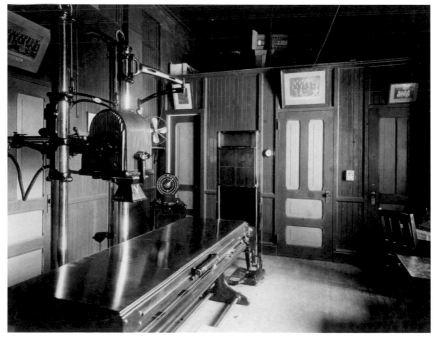

top, left to right
Life has never been easy for the field sales force, as St. Louis salesman F. C. Slemmer's mud-encrusted car attests.

A Victor factory service training class circa 1927.

bottom, left to right
A shipment destined for Perth Amboy, New Jersey leaves the Victor loading dock.

Model A shockproof unit installed at Clinica Herrick, Panama City, Panama. (c. 1930)

Not to be outdone, a major merger also had just been completed in France where Ropiquet-Hozart & Roycourt combined with Gaiffe Gallot & Pilon to create one of the most famous marques in radiology—Compagnie Générale de Radiologie (CGR).

The first three-and-a-half decades of the x-ray had now been written. From the initial discovery to the emergence of the first intimations of the modern imaging industry, the technical tools of x-ray generation and utilization had progressed at a fantastic pace, as had the medical applications of this marvelous ray. Some very bitter lessons had to be learned along the way, of course, but both the medical profession and industry worked hard to control and minimize the very great dangers posed by this powerful tool.

The successes and sacrifices of all these pioneers helped assure the essential role of the x-ray in modern medical practice even to this day.

No. 1

opposite, left
X-ray products weren't Victor's only offerings. Wantz also invented a variety of electromedical devices, such as the Victor Fulguration coil used to treat acute pain.

opposite, right, top to bottom
Among Victor's varied offering was electrocardiographs shown being assembled at the Chicago factory in 1929.

Victor Multiplex Stereoscope allowed two physicians to view images in 3-D simultaneously.

this page
GE's x-ray line also included dental diagnostic gear. The long-lived CDX dental x-ray unit (left) was on display at the New York City sales office in 1929.

The Middle Years

1930-1959

There could hardly have been a less auspicious time to start up a new business organization. When the GE X-Ray Corporation was launched on January 18, 1930, "Black Monday" and "Black Tuesday"—the second and third worst days in the history of the U.S. stock market and, arguably, the most catastrophic—were hardly 3 months in the past.

The previous September and October, the market had lost 40% of its value. By the end of November, investors had seen some $100 billion (in today's value) in assets vanish into thin air. The Dow Jones Industrial Average wouldn't hit bottom until mid-1932 at 40.60, nearly 90% below its September 1929 high of 386.10. As terrible as this debacle had been for investors, bankers, brokers, and businesses, it was what happened in the months and years following Wall Street's crash that had such a disastrous impact upon the American and world economies, "The Great Depression."

In the U.S. and around the globe, orders were canceled, international trade declined, credit dried up, monetary supplies curtailed, factories shuttered, jobs lost, and wages, tax revenues, prices, and profits all plunged.

Surviving in a tough market

GE wasn't immune to these ills, of course. The steps that were necessary to keep the Research Laboratory alive, for example, reflected similar measures instituted throughout the company, including the new GE X-Ray Corporation.

By the spring of 1932, Dr. Whitney had decided to step down as director, in large part due to the stresses and economic storms occasioned by the stock market crash. Dr. Coolidge was selected to replace him in this prestigious position effective November 1, 1932, just days before Franklin D. Roosevelt was elected to the first of his four terms as U.S. president. Among FDR's campaign pledges were promises to institute a 5-day workweek (in order to spread the jobs that were available among more workers), give Federal aid to the unemployed, and let no one starve!

The economic situation was truly that grim.

As GE sales tumbled (they were just one half of their 1930 peak of $396 million by 1935), Dr. Coolidge put the Research Laboratory on a 4-day workweek, slashed expenses by one third, and brought the workforce down to 270 people from the 1929 high of 555. Staff reductions among the professional employees, wherever possible, were made by finding academic positions for the scientists; support people were largely moved to other divisions.

These survival strategies, fully supported by Gerard Swope, GE's president at the time, began paying off as early as late 1933, when Swope urged Coolidge to "recruit a few chemists to begin developing new products." Some important discoveries and great products were to result, such as Flamenol®, a tough insulating polymer for copper wiring.

Similarly tough measures were also needed at the GE X-Ray Corporation, of course. It was in the fortunate position of being able to protect its leadership position even in a declining market, thanks to the patents the company had earned for ductile tungsten and the Coolidge tube. In addition, it had a thriving business in electro-medical products, such as air pumps, galvanic and sinusoidal devices, stereoscopes, centrifuges, bone surgery engines, cautery apparatus, lamps, eye magnets, thermal treatment devices, and many others.

Technological innovation, always the linchpin of GE's business success, was in evidence at the GE X-Ray Corporation even during these dark days. In 1931, 1000-mA diagnostic and 300-kVp therapy tubes were introduced. Thanks to Dr. Coolidge's work on the "cascade" principle, the most powerful x-ray machine developed up to that time—a 900,000-volt therapy unit—was installed at Memorial Hospital in New York City. In 1933, 800-kV x-ray therapy units were installed at Mercy Hospital in Chicago and Swedish Hospital in Seattle. The next year saw the announcement of three important new oil-immersed x-ray units—a 220-kVp model for x-ray therapy applications and 220- and 300-kVp models for industrial applications.

In an era of high-tech medical imaging, patient monitoring and analysis, biopharmaceuticals, life science ventures, and all the other extremely sophisticated initiatives that define today's GE Healthcare, it is easy to overlook the important role industrial x-ray once played in sustaining and driving this business. In fact, the GE X-Ray Corporation's strength and innovative skills in this area of technology were to prove of strategic national importance when U.S. industry was mobilized for the coming war effort.

This was also a significant period for GE X-Ray in another way. In 1933, C. F. Samms brought his nearly 40-year career as Victor president to a close with his retirement. He was succeeded by John H. Clough, who would lead the business out of the Depression, through World War II, and into its eventual new home in Milwaukee.

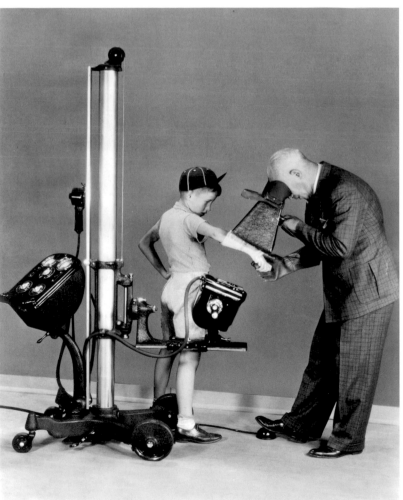

top, left to right
Demand for Model 39 tables remained reliable even in the difficult market conditions of the 1930s.

Dr. Willis R. Whitney (1868–1958) was the first director of GE's Research Laboratory.

bottom, left to right
Another good performer was the Model D mobile unit. Here, the doctor is checking a knitting bone using a hand-held fluoro viewer.

Assembling x-ray hand timers at GE X-ray. (1934)

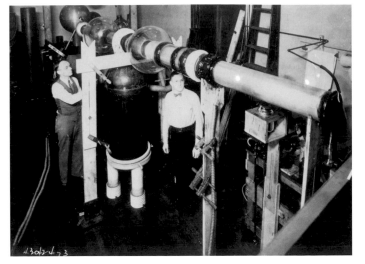

800 kV x-ray therapy unit at Chicago's Mercy Hospital Institute of Radiation Therapy. Dr. Coolidge is at lower left in light suit.

Lessons in Leadership

John Hewson Clough (1891–1975) *was born in Canada but grew up in Batavia, New York. He enrolled in the University of Rochester in 1912 and soon was stricken by a serious illness. He never returned to college. In 1913, he got a job as a steel mill inspector, prompting him to study metallurgy at night school. He joined GE's Research Laboratory later that year, looking for ways to keep tungsten on contact buttons. After service in Europe during WWI, he returned to the Research Laboratory where he became interested in Dr. Coolidge's work. This led him to the Central Station Department, which handled GE's x-ray business. He was soon made the liaison between GE and the Victor X-Ray Corporation and, in 1925, moved to Chicago as assistant to Mr. Samms. He was elected president of the GE X-Ray Corporation in September 1933 and retired in June 1950.*

Despite the Depression, many advances were occurring in x-ray tubes and related areas of technology. In 1934, GE brought out the first rotating anode tube to be manufactured in the U.S., a 400-kV constant-potential x-ray unit in 1935, a copper-backed rotating anode tube with higher heat storage in 1937, the first oil-immersed rotating anode tube with a solid tungsten disk for the anode in 1938, and a 1-million-volt x-ray unit in 1939.

In France, CGR also was making progress. It manufactured its first rotating anti-cathode tube in 1937, not long before Thomson acquired a majority stake in the business.

Meanwhile, back at the Research Laboratory in Schenectady, another GE scientific luminary, Dr. Irving S. Langmuir, had earned a patent for image amplification, a method of increasing the brightness and visibility of x-ray fluoroscopy images.

Footsteps of Pioneers

Irving S. Langmuir (1881–1957) *was born in Brooklyn, New York and educated as a chemist at the University of Gottingen in Germany. Unhappy in a teaching post, he took advantage of the opportunity in 1909 to work with Dr. Whitney and the other scientists at the GE Research Laboratory as a summer employee. He was immediately recognized as an extremely capable scientist and inventor and offered a permanent position. His early work resulted in such advances as gas-filled incandescent lamps that greatly improved lighting; improvements in vacuum tubes, which helped advance radio and electronics; and many others. He is best remembered for his contributions to surface chemistry, for which he received the 1932 Nobel Prize. He did more than anyone to prove the value of industrial research.*

The big news in 1938 was J. B. Wantz's announcement of his retirement after 44 years in charge of Victor's and GE X-Ray's manufacturing activities. However, he remained active in the business throughout the war years in his new capacity of consulting engineer. He was succeeded as factory manager by F. E. Scheven.

Gearing up for war

As war consumed Europe and Asia, big changes were occurring at GE. In late 1939, Owen D. Young, chairman, and Gerard Swope, president, decided to step down together to make way for the new team of Philip D. Reed and Charles E. Wilson, chairman and president, respectively. Their retirements were brief, however. Shortly after the attack on Pearl Harbor and America's entrance into the war, Reed was recruited to help lead the Lend Lease Mission to England, while Wilson became vice chairman of the War Production Board. So Young and Swope agreed to resume their previous GE roles for the duration of the war. That turned out to have significant implications.

top
J. H. Clough led the GE X-Ray Corporation from 1933 until 1950.

middle, left to right
A Cleveland physician's wife, Mrs. L. K. Barwell, boards an airplane at Curtis-Reynolds Airport in Chicago after picking up a Model F shockproof unit at the GE X-Ray factory.

The CRT-1-2 from about 1940 was an early GE rotating anode x-ray tube.

bottom
John Clough (l), GE X-Ray president, and J. B. Wantz, engineering vice president, compare a tiny CDX (dental) tube with a 400 kV therapy tube.

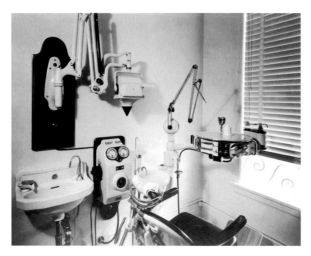

top, left to right

Irving Langmuir, a GE scientist, won the 1932 Nobel Prize in chemistry.

A modern dental treatment room with a CDX wall-mounted x-ray unit. (1940)

Unloading a Model F-3 portable x-ray unit for the first aid station at the 1940 Winter Sports Carnival, Mt. Hood, Oregon.

middle, left to right

GE X-Ray president John Clough (left) discusses advertising materials during a wartime visit by GE President Gerard Swope. At right is W. S. Kendrick, GE X-Ray vice president.

Charles E. Wilson (1886–1972), GE President, 1940–42, 1945–50.

bottom, left to right

John Clough (third from right), GE X-Ray president, and B. H. Doble (right), export sales manager, demonstrate a GE x-ray unit donated to the Polish Ambulance Relief drive. (March 1940)

GE X-Ray Corporation's Chicago factory in 1942.

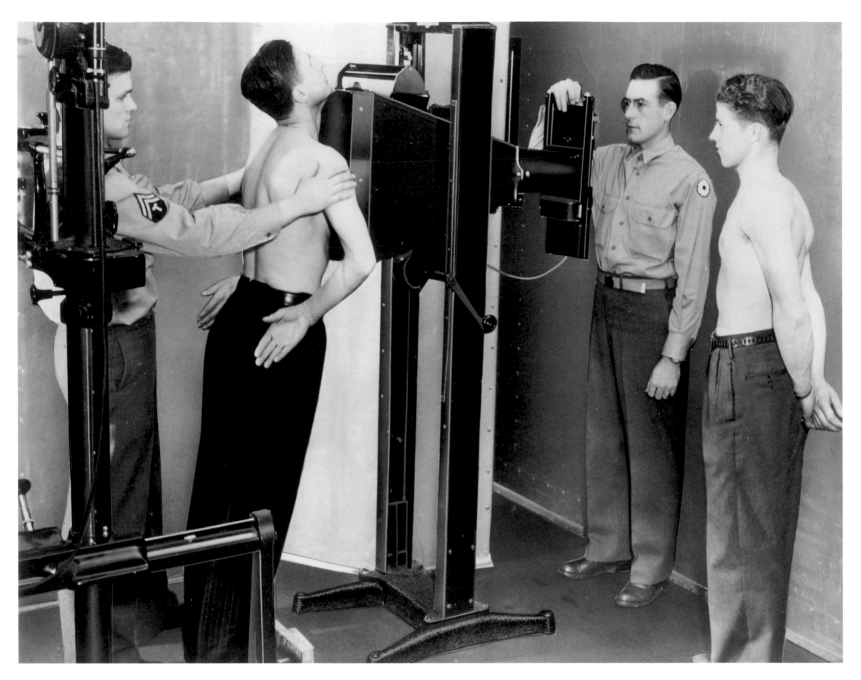

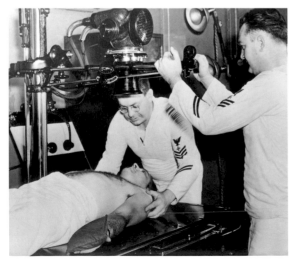

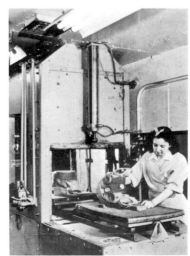

top
All WWII inductees received a chest x-ray.

bottom, left to right
A GE KX-8-33 table with DX tube installed aboard the U.S. Navy hospital ship, *U.S.S. Solace.*

An operator at the New York Shipbuilding Corp., Camden N.J., radiographs a heavy valve casting. (October 1944)

An inspector x-rays welds in a cast aluminum cylinder head for Ford-built 2,000 hp Pratt & Whitney aircraft engines.

An important part of Wilson's new duties with the War Production Board was to rationalize the production capabilities of American industry in order to obtain the greatest efficiencies and production output at the earliest possible moment. In many instances, that meant assigning manufacturers to specialize in producing a certain range of products where their unique experience and capabilities would have the greatest impact. That's how Ford Motor Company, for instance, became a major producer of B-24 bombers, and how A.O. Smith Corporation, Milwaukee, Wisconsin, became the largest U.S. supplier of bomb casings—fully 80% (over 5 million) of the wartime total. That's also how GE X-Ray was assigned the primary role of producing industrial x-ray gear to support the war effort. Those extremely powerful "cascade" tubes developed by Dr. Coolidge and his colleagues at the Research Laboratory were exactly what the armaments industry needed to perform nondestructive inspections of castings, armor plate, weldments, and all the other critical parts in heavy weaponry (including all those millions of bomb and shell casing being made in Milwaukee and in scores of other ordnance plants throughout the nation).

Producing tools for victory

By mid-1942, GE X-Ray, like many other vital war production plants, was gearing up to operate on a full-time basis. James S. Thelen, factory superintendent, told a meeting of the Quarter Century Club in the spring of that year,

> The 48-hour week . . . is something few of us like to have as a regular thing, but it has to be done if we expect to get the most from our equipment. And the 48-hour week is, of course, only a start in the direction of realizing the full capacity of our factory. Before we are through, we may be running 24 hours a day, 7 days a week.

Extended war production hours allowed GE X-Ray to rush much needed industrial x-ray gear to many giant industrial plants across the nation that were making the tools of war. Many of them were successfully relying on these GE devices to improve and speed their own manufacturing and inspection processes. For example, in a big Midwest foundry (not named at the time due to wartime secrecy restrictions), gun mount production had risen so rapidly that inspection facilities couldn't keep up. GE X-Ray engineers were called in to study the problem and recommended the installation of a GE million-volt x-ray unit that would allow several gun mounts to be examined simultaneously with one exposure. As a result, the faster inspections allowed the plant to boost production by a factor of 10!

Similarly, a shipyard making important castings for naval vessels developed a severe production bottleneck due to an inspection process that required several days to thoroughly examine a single unit. A GE 1000 kV machine was installed, cutting the inspection time to less than 1 hour. Not only was production speeded, but quality was also boosted, since the x-ray films provided a reliable guide to welding repairs when faults in the huge castings were detected.

At one of the nation's largest war plants (later identified as Ford Motor Company in Dearborn, Michigan), another GE 1000 KV unit reduced by six times the man hours required to examine cast steel crankshafts for liquid-cooled aircraft engines.

Interestingly, the September 1944 edition of *GEXCO NEWS*—the GE employee newspaper—carried a feature story on how one of GE's million-volt industrial x-ray units was helping Allis-Chalmers Manufacturing Company produce high-quality turbosuperchargers for aircraft engines at their Supercharger Works near Milwaukee. The powerful unit was able to radiograph three-dozen "hot wheels"—the working heart of the supercharger—from many different angles in a single operation, saving considerable inspection time, improving quality, and increasing output. Though no

top to bottom
These two photos illustrated the *GEXCO NEWS* article about the million-volt x-ray unit at the Allis-Chalmers Supercharger Works in Milwaukee. It later became GE X-Ray's home. (Old-timers will recognize the wood-block floors and tiled walls.)

The Allis Chalmers Supercharger Works in West Milwaukee manufactured aircraft engine superchargers that allowed bombers and fighters to fly at high altitudes.

top to bottom

Making plans to ship the first 2-million volt tube from the Chicago factory to Schenectady (l–r, Dr. R. H. Morris, Dr. Coolidge, Z. T. Altees, head of vacuum tube engineering, and F. E. Scheven, facility manager).

This photograph from *GEXCO NEWS* shows 155mm shell castings being x-rayed by a million-volt GE x-ray unit (behind wall) at the Milan, Tennessee, ordnance plant. (August 1944)

Electromedical devices on display at the "Weapons of War" exhibit in Chicago. (1943)

one knew it at the time, this same plant was to play a huge role in GE X-Ray's post-war future. (By the way, General Electric Company also manufactured tens of thousands of turbosuperchargers during the war at plants in Everett, Massachusetts, and Fort Wayne, Indiana.)

Though it was a closely guarded secret until the war ended, the men and women of GE X-Ray were also producing *2,000,000-volt* industrial x-ray units from 1944 onward. These units were used at the Research Laboratory and in various war production applications. They were especially effective in examining large shells and bombs to assure the explosive materials were properly loaded and stable.

With these kinds of results, it's no surprise war contracts were flooding into the plant at Jackson & Robey, nor that Mr. Clough and his staff were looking for new ways to increase production. Extended hours were only part of the solution. Another was the unprecedented effort to recruit women to fill factory positions traditionally held by men. As Jim Thelen pointed out at the time, "More women will be employed in this industry, as well as in all others, simply because men will not be available. Women are being used to take up the jobs which are left open by the promotion of men employees."

This breakthrough in industrial employment opportunities for women occasioned by the war provided a superb proving ground that demonstrated women could perform just as well as men in the modern factory.

In addition to industrial x-ray apparatus, GE X-Ray's wartime production was divided among several other important categories: medical apparatus for the armed forces, medical apparatus for civilian health and industrial hospitals, and so-called special war products. Interestingly, the latter category represented a substantial portion of GE X-Ray's total output, especially gaussing and degaussing equipment used to help protect U.S. Navy minesweepers from magnetic mines and torpedoes. GE X-Ray was selected for this role because of its expertise in high-voltage controls and cabling.

Of course, the company continued to produce x-ray gear for hospitals, clinics, doctor's offices, and dental labs during the war. Industrial equipment got the priority, both in terms of production and development, such as a 2-million-volt tube that appeared in 1943. At the other extreme, a beryllium window tube for low energy medical work also came out that same year.

As a measure of GE X-Ray's contributions, it was presented the coveted Army-Navy "E" flag award in early 1943 for outstanding production performance. Each employee also received a miniature "E" pin they proudly wore on their clothing. Although nine other GE units had received the "E" award by that time, GE X-Ray was the first General Electric subsidiary company to be so honored. It went on to add several "White Stars" to the "E" flag during the course of the war, symbolizing continued quality and quantity in production.

The company supplied much more than mere hardware to the war effort. Some 50,000 General Electric men and women served in the armed forces during WWII, and 1,055 of them gave their lives in the service of their country. Thirteen of them were from the GE X-Ray Corporation.

It may come as a surprise to learn that despite the global compass of WWII, GE X-Ray's export business remained very active, though at a reduced level. In the fall of 1944, for instance, Mr. Clough announced the formation of a new medical products company to serve as the export outlet for GE x-ray products. It would continue distributing the products of some three dozen U.S. surgical equipment manufacturers that had been relying on GE X-Ray to distribute their products offshore. The new General Electric Medical Products Company was a collaboration between GE X-Ray and International General Electric. It allowed GE's service and sales activities to be greatly intensified in the 60 or so countries where the former Export Department had

top to bottom

Roentgenoscopic units being assembled in Dept. L. (1945)

GE X-Ray won the Army-Navy "E" award in February 1943 for excellence in production. It proudly flies with Old Glory and the pennant signifying strong support of the War Bond drive.

Employees assembling "care packages" for their GE X-Ray colleagues serving with the armed forces.

top
The engineering department at the Jackson & Damon factory. (March 1944)

bottom, left to right
A common sight in American cities and towns during the war and after was mobile tuberculosis (TB) screening vans. Virginia, Minnesota, hosted this visit in 1944.

These students at Scott High School, Little Rock, Arkansas, are lined up for their TB chest x-rays. (1944)

Workplace TB screening was frequent, such as at the Stromberg-Carlson Co. plant in Rochester, N.Y. (1945)

new applications in peace. The situation was much the same in the medical x-ray industry. The end of the war also meant radiologists and dentists were clamoring to update equipment that was 5, 10, even 20 years old or more. The entire x-ray industry was under intense pressure and scrambling to find ways to keep up with the unprecedented demand.

Naturally, being in the middle of all this excitement, the GE X-Ray Corporation found itself both in an enviable competitive position and in a serious jam. In the previous 25 years, it had grown from a total staff of about 400 to around 3,000 employees by the end of the war. The organization was bursting at the seams, whether in terms of employment, orders, opportunities, or expectations.

Unfortunately, another place literally bursting at the seams was the old plant at Jackson & Robey. It had expanded to a collection of five buildings, some dating from the turn of the century, and now was hemmed in on a city lot with no more room to expand. Also, its obsolete, multistory construction style allowed no economical way to be upgraded to the latest production systems and methods. In an effort to forestall this problem, in the summer of 1945, President Clough had relocated the entire general office operation to the Insurance Exchange Building several blocks away at 175 W. Jackson Boulevard. This move freed up approximately 35,000 square feet of space that was quickly put to use to meet war production commitments and start attacking the huge backlog of civilian orders.

Even these heroic efforts weren't enough. The old plant simply couldn't keep up with the demand. Something clearly had to be done and done soon!

The perfect solution was found just 90 miles to the north.

above, left
Enrico Fermi, Nobelist and University of Chicago professor, adjusting controls of the GE 100 MeV betatron at Goldblatt Memorial Cancer Center.

top to bottom
This newspaper photo from December 1941 shows early construction activities at what would become the Electric Avenue factory. This view from near the present main gate looks southeast toward Lincoln Avenue.

The former Allis Chalmers Supercharger Works on McGeogh Street in West Milwaukee. (1946)

Aerial View Electric Ave Area

operated through various affiliates, distributors, and subsidiaries. All of the operating officers were long-time GE X-Ray executives; Clark H. Minor, president of International General Electric, was the chairman.

On to the future

With WWII successfully concluded, American industry was quick to convert away from war production to meet the huge, pent-up demand for consumer goods. The technical ingenuity that had been directed toward the war effort was now being refocused on the needs of the local healthcare provider. Advanced devices previously reserved for the military were now becoming available to civilian customers without restriction.

In early 1946, for example, GE announced the University of Chicago had placed the first order for a *100,000,000-volt* betatron, a giant electron accelerator designed for x-ray and atomic research. Only one other such machine was then in existence—at GE's Research Laboratory in Schenectady. About this same time, GE X-Ray also announced plans to construct its first 50,000,000-volt betatron for therapy applications and its intention to build and market future models up to 75,000,000 volts. Another program was launched to develop and market 10,000,000-volt units for industrial radiography uses.

As factories were retooled and expanded, and as new products were developed and introduced, the nation went on a huge buying binge driven by years of deprivation and by the fabulous new technologies developed for war and now finding exciting

"Made in Milwaukee"

On the southwestern edge of Milwaukee, Wisconsin, company officials located a surplus war production plant that filled the billl. A modern, air-conditioned, ground-level facility, it was the same plant where GE industrial x-ray gear had helped Allis-Chalmers Manufacturing Company produce high-quality turbosuperchargers for aircraft engines. Now, it provided everything needed for efficient, cost-effective, straight-line production, plus the benefit of being located on a 43-acre site offering ample space for expansion and employee parking. There was probably no other company in the nation that could have made better use of the total facility than GE-X-Ray.

In August 1946, the $2 million purchase was completed and the title transferred to GE from the War Assets Administration. The name of the street serving the site was changed from McGeogh Street to Electric Avenue, the "GE X-Ray" sign was hoisted atop the building (it was illuminated for the first time on September 30, 1948), and the GE X-Ray Corporation opened its modern new home.

The Milwaukee Road

Government restrictions during and after World War II made it impossible for the GE X-Ray Corporation to build a much-needed new home. Having searched futilely throughout the Chicagoland area for a solution, the Allis-Chalmers supercharger plant near Milwaukee was finally located. GE's offer to purchase the site from the War Assets Administration was accepted on April 9, 1946, and the title officially transferred on August 27.

The first product to be manufactured in the new plant was the CDX dental x-ray unit. It was selected for the honor because it not only was one of GE's "best sellers" at the time but also because it was complete in itself—no separate control stand and generator—and it could be shipped independently from Milwaukee for immediate installation. On the last day of 1946, the first 12 "Made in Milwaukee" CDX units were shipped.

Next came the Model F portable x-ray unit, which, like the CDX, was self-contained, called for comparatively simple manufacturing methods, and was produced in high volumes. Over the following months, additional high-volume products were moved from Chicago to Milwaukee, along with the people and tools to manufacture them.

A major milestone was reached in September 1947, when the entire Engineering Division completed its move north. By the time the new year rolled around, some 700 employees had relocated, boosting total Milwaukee employment to about 1,800 men and women. A. V. Muskett, former engineering consultant to Charles E. Wilson, GE President, was appointed works manager, and the new operation was underway.

Transferring an entire business from one city to another naturally took quite some time. Equipment had to be crated and shipped, employees relocated, files transferred, and all the rest of it. In fact, it wasn't until January 1, 1948, that the Chicago plant was officially closed. Even then, the general offices remained at 175 W. Jackson Boulevard in Chicago for some months longer. The die had been cast, however, and products manufactured at Electric Avenue and in nearby sister plants would proudly carry the "Made In Milwaukee" label in the future.

The State of Wisconsin's official welcome was extended by Governor Oscar Rennebohm who wrote:

Now that the installation of the General Electric X-Ray Corporation is about completed in Milwaukee, I take this means of extending a cordial welcome to Wisconsin.

top to bottom

F. E. Scheven (left), vice president of manufacturing, brings a group from the Quarter Century Club in Chicago for a premove visit to GE X-Ray's new home in West Milwaukee.

Ed Cedik, screw machine department foreman, closes the door to his office in the old Chicago plant for the last time in December 1947.

GE X-Ray machine shop about 1950.

It is my understanding that you have a fine plant which represents a substantial addition to our State's industrial resources. And there could be no more appropriate time to get underway than the present when Wisconsin, as you know, is celebrating its Centennial.

While most of your employees, I presume, are Wisconsin people who know all about our State and its advantages, I am confident that those of your people who are now living in Wisconsin for the first time will soon learn to like the Badger State as much as we do who have called it home all our lives.

Please accept my best wishes, extended in behalf of all the people of Wisconsin, that your success as a Wisconsin institution may be outstanding in every way.

Governor Rennebohm couldn't have guessed just how accurate his prediction would prove in coming years.

A history lesson

On September 13, 1948, everyone on Electric Avenue received a dramatic reminder of just how closely they were tied to the history of the x-ray. Late that end-of-summer morning, a special train pulled up at the nearby street crossing and down the steps came Dr. William D. Coolidge and his wife, Dorothy, accompanied by GE President Charles E. Wilson. Dr. and Mrs. Coolidge had been invited from their home in Schenectady to attend the dedication of the new "Coolidge Laboratory" at GE X-Ray. At the time it opened, and for many years thereafter, it was the largest developmental laboratory in the world exclusively devoted to advancing x-ray technology. What better tribute to commemorate this remarkable man and perpetuate the achievements of his brilliant career?

Before the hundreds of guests attending the dedication ceremonies, Dr. Coolidge concluded his remarks by saying:

The only predictions for the future which I will make are, first, that fundamental research, which is now receiving much of the attention and support which it merits, will, as in the past, and with increasing tempo, supply new scientific facts and principles; and, second, that this laboratory, designed for applied research and development, will, aided by the cooperation of the medical profession, promptly and effectively use such new discoveries to extend and strengthen the X-ray art.

Mr. Wilson had a few well-chosen words of his own to share at the celebratory dinner that evening in Milwaukee's Schroeder Hotel:

The x-ray tube, to my mind, has long been one of the most dramatic achievements of the laboratory. From the beginning it was bound up in colorful human striving, and in this, one of the central figures of modern times has undoubtedly been that of Dr. William D. Coolidge.

During the nearly 27 years of life still before him, Dr. Coolidge would witness an incredible variety of advances in every area of radiography and fluoroscopy, as well as the emergence of an array of fantastic new imaging techniques. Even his fertile imagination must have been astonished by the many developments to come in such fields as nuclear imaging, ultrasound, and computed tomography.

In early 1949, perhaps inspired by Dr. Coolidge's stellar example, Art Kizaur became the first GE X-Ray engineer to win the coveted GE Coffin Award in recognition of his "outstanding contributions to the x-ray industry by producing an advanced and

top to bottom

Engineering Building, Electric Avenue (1946). It was renamed the Coolidge Laboratory in 1948.

Dr. and Mrs. Coolidge at the 1948 dedication of the William D. Coolidge Laboratory in Milwaukee. Dr. A. C. Christies (left) of Washington, D.C., a nationally known radiologist, was a special guest.

Part of the audience attending the Coolidge Lab dedication.

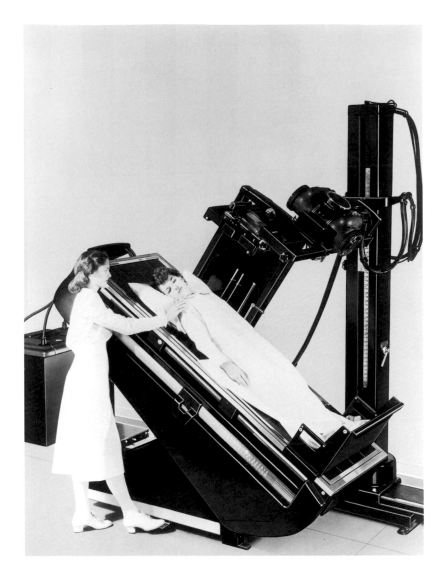

radically new design of x-ray apparatus"—the Maxiscope® deluxe diagnostic x-ray unit." Named in honor of Charles A. Coffin, GE's first president, this award for many years was the top company recognition for exceptional employee contributions.

Art Kizaur's Coffin Award was not the last for the X-Ray Department. Just 4 years later, John Jacobs, manager of the advanced development lab, won another for his work in "converting cadmium sulfide crystals into a highly sensitive automatic detector for inspecting industrial and military products." More similarly prestigious corporate awards lay ahead for some of Milwaukee's technology superstars.

Lessons in Leadership

John Heywood Smith (1904–1991) was born in Springville, Utah and earned a B.S. in Economics at the University of Pennsylvania, where he was selected to the Grantland Rice All American First Team (football) in 1927. He later taught at Brigham Young University where he was head football line coach and business manager of the athletic department. In 1936, he returned to Penn as a business instructor and football coach, while also pursuing graduate studies. During World War II, he was the procurement manager for a Philadelphia shipyard. Smith came to GE X-Ray in early 1947, as assistant to the president, became marketing vice president 6 months later, executive vice president in 1948, president in 1950, and X-Ray Department general manager in 1951. He was appointed professor of commerce at the University of Wisconsin-Milwaukee in 1957 and retired in 1970.

Having successfully shepherded the business through this tumultuous period of depression, war, and relocation, J. H. Clough decided the time had come for him to announce his retirement. A successor had already been groomed for this leadership role. John H. Smith had stepped up to replace W. S. Kendrick as vice president when he retired in 1949. Now, just a year later, he was selected to move into the president's office.

But the changes were just beginning.

Decentralization

New faces were also appearing at the corporate level where Ralph J. Cordiner was elected GE president in 1950. He succeeded Charles E. Wilson who had resigned at President Truman's request to become director of the Office of Defense Mobilization in response to the international emergency developing on the Korean Peninsula. As one of his final official GE duties, Wilson had the pleasure of dedicating the GE Research

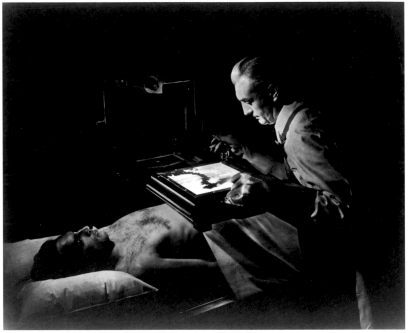

above, left
The Maxiscope 500 system.

above, right, top to bottom
Maxiscope fluoro screen.

John H. Smith, President, GE X-Ray Corporation, 1950–51; General Manager, GE X-Ray Department, 1951–57.

Laboratory's new home just outside Schenectady. The occasion also was the 50th anniversary of the founding of the Research Laboratory. The complex represented one of the world's largest and most modern industrial research laboratories then and today!

Cordiner immediately embarked upon a massive restructuring program based upon the decentralization concept to better manage GE's burgeoning growth. His idea was to divide the company into smaller, more easily managed units called departments, each under the leadership of its own general manager. As he described it, these individual businesses would not be "too big for one man to get his arms around." The expectation was better decisions would be made more quickly than would be possible in a huge, centrally planned and controlled organization.

Cordiner's new vision for General Electric was implemented officially on July 1, 1951, with the creation of about 120 operating departments. Most of the former affiliated companies also became departments, including the GE X-Ray Corporation, which now became known simply as the X-Ray Department. He also would leave an indelible mark on the company in another key way. At his urging, GE opened its renowned Management Development Institute at Crotonville, New York, in 1956. Its specific mission was to develop and teach the new management skills that the decentralization program demanded. It has gone on, of course, to become the most admired business management training center of its kind, whether in terms of preparing executive talent for major leadership roles or developing mid-career management skills.

The fabulous '50s

The 1950s proved to be one of the most exciting and fertile periods in the entire history of the x-ray, indeed, of medicine itself. Thousands of bright young physicians, scientists, and engineers had resumed their interrupted careers and were determined to make up for lost time. In virtually every area of medicine, science, and technology, they were providing the energy and intellectual muscle to aggressively pursue new breakthroughs and practical applications.

The field of radiology was a major beneficiary of this trend, thanks both to the enthusiastic advances on the medical front and expanded capabilities industry could now deploy. Among the many technical advances that crowded onto the market during the first part of the decade, one of the most striking was "Made In Milwaukee." GE's new Imperial® table for radiography and fluoroscopy was introduced in 1952 and immediately set the standard for efficiency, flexibility, and productivity. The table, with power-assisted longitudinal and transverse tabletop movements, was configured as a chord mounted inside a ring-shaped support. This permitted up to 360 degrees of table angulation in either direction with the axis of rotation above the tabletop for smooth "90/90" fluoro positioning. Combined with an under-table fluoro tube and over-table, ceiling-suspended fluoroscope, the radiologist enjoyed unprecedented ease in conducting a wide assortment of these bread-and-butter procedures. And when a radiograph was needed, a built-in overhead radiographic tube could be quickly swung into action.

GE Imperial R&F tables flew out the door and soon spawned a host of imitators.

Excellent progress was also being made on the industrial side of the business where the new Hytafill® x-ray unit was introduced to monitor and control canning lines. As closed containers sped through the inspection chamber, a beam of x-rays would measure the level of the contents. If the fill didn't meet specifications, a puff of compressed air would automatically eject the offending can from the production line. Soft drink canners, brewers, food producers, and manufacturers of all kinds were enthusiastic users of the Hytafill product.

Another leadership product appeared in April 1954, when GE's General Engineering Laboratory in Schenectady announced the development of the x-ray microscope.

top to bottom
Ralph J. Cordiner, GE President, 1950–58.

John McGown, GE X-Ray manufacturing manager, demonstrates the Military X-ray Unit to a group of high-ranking government and military officials in 1951. The armed forces ordered 225 of these units, one of the largest contracts for x-ray equipment ever placed up until that time.

In 1953, Madison General Hospital physicians used a GE Maxicon system to demonstrate fluoroscopy-guided cardiovascular catheterization for leaders of the Wisconsin Heart Association (l-r, George Powe, M.D., Dodgeville; Igor Renk, Sun Prairie; and Charles Crumpton, M.D., Madison.) The "patient" was George O'Brien, M.D., Madison.

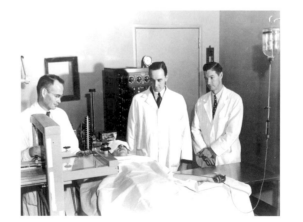

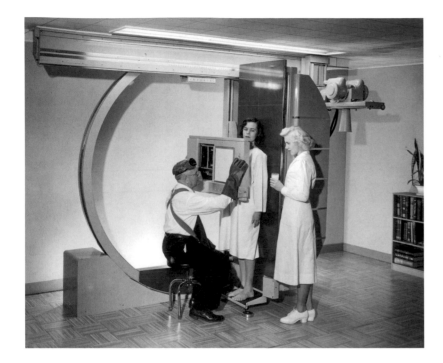

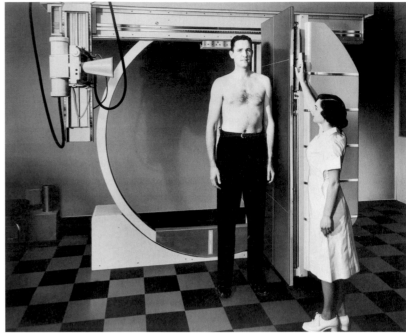

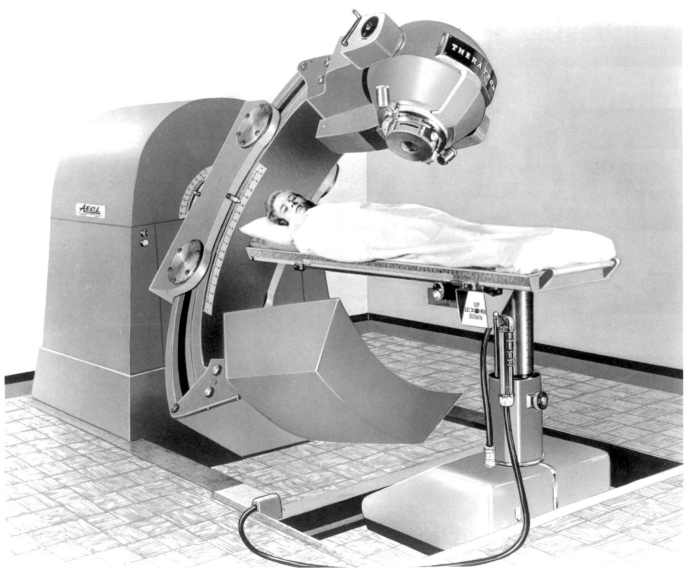

top, left to right
Routine fluoroscopy on the Imperial Table.

George Mikan, known as "Mr. Basketball," was the 6'10" star of the Minneapolis Lakers. The Imperial Table could even accommodate his long frame, as this 1954 publicity photo proves.

bottom
GE distributed Atomic Energy of Canada's Theratron "B" cobalt therapy system and related products in the U.S. more than 2 decades.

GE X-Ray was soon selected to take over production of this extremely sophisticated scientific instrument. April was a busy month, since it also was when GE X-ray and Atomic Energy of Canada Ltd. (AECL) signed an agreement to join forces to market AECL's Cobalt 60 therapy units in the U.S. This partnership continued for over 20 years until GE decided to withdraw from the radiotherapy market.

GE and industry advances continued apace in every area of medical x-ray technology—light-localized beam collimators, overhead image intensifiers, floating fulcrum tables with power driven movements, improved Bucky trays, cineradiography, better radiation protection for both patient and operator, more powerful generators and tubes, auto exposure sensors, automatic film processing, and many others.

A particularly important development was the 1957 introduction of what is believed to have been the first remote control x-ray table. CGR received the credit for this key advance. That also was the year when the 908 Section was established in the Electric Avenue factory to produce an astonishing product. More about that later.

During this period, the X-Ray Department also had a small business producing "radar recording aerial cameras" for the U.S. Air Force. The contract for these reconnaissance cameras was relatively small, only $2–$3 million, since they were primarily used in the U-2 spy plane. The major camera companies weren't interested, so GE X-Ray's expertise in large-format film technologies earned it the job.

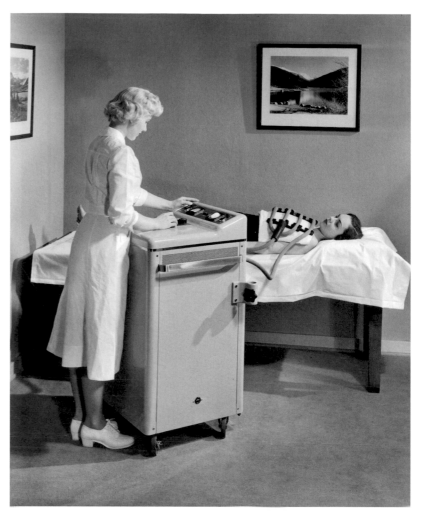

left
John LaRocco, who became conventions and exhibits manager, assembles mounting rings for the Imperial Table

right, top to bottom
The Model F III Inductotherm was the latest (1955) entry in a business begun by Victor Electric nearly half a century before.

This well-equipped dental x-ray room (circa 1941) included a CDX dental x-ray unit and a GE Model B thermospectral lamp.

Fred Strouf (right), dental x-ray sales manager, introduces new products to his field sales managers in 1955.

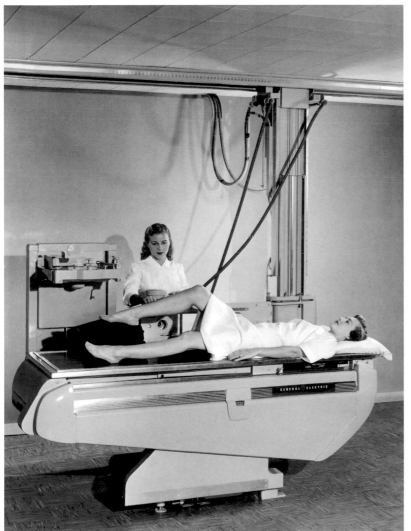

Changes were once more astir in the X-Ray Department's front office. In July 1957, John H. Smith decided to resume his college teaching career and accepted a business professorship at the University of Wisconsin-Milwaukee. An editorial in the *Milwaukee Sentinel* praised him for his decision to return to teaching, noting:

> Here, truly, can it be said that industry's loss is education's gain. We can be grateful, however, that John Smith is making this shift within our community, to which he already has contributed richly, not only as an outstanding executive but via his tremendously active interest in social, civic, and humanitarian affairs.

Dr. Lyman R. Fink took over the top management position at GE X-Ray that September, but less than a year-and-a-half later was selected to lead GE's new Atomic Products Division. He took up his new duties effective February 1, 1959.

Lessons in Leadership

Lyman R. Fink, *a native of Elk Point, South Dakota, joined General Electric's Aeronautics and Ordnance Systems Division in 1937, having earned B.S., M.S., and Ph.D. degrees in electrical engineering from the University of California. He was appointed assistant manager of the Electronics Laboratory, Syracuse, New York, in 1947, and manager the following year. From 1949–55, he was manager of engineering for the Radio and Television Department. He was made a Fellow of the Institute of Radio Engineers in 1953. He served as Manager, Research Application, at the Research Laboratory until his appointment as X-Ray Department general manager in September 1957. Dr. Fink received the Coffin Award, then GE's top honor, for his work on the design and development of a radar gunfire control system for the U.S. Navy.*

Succeeding him was J. W. (Walt) Nelson, Jr., who was destined to guide the X-Ray Department to the very threshold of its modern era.

left, top to bottom
The Patrician table. (1956)

The Regent Table performed both fluoroscopy and radiography.

right
Lyman R. Fink, General Manager, X-Ray Department, 1957–59.

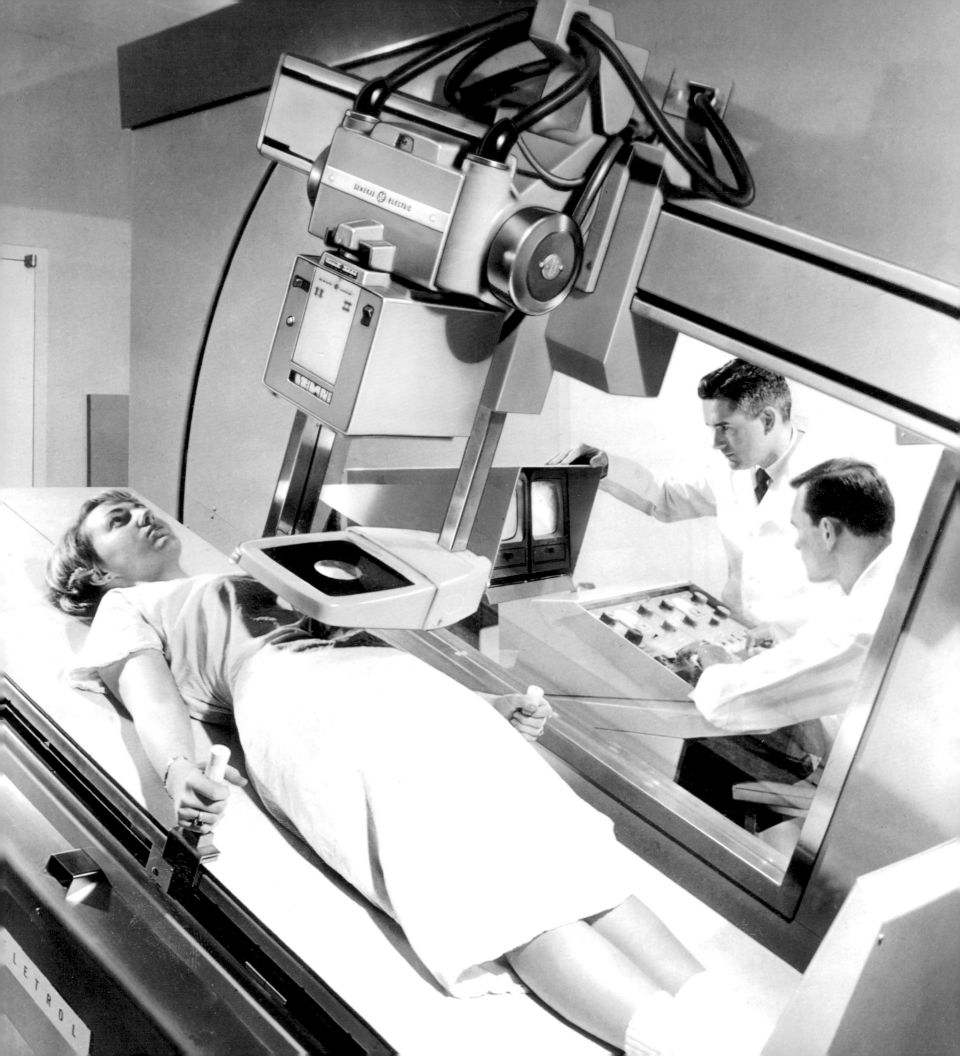

The Nelson Era

1959-1969

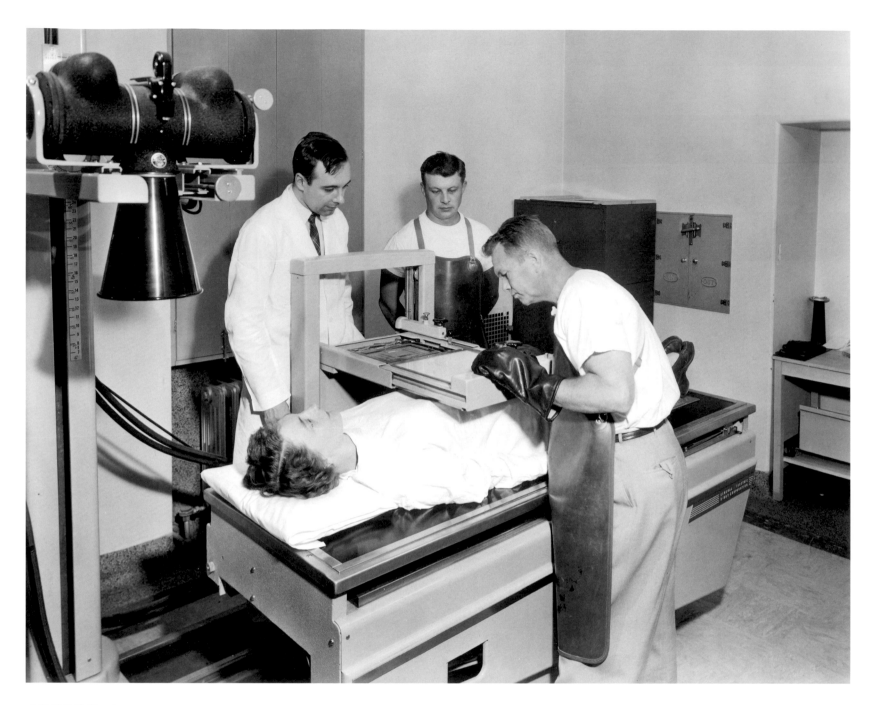

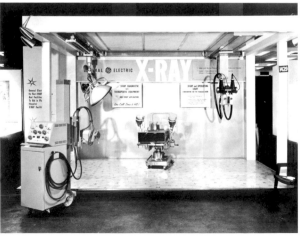

top to bottom, left to right

GE fluoroscopy equipment in use at the Milwaukee Cancer Diagnostic Clinic (l–r: x-ray technologists Richard Krill and Roger A. Schultz, R.T.; radiologist Donald Knutson, M.D.).

James W. Nelson, Jr., General Manager, GE X-Ray Department, 1959–68; General Manager, GE Medical Systems Department, 1968–69.

GE X-Ray's modest booth at the 1959 American Hospital Association meeting. The exhibits manager at the time was Connie Wantz, son of Victor Electric cofounder, J. B. Wantz.

As Walt Nelson assumed the leadership role at the X-Ray Department, the exciting progress enjoyed by the x-ray imaging industry during the 1950s was, if anything, accelerating.

Positive market developments weren't limited to just GE X-Ray. Virtually the entire General Electric Company was caught up in astonishing new technologies and breathtaking new opportunities. Perhaps the most amazing was in the rapidly expanding field of space exploration. The shock of the U.S.S.R.'s launch of Sputnik I in the autumn of 1957 had prompted the U.S. to redouble its aerospace efforts. Already, a GE built spacecraft had been key to recovering the first ever payload from outer space. Soon thereafter, the RVX-2A experimental reentry vehicle brought back the first color photographs of the earth from altitudes up to 700 miles.

Another sophisticated GE spacecraft, the Nuclear Emulsion Recovery Vehicle, allowed NASA to explore the Van Allen Radiation Belt, achieving altitudes as high as 1,250 miles.

Meanwhile, in the cutting-edge technology of nuclear power generation, the first large-scale, privately financed nuclear power plant went into service in 1960 at Commonwealth Edison Company's Dresden site near Chicago. The GE reactor in this plant was coupled to a company-supplied turbine, the first ever built to operate on steam created by nuclear fission.

Success was also being achieved on a much smaller scale, such as the Carboloy™ cemented carbide balls that GE's Metallurgical Products Department was supplying for a new generation of ballpoint pens. Just 1mm in diameter, these tiny pellets cost less than a penny apiece but delivered huge improvements in operating life and smooth performance.

Lessons in Leadership

James Walter Nelson, Jr. (1919–2009) earned degrees in engineering and physics from the University of California and later pursued graduate studies at both Syracuse and Stanford universities. While at Berkeley, he was a research associate in the Radiation Center, working with such luminaries as Dr. Ernest Lawrence, inventor of the cyclotron, and Dr. Luis W. Alvarez, Nobel Laureate. From 1943 to 1946, he served at the Air Force Engineering Center developing airborne microwave radar and armament systems, then joined GE's Electronics Division where he worked in various engineering, research, and marketing positions. He returned to California in 1953 to help establish GE's Microwave Laboratory at Palo Alto, becoming its manager in 1956. He left GE in 1970 and later purchased a manufacturing company that he ran for 15 years before retiring in Milwaukee.

Revitalizing the franchise

The successes of the 1950s notwithstanding, as Walt Nelson took over in the fall of 1959, the medical x-ray segment of the business was languishing. The basic technologies being employed were hardly different from those used in x-ray equipment a decade or two earlier. Relay controls were common and generators were primarily

single-phase designs, sometimes still with rheostat switches to set kVp, mA, and exposure times. Even the popular CDX™ dental x-ray unit was only available in basic white or graphite black, the latter color the traditional finish dating back virtually to the founding of Victor Electric. (One of Nelson's first "high-tech" innovations was to introduce a palette of 30 new colors for the CDX!)

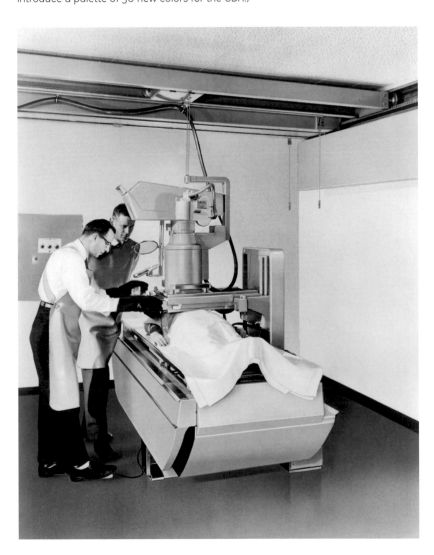

Mirror optics were used to give the radiologist a view of the image intensifier screen in 1960s-era fluoroscopy systems.

top, left to right
GE has been continuously producing
x-ray tubes since 1896. This Electric
Avenue technician is checking the focal
spot on a dental x-ray tube. (1961)

An engineer tests an x-ray tube.

bottom, left to right
A GE field service technician tests
a KX-20-II x-ray generator. (1960)

Aristocrat Table with the Model 52
headstand.

The competitive situation also was extremely challenging. Picker Corporation, which had started out in business recovering latent silver in used x-ray film, had emerged from WWII admirably poised to step into the civilian market with new products based on the medical equipment it had developed and manufactured in volume for the military. GE X-Ray, on the other hand, had deferred developments in the medical x-ray field in order to concentrate on the specialized electrical equipment and special war products it had been asked to produce. As a consequence, Picker had gained an edge over GE in both product and market leadership, which it maintained throughout most of the 1960s; GE spent the intervening years trying to catch up. Leading-edge innovation wasn't high on GE's list of priorities, though important new products such as the Imperial® table did make their appearances in the 1950s.

The most serious competitive threat of all, however, was the emergence of Siemens and Philips as major players in the U.S. market. Then, as now, both were aggressive marketers and respected for their advanced, high-quality products. American radiologists found their equipment particularly well suited to the needs of the modern imaging department and were buying it in greater and greater quantities. As a result, though the domestic manufacturers were seeing an overall increase in their sales figures, they nonetheless were losing significant market share to the Europeans.

GE X-Ray's primary competitive asset, then as now, was its strong, dedicated field sales and service organization. More than 700 people were deployed around the country selling, installing, and keeping GE x-ray equipment operating. If customers needed help at 2 a.m. on a Sunday morning, they could count on a GE service technician being there. This was the shield that protected the business while engineers and marketers attempted to close the competitive gap.

By the late 1950s, the electronic revolution was just around the corner. Solid-state components were emerging from the development lab, though very few had yet found their way into the x-ray equipment of the day.

Perhaps the most significant early step taken by Nelson (aside from the new CDX color palette, of course) was to reinvigorate the engineering function. A new engineering manager, Bob Hodgers, was brought in from GE Engineering Services and quickly got to work. Within a matter of just 2 years, the engineering section was expanded by 50%, and a flood of upgraded products using the latest electronic technologies began to appear. Major development efforts were concentrated on image intensifiers and three-phase x-ray generators, the latter a brand-new leading edge technology from Europe. These devices were essential for many of the more sophisticated applications then emerging, such as special procedures rooms and mammography systems.

It took time to architect the next new generation of hardware, but by about 1963, these efforts were beginning to pay off in terms of stronger sales. By the middle of the decade, virtually the entire GE medical x-ray catalog consisted of modern new products specifically geared to the needs of U.S. customers. Not only did this allow the market share position versus Picker to be stabilized, it also positioned GE to better withstand the severe competitive challenges from Europe. However, it would take GE many years to become the unquestioned leader in its home market.

The 1965 meeting of the Radiological Society of North America (RSNA) provided excellent evidence that GE X-Ray was at last embarked upon the road toward its resurgence. Featured products on display included: the Fluoromount™ positioner that facilitated fluoroscopy and cine during cardiac catheterization studies; Fluoricon™ Compact Video System with twice the resolution; Monarch® Table with the Model 63 spot-filmer; Fluoricon™ dual-field imaging intensification system with 70mm spot-film camera; Mobile 225 x-ray unit; DXR-1050 x-ray generator; and the new Fluoroline™ 80 film viewer

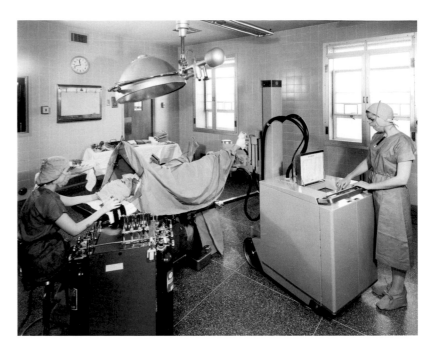

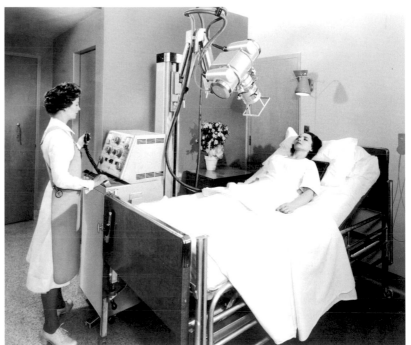

top to bottom
An EP-300 Mobile Unit being used for a hip-pinning procedure at Good Samaritan Hospital, Cincinnati, Ohio. (1962)

The Mobile 200 x-ray unit brought a wide range of radiographic capabilities to the patient's bedside.

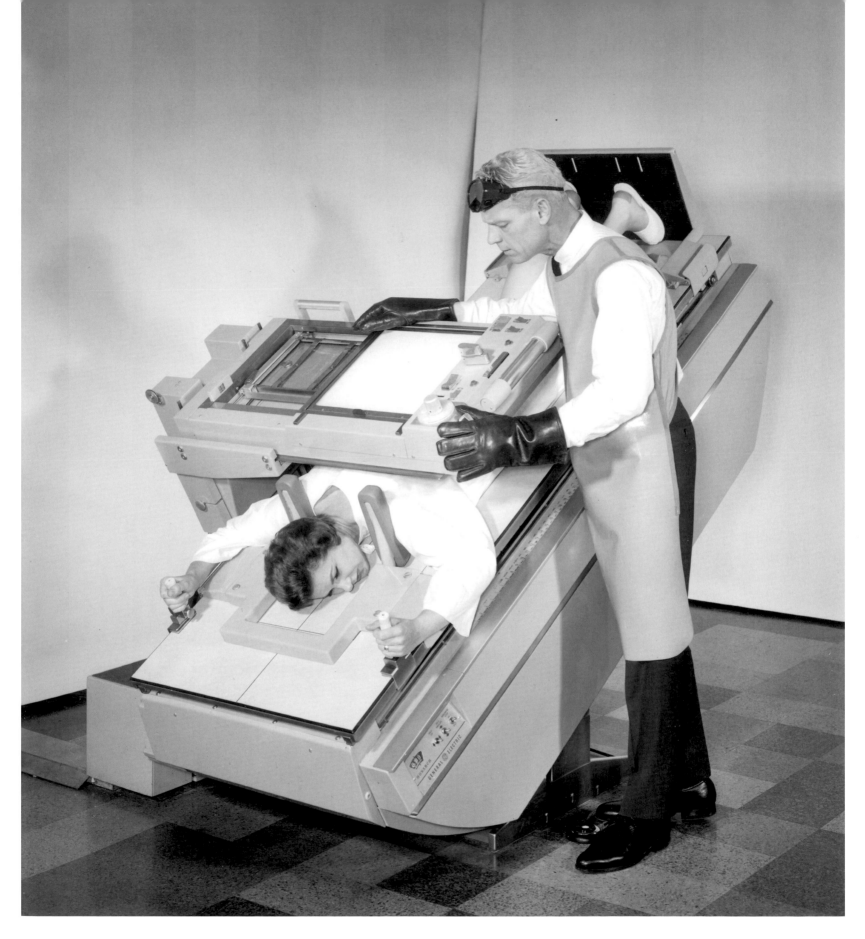

The Monarch Table with Model 63 spot-filmer.

Image intensification matures

Image intensification is an especially good example of GE's development efforts. Though Irving Langmiur had been awarded the original image intensifier patent in 1937, it's clear his design, which yielded a brightness gain of only about 100X, would not have been satisfactory for routine clinical applications. It remained for others to modify and improve his basic design in order to perfect an image intensifier with a brightness gain of at least 1000X. This was the key threshold, since it would allow fluoroscopists to conduct exams in normal room lighting, with no need to dark-adapt their vision as with old-style fluoro screens. This was more than a mere matter of convenience. Viewing images in normal room lighting allowed them to rely on their central cone vision (fine detail discrimination), rather than rod vision (gross detail discrimination).

Development of image intensification had been slowed by the demands of war, so it wasn't until 1953 that Westinghouse Corporation introduced the first commercial model. It used a mirror-optics system to reflect the image from the output phosphor of the fluoro tube to the physician's eyes. Without a proprietary product of its own, GE X-Ray fitted Westinghouse's Fluorex® intensifier to the extremely popular Imperial table, giving fluoroscopists easy access to an unprecedented range of angulations. Other manufacturers recognized a good thing when they saw it and soon were offering ceiling-suspended image intensification systems of their own.

GE, of course, wanted its own image intensifier, so it launched a major technology initiative to develop a large-area tube called the TVX. This was an x-ray television tube with a photoconductive surface built on lead oxides for direct viewing. Unfortunately, it turned out that lead oxides tend to migrate over time and "poison" the cathode. TVX images were initially very good, but within a short while they would seriously degrade. The TVX was abandoned and a sourcing agreement with a French image tube supplier was signed. This relationship was a harbinger of a much more significant French partnership to come in GE X-Ray's distant future.

Another concern was to find ways to decrease patient exposure and increase the diagnostic information during such complex fluoroscopic procedures as cardiac catheterizations and angiography. This was no small matter since the extended fluoro times typically needed for these studies could quickly reach unsafe exposure levels for both the patient and operator. To make the process safer and more efficient, substantial improvements were needed throughout the entire imaging chain, from the generator and tube through the image output and viewing devices.

A major advance was the development of closed-circuit TV systems to display fluoroscopic images. First demonstrated in 1948, this technique replaced the mirror optics system inside the fluoroscope with a high-resolution television pickup tube coupled to a high-resolution TV monitor. As the sensitivity and resolution of these components continued to increase, less and less radiation was needed to conduct a satisfactory exam. Before many years elapsed, virtually all new fluoroscopy systems incorporated TV image presentation.

Television was also a key to GE's development of remote control R&F units later in the 1960s, especially the home-grown Teletrol® system and the Telegem 15® that was sourced from its subsidiary in Belgium, General Electric Medical. With these units, the radiologist could be entirely outside the examination room—and the exposure field—during the examination. By remotely angulating the table and adjusting the tabletop, virtually any necessary view was available. There was even a remotely operated hydraulic palpator the radiologist could use to gently press the patient's stomach or abdomen. Technologists in protective aprons were always present in the room to assist the patient and change film cassettes.

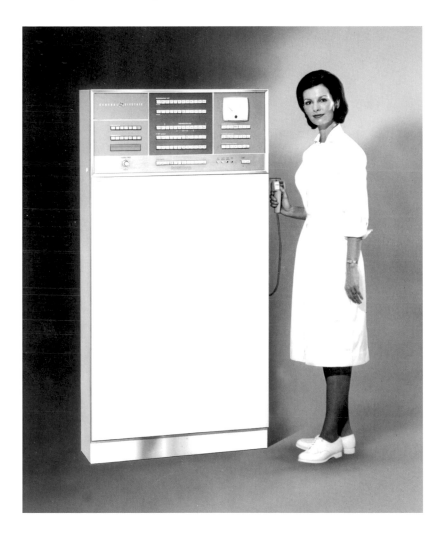

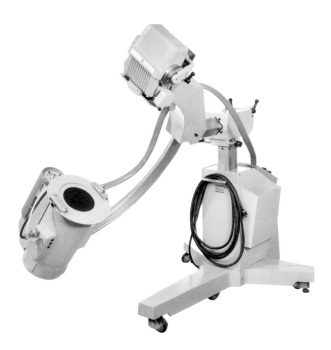

left
GE Mobile Image Intensifier. (1964)

above
The DXR-1050 x-ray generator was among the first of GE's new designs. (1964)

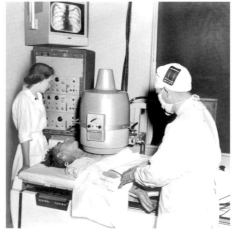

top
Sealing face plates on 12-inch TVX camera tubes.

bottom, left to right
Dr. J. E. Jacobs (right) demonstrates the TVX system to long-time Milwaukee television announcer John Drury.

The TVX system guiding a heart catheterization. (1959)

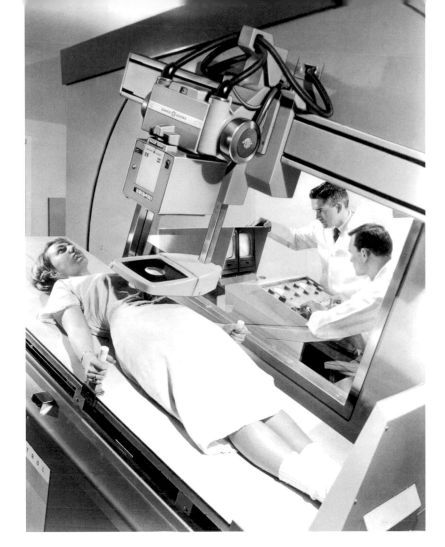

contributions in the mid-1960s: 1) the first 500-cycle, battery-powered mobile x-ray generator, which later was the model for the extremely successful CMX/AMX series of high-performance mobile x-ray units; and 2) the first solid state, three-phase x-ray generator, which made possible improved x-ray tube loading, higher energy, faster exposures and significantly reduced radiation per exposure.

Good things were also happening in the area of x-ray supplies and accessories where GE had introduced two new automated film retrieval systems, the Monoscan™ and the Monotrieve™ units. These devices gave busy hospital x-ray departments an efficient solution to storing and retrieving the thousands of radiographs they made each month. Each scalable system could store literally hundreds of individual patient film files in each five-shelf section and recall any file needed in moments. Additional sections could be added as the film inventory grew.

Monoscan and Monotrieve systems were, arguably, the earliest predecessors of GE's later entry into PACS—Picture Archiving and Communication Systems that use sophisticated digital storage technology to archive x-ray images as digital files for easy retrieval and review.

Meanwhile, on the industrial x-ray side, the improved Hytafill® 1000 product made its market debut in early 1961. It featured a capacity of up to 1,200 inspections per minute (that's 20 per second!) with a routine accuracy of approximately 1/32 of an inch (and up to 1/64 of an inch under certain conditions). This eliminated the underfilling of containers, which otherwise annoyed both customers and government weights and measures inspectors. It also eliminated overfilling, an equally vexing problem since it gave away product on the one hand and, if the contents happened to be beer, irritated tax authorities on the other. (An effort was even made to sell Hytafill units to the French wine industry, but it turned out no Frenchman was ready then, or now, to sip his Beaujolais nouveau from a can!)

The Hytafill system was also a great example of synergy, since it used exactly the same reliable "Made in Milwaukee" x-ray tube as the CDX dental x-ray unit.

Another major advantage made possible by remote control R&F systems was the greatly improved image quality resulting from the increased tube-screen (i.e., tube-input phosphor) distance. This was a particular advantage of GE's Teletrol system, which reversed the traditional placement of the x-ray tube beneath the table with the image intensifier suspended above. With the x-ray tube now overhead, it was very easy to increase the critical tube-screen distance. This arrangement also made it possible to produce spotfilms fully equal in quality to tabletop radiographs.

Growing the market

During the first half-century of its existence, Victor and GE X-Ray had marketed a huge variety of devices far beyond traditional x-ray equipment. Early sales catalogs encompassed an astonishing array of electro-medical offerings ranging from air pumps and centrifuges to Inductotherms® and proprietary surgical instruments. But such products largely had been abandoned in the decade or so following WWII in favor of exploiting the huge opportunities available in medical and industrial x-ray.

Image intensification, as we've seen, was a key development driving GE's recovery in the medical market, closely followed by powerful new generators and an entirely new family of R&F table systems. In addition, the business was continuing to strengthen its traditional role as a leading manufacturer of proprietary x-ray tubes with a stream of innovations based on new materials and designs.

One of the technology superstars who contributed so much during this period was Don Graves, who headed up controls and generators engineering. Don began his GE career in the old Chicago operation and made the move to Milwaukee in the fall of 1947, along with the rest of the engineering section. He was credited with two major

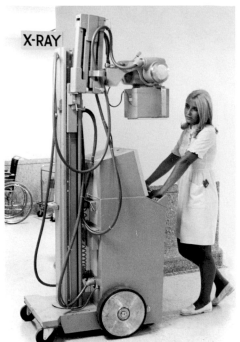

above, left
GE's first remote-control R&F system was the Teletrol unit.

left
The battery-powered CMX110 automobile x-ray unit could make x-rays anywhere in the hospital. GE has manufactured thousands of similar units over the years.

The industrial business was also producing a surprising variety of other imaginative products. In addition to the supervoltage units used to examine large parts, GE was marketing the Raymike® gauge for steel mills, the Inframike® moisture gauge for paper mills, and even a line of x-ray spectrometers for chemical analysis.

Remixing the offering

In light of all this activity, the company decided the X-Ray Department had plenty on its plate managing growth in traditional medical x-ray markets while also nurturing new initiatives in such nontraditional areas of medical technology as pacemakers, patient monitoring, nuclear medicine, and so forth. So, in May 1968, the decision was made to transfer the industrial x-ray businesses to Process Management and Control, a unit of the Industrial Process Control Division. Later that summer, the business was physically transferred as well, this time to the new Analytical Measurements Business Section that had been established in West Lynn, Massachusetts.

Just a couple of years later, GE decided to withdraw completely from the industrial x-ray business, marking the end of its long and distinguished record of leadership in this technology. However, the tube operation in Milwaukee continued to make industrial x-ray tubes until March 1978, when the last SMS 1000 came off the Electric Avenue production line.

Meanwhile, Walt Nelson was convinced there were tremendous growth opportunities to be explored in the export market. Both Victor X-Ray and GE X-Ray Corporation had been extremely active in the export field. GE X-Ray had even teamed with International General Electric (IGE) to form a dedicated export subsidiary—General Electric Medical Products Company (GEMPCO)—in late 1944. GEMPCO had gone on to gain a strong position in x-ray exports during the temporary absence of several major European competitors.

In the fall of 1951, IGE had taken full responsibility for selling and servicing GEMPCO supplied products abroad, including GE medical x-ray gear and a wide range of proprietary surgical products. (IGE also successfully distributed GE industrial x-ray gear as well.) The entire GEMPCO organization was subsumed by IGE shortly thereafter and moved to New York City as the IGE X-Ray Division.

Now, just 10 years later, the wheel turned full circle when Nelson reestablished GE X-Ray's own international sales organization at the Milwaukee headquarters. Bob Parkhurst was named manager of international sales and soon relocated from IGE, along with a nucleus of key sales personnel. In coming years, "Parkie" was a familiar figure around Milwaukee and the world advocating for export customers, distributors, and dealers. It was only when the business became truly "internationalized" with the establishment of permanent marketing and sales subsidiaries in the major export markets that he finally stepped down from a job well done.

Feeling the beat

As the turnaround in medical x-ray equipment gained traction, more and more attention began to be focused on marketing opportunities in non-x-ray areas of medical technology. One of the most fascinating was implantable cardiac pulse generators, also known as "pacemakers."

The genesis of the pacemaker can be traced to Dr. Wilson Greatbatch, a physician at the Veterans Administration Hospital in Buffalo, New York, who had built a rudimentary cardiac defibrillator in the 1950s. Fibrillation is a condition in which the heart muscles begin contracting in a random, uncoordinated manner and often results in the death of the victim. His idea was to apply a strong, external electrical current to the heart to restore normal sinus rhythm. Dr. Greatbatch's first experiments were conducted using ice picks as electrodes to conduct raw electric current to the patient's heart. Though that technique wasn't always successful, these early efforts eventually led to the development of capacitor-discharge defibrillators that became the standard treatment for arrhythmias.

With this encouragement, Dr. Greatbatch next turned his attention to building a transistorized pulse generator that would produce the appropriate electrical waveforms to control the heartbeat. His first attempts were directed at an external device that had to somehow be connected to the heart through chest-implanted leads. Since it was now 1960 and reliable transistors had become available, he soon took the technological leap toward an implantable, battery-powered device.

Meanwhile, the GE Electronics Laboratory in Syracuse, New York, had taken on the challenge of designing and building an implantable heart stimulator of its own. They were working closely with Dr. Adrian Kantrowtiz, director of cardiovascular surgery at Maimonides Hospital in Brooklyn, another early pioneer in the field. The company was sufficiently encouraged by the progress that the decision was made to transfer the pacemaker program to the X-Ray Department in mid-1961 for further development and commercialization.

Walt Nelson selected Bob Hodgers, his engineering manager, to head this project, as well as parallel development programs in patient monitoring and nurse communications. The team set up offices and labs in a portion of the Hotpoint plant that adjoined the Electric Avenue facility to the east. They were to remain there until a brand new plant was built near General Mitchell Field a few years later.

As the pacemaker program grew, Phil Read was brought over from his job as manager of x-ray components engineering to assume leadership of the Biomedical Systems Section. It would eventually be rechristened Cardio-Surgical Systems with responsibility for developing, manufacturing, and marketing pacemakers, patient monitoring products, and blood chemistry systems.

A number of technology challenges had to be overcome to bring GE's pacemaker

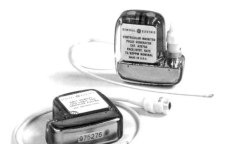

left to right
The Mobile KXC-3 industrial x-ray unit.

GE Portable DC defibrillator.

GE pacemakers built on Edgerton Avenue.

opposite, top
GE implantable pacemakers were assembled in a sterile environment to eliminate opportunities for contamination.

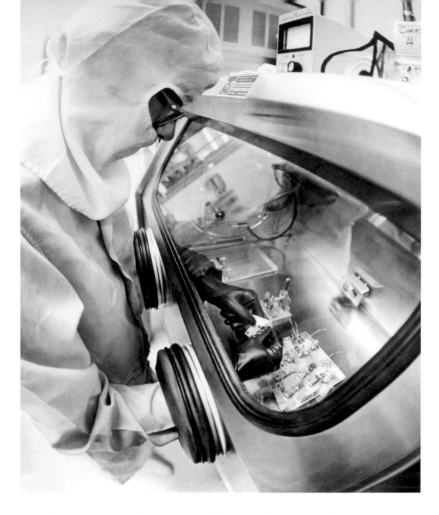

in terms of system reliability and performance. It confirmed reliably connecting the leads to myocardium remained a critical problem, so a huge campaign was launched to develop electrodes that would last as long as the batteries. At least a million dollars (big money at that time) was ultimately invested in this focused effort, but the problem was solved.

Meanwhile, Dr. Kantrowitz was conducting human clinical trials at Maimonides Hospital. GE provided free pacemakers, and he contributed the surgery to treat 200 patients who otherwise could never have afforded the procedure. Considerable information of great value was gleaned from these studies, such as the desirability of having separate leads and power packs. This design modification made it possible to easily install new batteries simply by unplugging the old unit and snapping on the new. The lead itself, which was the only component directly connected to the heart, could remain in place. Thus, the entire battery replacement procedure took only minutes and was usually performed under local anesthesia.

During the 15 years General Electric actively marketed pacemaker products, it developed a wide selection of offerings, from basic fixed-rate units to models that the patient could switch to faster or slower pulse modes. One model even featured rechargeable batteries; another was a "demand" unit that continuously analyzed the heart's natural pacer voltage and fired only when assistance was needed.

The final additions to GE's cardiac pacemaker line were the Sentry 75™ ventricular inhibited and Sentry 76™ asynchronous pulse generators. Both featured advanced mercury/zinc power cells and sophisticated electronics for extended operating life of an anticipated 4–6 years.

Ironically, in early 1972, the increasing life of GE pacemaker batteries had indirectly led to the first recall of its kind. Whereas the original industry standard battery manufactured by Mallory usually ran down within a matter of months, requiring the entire pacemaker to be replaced, improved batteries had extended implants to 12–18 months or longer. This allowed sufficient time for the body's natural moisture to penetrate into the circuitry and affect reliability. As a result, several hundred GE pacemaker patients were advised to have their units replaced. Another recall was initiated in 1974 for similar reasons.

Other manufacturers were also beginning to experience recalls of their own. In 1973 and 1974, Cordis Corporation recalled approximately 18,500 pacemakers, while Biotronik Corporation of Germany recalled about 1,350 units in early 1974 and Vitatron Medical recalled over 500 units the following June.

Not long after all these events unfolded, General Electric Company assessed the situation and made the decision to withdraw from the cardiac pacemaker market. Appropriate arrangements were made to support the GE units still in use, and the operation was terminated in 1976, ending an exciting decade-and-a-half at the far frontiers of biomedicine.

to market. Foremost was developing a reliable electrode to connect the pulse generator to the myocardium. This flexible wire had to somehow be attached to the beating heat and remain secure for literally 10s of millions of flexures (80 bpm x 60 min x 24 hrs x 365 days x 2 yrs = 84 million!). Though these leads were not the value-added part of the problem, they represented the greatest technical obstacle.

Another challenge was the size and life of batteries. At that time, researchers were reluctant to put mercury cells inside of patients because of the potential toxicity. Rather, small batteries based on silver were used initially and could deliver up to 2 years of tolerable life. As the industry gained more experience and confidence in encapsulation techniques grew, mercury/zinc batteries became the industry standard for many years until lithium cells were developed.

In 1966, the GE pacemaker development program completed the animal testing phase at the University of Michigan Medical Center, providing an excellent profile

left to right

To assure quality, employees in the GE pacemaker assembly facility on Edgerton Avenue were thoroughly trained and certified in a specified task.

Sentry 75 ventricular inhibited pulse generator.

Sentry 76 asynchronous pulse generator.

Gauging a new market

GE's experience in patient monitoring was similar in many details, though the final outcome ultimately proved to be entirely different.

As with pacemakers, the X-Ray Department's path into patient monitoring started with Nelson's initiative to explore new growth opportunities beyond the traditional boundaries of the x-ray business. As he recalled during a later interview, "Early on, we were receiving encouragement to search out other businesses in the medical field. Bob Hodgers was sweeping out the university/medical center community to identify opportunities that meshed with our field sales and service organization."

Several possibilities soon sprang into view, including medical testing laboratories that performed basic patient blood panels on behalf of physicians and hospitals. Though the potential opportunity was very exciting, the market was dominated by a company called Technicon. Since its revenue already exceeded that of GE's medical x-ray business, the decision was made to look elsewhere for an opening without such formidable competition.

The search soon spotlighted the emerging field of electronic patient monitoring, where GE's inquiries into the auxiliary medical arena had led it to consult with such prestigious providers as the Mayo Clinic in Rochester, Minnesota. There, and at other medical institutions, large and small, officials frequently mentioned an urgent need for coronary and intensive care monitoring capabilities. They wanted electronic assistants that could help them reliably track the vital functions of those pre- and post-operative patients who required around-the-clock monitoring. Attempts to provide these services manually had proven to be too great a burden on the nursing staff. Such efforts were also less than satisfactory for high-risk patients. While the nurse might be checking one patient's blood pressure down the hall, another might go into an undetected total arrest somewhere else. Something had to be done and remote monitoring offered a promising solution.

GE X-Ray built its first experimental patient monitoring system for St. Mary's Hospital in Rochester, the major facility where Mayo Clinic patients receive their in-patient care. Though the company had been making electrocardiographic (ECG) devices for quite some time, now this technology had to be upgraded, modernized, and integrated with various new components that could detect, monitor, and analyze a range of vital physiological function—heart rate, pulse, arrhythmia, systolic and diastolic pressures, blood oxygen level, respiration, temperature, and so forth. All of this had to somehow be made conveniently available to the nursing staff on a 24×7 basis. . . just as soon as much of the technology was invented.

The new patient monitoring engineering team in Milwaukee soon articulated a modularized system that could collect the data on all these vital signs directly from each patient and communicate it to TV displays at a central nurse station. Built-in alarms would sound an alert when a preset parameter was exceeded, allowing the duty nurse to respond immediately to the affected patient's bedside. No time was lost, and no potential emergency was overlooked. Along with continuous monitoring was a requirement for patient-to-nurse and nurse-to-nurse voice communications. So such capabilities also were built into these early models.

GE formally introduced its line of electronic patient monitoring products in 1962. Supported by its large field sales and service organization, the new line found ready acceptance, and the company soon became a major player in this market. As the product line continued to expand in scope and sophistication, the installed base continued to grow, leading management to eventually create a dedicated field sales and service group.

In the coming years, GE gained a substantial share of the patient monitoring equipment market in the U.S. and Canada, and was credited with a number of innovations, such as the *in vivo* pCO2 module that measured the partial pressure of carbon dioxide in the blood stream in real time. GE's 3100-Series modularized line was particularly well received, since it allowed users to quickly and easily assemble an intensive-care or coronary-care system of the configuration and scale that precisely matched their needs. There was even a telemetry system that provided continuous wireless ECG monitoring of intermediate care and ambulatory patients. No longer were they tied to the bedside modules by the various electrodes but could move freely within a defined area.

GE added new energy to the patient monitoring market when the computerized PDS (Patient Data System) product line was introduced in early 1974. This innovative "third generation" technology brought an entirely new level of sophistication and accuracy to the ICU/CCU environment. Its sensitive electronics could detect even minor complications in a monitored patient's vital signs, providing an early warning of potentially more serious changes. A major PDS advantage was its integral computer that could precisely measure such complex information as arrhythmias. It also was used to store, recall, and display complete patient trend information, including a history of parameters recorded during the previous 24 hours. Another unique feature was the "vector contour plot," which presented up to eight patient parameters as a segmented circle on a TV monitor. A change in any of them caused the corresponding segment to distort, providing the nursing staff a quick visual alert.

Despite the company's viable position in patient monitoring, change was in the air. In 1982, in response to the heavy demands being placed upon its resources by the great success in computed tomography and the major development program in magnetic resonance, GE reluctantly decided to transfer the patient monitoring business to Marquette Electronics, Inc. This innovative Milwaukee firm, founded in 1965, had earned an excellent reputation as a technology-oriented supplier of specialized electrocardiographic equipment and computerized analysis systems for hospitals and clinics. Now, the addition of GE's monitoring line and technical talent would allow

Besides its rock-solid lineup of conventional intraoral x-ray units, GE also was a co-pioneer, along with S.S. White, in panoramic dental radiography. GE's first panoramic system, the Panoramic 3000, allowed the patient's entire dental structure from temperomandibular (TM) joint to temperomandibular joint to be imaged in only 2 minutes on a single piece of x-ray film. However, it was the greatly improved and speedier Panelipse™ system introduced a couple of years later that really established GE as a leader in this segment. In addition to all the features of the Panoramic 3000, it also made it possible to easily adjust the axis of rotation to match the dental arch of each individual patient. The result was clearer, more detailed diagnostic images.

GE's continuing success in the dental x-ray market eventually required the construction of a 40,000 square foot assembly center near General Mitchell Field to house Frank Seminerio's team. In conjunction with three other dental products manufacturing

Marquette to broaden its reach into all areas of the market, especially intensive and coronary care monitoring systems. GE, which retained an equity position in the expanded firm, watched with pride as its protégé grew from this strengthened base into one of the most successful firms ever to serve this market.

All of these activities in non-x-ray product areas had led Nelson to create the Biomedical Business Section in mid-1968. Dr Peter Wargo, who had been the department's engineering manager since April of 1964, was appointed to lead the new group.

"For quite some time, we have been laying the groundwork and shaping this rapidly growing business to meet the new requirements for medical products," Nelson noted when making the announcement. "Now we are ready to move ahead by getting our organization and facility rearranged so that we can stay ahead of our competitors."

Nelson's optimism was well founded. The department's biomedical products sales in 1968 were double those of 1967 and tripled the following year. This vigorous growth was supported by a large, new manufacturing facility near the Milwaukee airport that was exclusively devoted to biomedical products and components.

A view of success

A similar story had been written in one of GE X-Ray's oldest businesses, dental x-ray equipment.

Among the very first products manufactured by Victor Electric Company was an electric motor to power dental drills. Though it's not certain when the x-ray was first used for a dental examination, examples still exist from the earliest years of the 20th century. What is known is the Coolidge oil-immersed, shockproof dental x-ray unit was announced in 1919. For the next 65 years or so, GE's name was to be closely associated with technical and market leadership in dental radiography.

As we've already seen, CDX self-contained dental x-ray units were a best seller from the 1930s until the early 1960s. They were beautifully engineered, sturdily built, and easy to operate. And though only available in basic black or stodgy white for most of its life, they were extremely reliable and never seemed to wear out. There may even be a few CDXs still operating out there somewhere today!

During the rush to upgrade GE X-Ray's market offerings during the early years of the Nelson era, dental x-ray products also received considerable attention. New wall-mounted models were introduced in a variety of decorator colors, and a full catalog of supplies and accessories—x-ray film, processing chemicals, automatic film developers, view boxes, and much more—was created. GE, of course, continued to manufacture its highly regarded line of dental x-ray tubes at Electric Avenue.

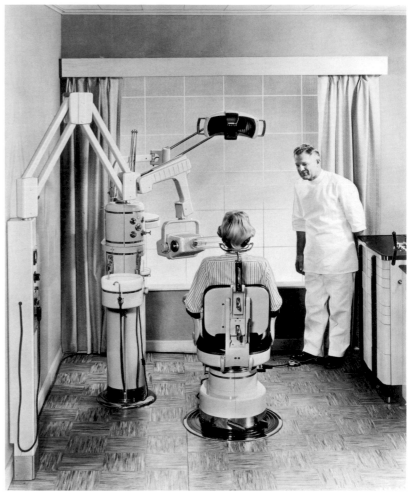

left
PDS central monitoring station.

above
The GE-70 dental x-ray unit. (1954)

GE's Panelipse panoramic x-ray system imaged the entire dental structure from TM joint to TM joint in just 20 seconds.

locations in the Milwaukee area, plus a facility in Syracuse, New York, this new plant was soon working at full tilt to keep up with customer demand.

As with the patient monitoring business, dental x-ray was caught up in the need to focus the resources and management attention of the larger business upon the booming computed tomography and magnetic resonance product lines. Thus, the difficult decision had been made to concentrate exclusively on the medical diagnostic imaging marketplace. GE's dental x-ray operations were subsequently sold in 1983 to an investor group led by John McDonough who took over as general manager from Orlin Yenerich. It emerged as the Gendex Corporation and went public a couple of years later in an extremely successful stock offering. Today, Gendex remains one of the world's leading suppliers of panoramic and intraoral x-ray equipment, digital imaging systems, intraoral cameras, and software.

The "908" project

One of the least known and most fascinating chapters in the X-Ray Department's history was the key role it once played in the nuclear armaments industry.

Since the early 1950s, General Electric had been under contract to the Atomic Energy Commission's (AEC) Los Alamos Scientific Laboratory and the Sandia Corporation to develop and manufacture neutron generators—euphemistically known as "zippers." These were a family of classified, complex, compact, and costly electronic devices used by the AEC in most nuclear warheads. The X-Ray Department was chosen by GE to execute the contract.

Interestingly, the neutron generator had been invented by Walt Nelson's friend and mentor at the University of California, Luis Alvarez. Dr. Alvarez, who had been closely involved in the World War II Manhattan Project that developed the atomic bomb, won the 1968 Nobel Prize in Physics for "the discovery of a large number of resonance states, made possible through his development of the technique of using (the) hydrogen bubble chamber and data analysis." He also was credited with developing the Ground Controlled Approach system (GCA), which is still used to assist aircraft in landing safely during periods of poor visibility, and inventing the synchrotron. (In 1980, he and his son, Walter, a professor of geology at the University of California-Berkeley, presented the asteroid-impact theory as an explanation for the extinction of the dinosaurs.)

"Dr. Alvarez invented the basic concept there in the Berkeley research lab," Nelson recalled. "The Atomic Energy Commission needed a proven supplier and chose General Electric, partly because we had known capabilities in high-voltage and components."

Another key reason was the fact the heart of the neutron generator was a small, x-ray type tube loaded with a capsule of tritium. GE was very experienced in dealing with radiation and radioactive materials; it also possessed unmatched skills in making high voltage tubes that could operate with very fast, precisely timed pulses of high energy.

During the early years of the contract, most of the activity was concentrated on the engineering development of this extremely complicated technology. The so-called "908 Product Section" had been set up for this purpose under the leadership of Dr. Roy Beaton, who had an extensive background in the nuclear field and came to Milwaukee from the GE-managed Atomic Energy Commission plant in Hanford, Washington. Much of the engineering development work was conducted in the Coolidge Laboratory at Electric Avenue.

By 1957, the project had reached preproduction status. With it now clear that GE would be able to manufacture zippers reliably, the decision was made to set up a dedicated factory in Pinellas County, Florida. This facility, managed by Ad Persons, was to grow eventually into an 800,000 square foot plant employing some 2,500 people, as many as were at work in Milwaukee building all the other products.

In an early 1962 edition of *GEXTRA*, the plant newspaper, Dr. Beaton was quoted as saying:

> The 908 Product Section still has to operate with a 'security gag' in its mouth. It can be said that Milwaukee develops and Florida manufactures so-called 'zippers.' Because of its skills and demonstrated performance in this field, this section of the X-Ray Department for a number of years has been the largest development subcontractor of the Sandia Corporation and the Atomic Energy Commission's major production source.

Because of the critical role these devices played in the reliable operation of nuclear weapons, they were designed and manufactured to extremely precise specifications. Quality was absolute and cost no consideration. For example, 9 of every 10 zippers were tested to destruction in order to prove with near certainty that the survivor would work as designed.

In the autumn of 1965, the Atomic Energy Commission informed the X-Ray Department of its intention to transfer the 908 engineering development activity to the Florida plant. Over the following months, a number of engineers and technicians in R. F. Wilson's operation made the move from Milwaukee to the St. Petersburg, Florida, area. The following year, an amicable divorce agreement was concluded that led to the reconstitution of the Florida operation as the independent Neutron Devices Department.

X-RAY DEPARTMENT, MILWAUKEE 1, WISCONSIN   G. E. 76 5/8 Up 5/8   Thursday, February 15, 1962

908 WORK STEADY

MR. R. H. BEATON

This is another in a series of articles by the section managers as to what's ahead for X-Ray in 1962. Dr. R. H. Beaton is 908 Product Section General Manager with responsibility for operations here and at Pinellas Peninsula in Florida. When questioned as to what's ahead for 908, Dr. Beaton said, "the 908 Product Section still has to operate with a 'Security gag' in its mouth when it comes to discussing publicly what the nature of its business is, both at Milwaukee and at Florida."

"It can be said," he continued, "that Milwaukee develops and Florida manufactures so-called 'Zippers', a family of classified, complex, compact, and costly (less so today) electronic devices used by the Atomic Energy Commission in most nuclear warheads. Because of its skills and demonstrated performance in this field, this Section of the X-Ray Department for a number of years has been the largest development subcontractor of the Sandia Corporation, Albuquerque, N. M., and the Commission's major production source."

For 1962, as well as for any other year, business volume alone will not determine the extent of profitability on Cost-Plus-Fixed-Fee contract operations, which are the basis of all 908 activities, but profitability is expected roughly to match the 1961 budget.

"At Milwaukee," Roy said, "the business volume of Bob Wilson's 908 Product Engineering

BOND INTEREST TAXABLE

Today's article on how taxes affect participants of the various General Electric benefit plans continues the questions and answers regarding the Savings and Security Plan which started in yesterday's GEXTRA.

6. WHEN STOCK IS RECEIVED IN A DISTRIBUTION, HOW WILL THE RECIPIENT KNOW THE BASIS (TAX COST) OF THE SHARES FOR PURPOSES OF COMPUTING GAIN OR LOSS ON SALE?

The Company will advise recipients of the basis (tax cost) of any stock which is distributed. This information should be retained for income tax purposes, since it may be required to compute and substantiate the gain or loss reported in the income tax returns when shares included in the distribution are sold.

7. WHAT IS THE MINIMUM LENGTH OF TIME THAT SHARES OF STOCK RECEIVED IN A DISTRIBUTION UNDER THE PROGRAM MUST BE HELD BEFORE BEING SOLD IN ORDER FOR ANY EXCESS OF SELLING PRICE OVER BASIS (TAX COST) TO QUALIFY FOR LONG-TERM CAPITAL GAIN TREATMENT?

As a general rule, shares must be held for at least six months and one day after they are received in order for any gain on sale to qualify for long-term capital gain treatment. In other words, the holding period for tax purposes does <u>not</u> include the period during which the shares were held by the Savings and Security Trust. An exception to the general rule applies to the sale of shares received in a total distribution made within one taxable year because of retirement, other termination of employment, or death. On such sale any gain will be long-term capital gain up to the difference (if any) between basis and market value at the time of the total distribution, regardless of when the shares are

Dr. Roy Beaton, general manager of the 908 Product Section.

The Pinellas operation continued as a GE component for a number of years until the company finally decided not to renew its contract with the AEC. The operation was then transferred to the Ball Brothers Company, bringing to an end a very unusual chapter in GE's—and GE X-Ray's—long history.

Positioning for the future

As the 1960s progressed, a flood of new developments appeared from every corner of GE. In consumer products, the rechargeable automatic toothbrush was introduced, plus the first of a series of lightweight, hand-held appliances such as electric hair dryers, electric slicing knives, grass shears, hedge clippers, and so on. The laundry room received a boost with the introduction of GE's V-12 washer, the first automatic washer with a 12-pound capacity. Soon, the Mini-Basket™ washing system was added to improve small load washing.

At the other end of the spectrum, the Space Division developed the pioneering NIMBUS meteorological satellite to supply timely information on atmospheric and environmental conditions. A total of seven satellites in the NIMBUS series were ultimately produced. Later in the decade, GE also built LANDSAT, the first earth resources satellite system and the first of today's fully operational global systems that help inventory and manage earth's natural resources.

Major developments were also happening in GE's organizational structure. In 1965, The Research Laboratory and the Advanced Technology Laboratories (successor to the General Engineering Laboratory) were combined into a new organization called the General Electric Research and Development Center. Arthur M. Bueche was named to the newly created post of Vice President, Research & Development, taking his place in the long line of distinguished GE research directors that began in 1900 with Dr. Willis R. Whitney.

Another space highlight for GE occurred on July 20, 1969, when the Apollo 11's lunar module, *Eagle,* set down on the surface of the moon. A few hours later, on July 21, mission commander Neil Armstrong became the first human to leave his footprints on the surface of another celestial body. The boots he was wearing were made from GE silicone rubber, and the visor on his spacesuit used Lexan® polycarbonate resin, a product of GE Plastics.

Though with considerably less drama than the moon landing mission, the X-Ray Department had been exploring far afield for new opportunities of its own. In 1966, that search had led to the acquisition of General Medical Balteau, an x-ray equipment manufacturer located in Liege, Belgium. Walt immediately transferred Don Deike, his second ranking finance manager after Stan Small, to Liege to help integrate the new subsidiary into the GE X-Ray family. It was soon renamed General Electric Medical (GEM) and became a key source of remote-control R&F systems for the U.S. market. GEM also would provide the next leader of GE's medical imaging business—Julien ("Jim") Charlier.

Walt Nelson had met Jim Charlier during the exploratory talks. At the time, the Balteau works specialized in the manufacture of electric transformers with a small operation in medical x-ray based on the quality of their transformers. Charlier had introduced a remote control x-ray table of his design that became a market success and attracted GE's attention. Though a new factory had been built to produce medical equipment, the Balteau family lacked the resources to fully finance its potential growth opportunity. Thus, they decided to sell the medical business to a company that had the necessary financial and marketing strength to assure success. They soon settled on GE X-Ray as the right choice.

In mid-1964, GE X-Ray had become a component of the Chemical & Metallurgical Division under Charles E. Reed. On January 1, 1968, General Electric reorganized its various businesses into a new structure, increasing the number of divisions from 29 to 46. Charlie Reed was named Vice President-Group Executive for the Components

and Materials Group, and Reuben Gutoff, who formerly led the Chemical Development Operation in Bridgeport, Connecticut, was appointed general manager of the newly created Chemical and Medical Products Division, which included the X-Ray Department and Plastics. Other group components were the Appliance Components Division, Electronic Components Division, and the Industry Components and Metallurgical Division.

Later that same year, GE X-Ray's increasing activities in non-x-ray areas of medical technology led General Electric to again change the name of the business. Frankly, "X-Ray Department" no longer adequately described its wide-ranging interests, so it was rechristened Medical Systems Department, a title that would go through several permutations in years to come until finally emerging as GE Healthcare in the new century.

A number of other changes were also afoot that would substantially affect GE Medical Systems. The first, which also occurred in 1968, would not be apparent for several years. That was when Godfrey N. Hounsfield, a brilliant scientist in the employ of EMI, the British company best known for recording the Beatles, described for the first time a complete system for "computerized trans-axial tomography" imaging in a patent application. The second was the mid-1969 announcement that Jim Charlier had been selected as the new general manager of Medical Systems Department. Walt Nelson, after 10 exciting and productive years, was appointed Manager of Special Medical Projects for the Chemical and Medical Products Division.

The die had been cast for perhaps the most dramatic series of changes yet seen in GE's medical equipment business.

top to bottom

GE's 1966 corporate calendar was printed in Milwaukee. R. G. Burrington (left) of E. F. Schmidt Co., shares an advance copy of an illustration with Walt Nelson.

Charles E. Reed, Senior Vice President, Corporate Technology

Growing Medical Technology

Jim Nelson

When I joined the X-Ray Department in 1959, the medical business was around $40 million, about half equipment and half film and supplies. We were probably Eastman Kodak's largest customer; film and supplies carried a lot of our operating expense. The industrial x-ray business was in the $6–$8 million range.

The technology of the medical equipment was hardly different from that of a decade or two earlier. So we faced an overwhelming need to bring our whole product line into the new decade. There was a big change around the bend called "solid-state electronics" that was going to be reflected in x-ray systems first by image intensification.

Our industrial x-ray business built huge radiographic x-ray units that would penetrate large castings or could be used for almost anything else you wanted to inspect, such as solid fuel crystals in ballistic rocket motors. In addition, people were beginning to talk about sterilizing substances with x-rays or electrons, such as an Army program to sterilize meat to provide shelf-stable food for soldiers on the battlefield. I even inherited a $10 million development contract with American Tobacco to sterilize cigarettes. We had built the first of 50 of these million-dollar machines, when American Tobacco realized that it didn't make good marketing sense to suggest their products needed to be sterilized, so they quietly terminated the contract.

Two other important industrial x-ray product lines were x-ray spectrometers, which could be used to study the crystallographic makeup of materials, and our Hytafill product, which looked at the fluid fill in a can on a production line. We built them for practically every canning line in the U.S. and even shipped them to Europe. We were very happy this product had originated in Milwaukee, which had a reputation for canning a lot of beer!

Our third business was making small reconnaissance cameras for the Air Force to use in the U-2. This was an offshoot of the fact that we already produced large, film-loaded cameras—either roll film or film pack—for chest radiographs. It was only a $2–$3 million a year business, so the big camera companies weren't interested. Since we had the skill, the Air Force asked us to make them.

We had a fourth business building the "908" product that was colloquially called "zippers." These were neutron generators that delivered a pulse of neutrons with extremely high precision to detonate large atom and hydrogen bombs. The Atomic Energy Commission selected GE to develop and manufacture them because of our skill in making high-voltage x-ray tubes that operated with very fast, precisely timed high-voltage pulses. When the product neared preproduction status, and we knew we could make them reliably, a production facility was established in Florida, and the entire 908 section moved down there.

At that time, we were beginning to deliver the very first generation of automatic film processors. The Veterans Administration had actually given General Electric the order to develop the processor later known as the X-Omat a few years before. We, in turn, subcontracted the work to Eastman Kodak, which made a huge success of the product for many years.

One of my first actions was to bring in Bob Hodgers from Engineering Services to radically overhaul and expand our engineering organization. Bob was an outstanding engineering management administrator and in a matter of 2 years, our engineering organization had grown by 50%. More importantly, this move allowed us to revitalize our basic business in tables and generators, converting them to solid-state controls, rather than relay controls. Also, we started the initial development and production of improved generators, image intensifiers, remote tables, mobile units, and everything else we needed to regain market leadership.

We soon started to see this turnaround in technology reflected in unit sales. And by 1965, almost everything in our catalog was a new product. We did it by setting up product teams to tackle each major product, consisting of a market product planner, an engineer product designer, a manufacturing engineer, and an accountant. We knew nothing about Six Sigma or Black Belts, but a lot of the things we were doing intuitively were the precursors of what came later.

Another important thing we started was to focus on non-x-ray opportunities in the medical marketplace—patient care monitoring, nursing care communications, and implantable pacemakers.

The latter was especially interesting. The GE Electronics Lab in Syracuse (N.Y.) had undertaken the construction of an implantable stimulator in cooperation with Dr. Adrian Kantrowitz, a cardiovascular surgeon at Maimonides Hospital in New York City. The company transferred the technology to the X-Ray Department and, in mid-1961, we decided to have a go at evolving a pacemaker product. So in our laboratory here in Milwaukee, we started from the original Electronics Lab design and soon developed the first of a fairly sizable market basket of GE pacemakers.

We also searched out other applications for implanted stimulators, such as lung stimulators to get people out of iron lungs and renal stimulators to help control incontinence. As it turned out, polio had been conquered, so iron lungs were disappearing. And renal applications only became common three or four decades later. So we really were quite far ahead of the development curve in this area.

We also started probing the auxiliary medical arena, where we found a great need for coronary care and intensive care monitoring. Hospitals wanted electronic systems for around-the-clock monitoring of the vital functions of the pre- and post-operative patients. We built an experimental system for St. Mary's Hospital in Rochester, Minnesota, from which we standardized some designs that could monitor various physiological functions, such as pulse rate, systolic and diastolic pressures, blood oxygen level, and so on. We articulated a system with modules that could follow all those various parameters at a central display so that nurses could track high-risk patients.

Bob Hodgers was so excited about these electronics ventures that I assigned him the responsibility for developing the medical electronic business as a section manager. Pete Wargo then came in as the new engineering manager, bringing his extensive technical background from the Research Laboratory and the picture tube operation in Syracuse. He put an even higher emphasis upon our traditional business, expanding the engineering function by another 50%. Pete ran it for 3 years before moving over to head up our medical products business section.

I then brought in Herb Hannam in the engineering management role. He was also a Ph.D. engineer with a strong background in vidicon and light-sensitive materials, both of which were particularly relevant to the hottest growth part of our business—image intensifiers. Both of these very fine men—Pete Wargo and Herb Hannam—were practical engineering managers and greatly bolstered us as technical leaders in x-ray.

My first marketing manager was Gordon Williams ("Mr. X-Ray"), a good example of how a strong personality, backed by a devoted organization, can mold a business. He went to work for the Victor X-Ray Company as a sales trainee just after WWI and spent his early career in Colorado, where he became the district manager. He then was brought to Milwaukee to head the entire field sales organization and was the gold-standard asset that I inherited. He only worked for me for 3 years before he turned 65 and had to retire. But Gordon was a real powerhouse who built an outstanding selling organization filled with people extremely dedicated to him. The competition couldn't hire any of his people away; there was too much loyalty and respect.

We replaced Gordon with David Day who was sent here by the group executive in New York. In some organizations, putting in an outsider is the way to go but not here. Gordon had hand-groomed Austin West as his successor, so Austin was terribly disappointed when he didn't get the marketing job. However, by essentially adding another layer, I made Austin my sales and service manager, where he was still doing an outstanding job when I left the business.

David Day later left to become president of Picker Corporation (Cleveland) and was replaced by Vince McCabe. Vince was an insider and did well with the marketing organization. He was a short, feisty Irishman who made his career in apparatus sales and would have had a good future had he stayed there. He also was still here when I left.

John McGown was manager of manufacturing and he had originally gone to work for the GE X-Ray Corporation in Chicago. He made the move to Milwaukee and stayed here until he retired. He was a real pro and ran a good manufacturing shop. John was a tiger for cost reduction. Year after year, our manufacturing and engineering organizations made enough through cost reductions to produce all the profits we had to make. Now, that's Six Sigma before anybody invented the term!

Fred Strouf ran the dental x-ray business and Dex Webster ran the industrial x-ray business. Industrial was a $10 million business by then and was soon transferred over to the Analytical Measurements section in Lynn, Massachusetts. The dental x-ray business was also eventually divested but continues to thrive today as Gendex.

I really loved this business and was fortunate to have an outstanding staff at every level and in every function. I'm especially proud of the fact that by the time I departed, our U.S. market share had risen to around 35%, overtaking Picker and setting us on the road to worldwide success.

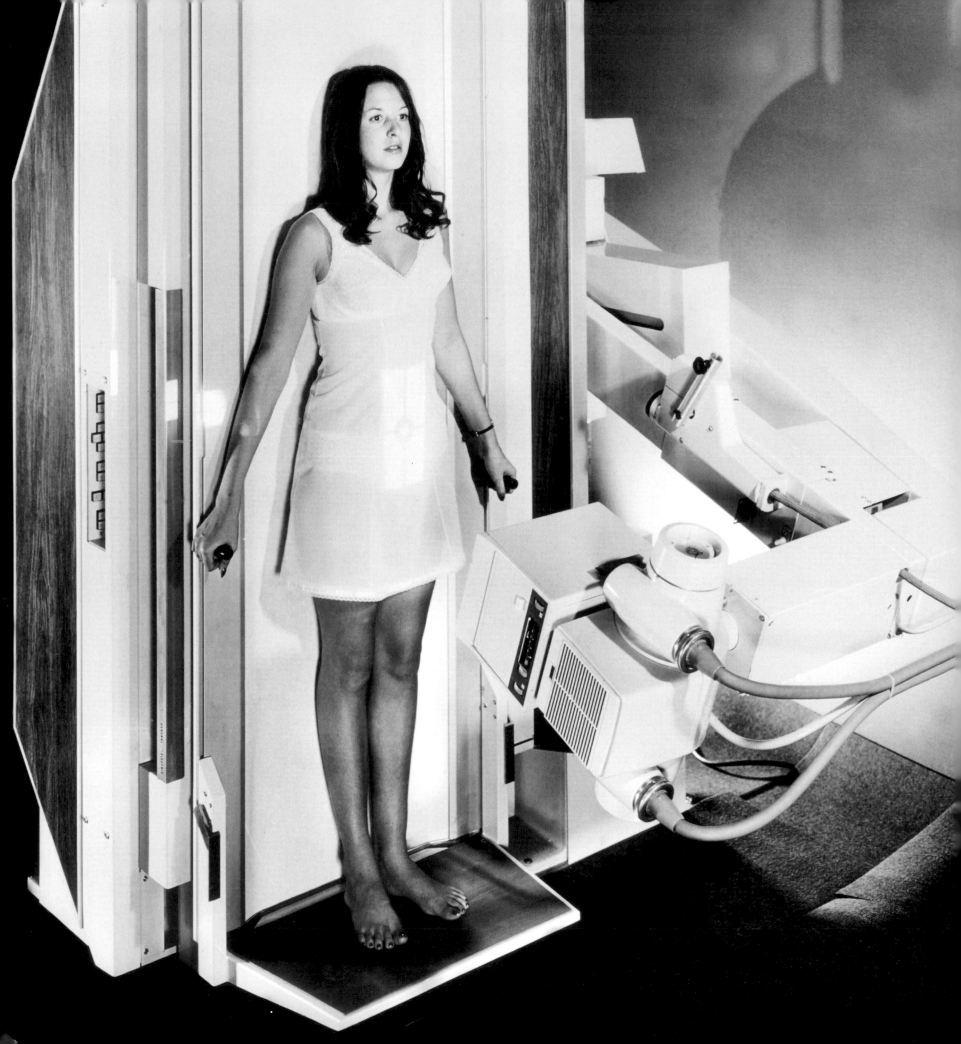

The Charlier Era

1969-1973

Julien "Jim" Charlier took over as general manager of the GE Medical Systems Department at a very uncertain moment in the history of the business. Not only was the entire company in the midst of a nationwide strike, but some senior corporate executives were expressing concerns about GE's potential liability should one of Milwaukee's medical products injure a patient. Confidential suggestions were even being floated at headquarters that the prudent course of action might be to exit the medical equipment market entirely.

This wasn't the only challenge facing Charlier and his new team. Upon his arrival, he soon discovered the business lacked a strategic business plan and was projecting its future business expectations based upon an accounting extrapolation from the previous year's results. In addition, despite many exciting advances in both traditional and emerging product areas, several serious product gaps remained, including the critical need for a premium remote control x-ray table system. One of his first actions was to implement a crash program to correct these deficiencies.

Lessons in Leadership

Julien R. Charlier (b. 1927) *began his career in 1949 as a factory worker at Usines Balteau, Liege, Belgium. He rapidly rose through the organization, becoming general manager of Balteau's small x-ray business in 1963. Jim was instrumental in arranging the sale of this operation to GE in 1966, leading to his appointment as general manager of GE Medical Systems in August 1969. He was elected a GE vice president in 1972. After completing the University of Chicago's executive MBA program in 1974, Jim returned to Europe as Chairman & CEO of the Cockerill Group. He then became Chairman & CEO of the DMC Group in Paris where he also was Vice President of the French Industrial Organization. He holds the Legion d'Honneur (France), Ordre de la Couronne and Ordre de Leopold (Belgium), and Ordre de St. Charles (Monte Carlo). Jim resides in Monaco.*

Not all was gloom, of course. Many developmental projects were already underway to update and strengthen key offerings across the medical x-ray product line. As we've seen, exciting progress was also being made in dental x-ray and the new biomedical businesses.

Perhaps the most satisfying early success enjoyed by Charlier was when he personally dedicated the new "Medical Systems Institute" in the autumn of 1969. Under the direction of John Stack, its staff of expert instructors—Gabe Melotte, Gene Cole, Dave Wilking, Mark Erhart, Warren Herwig, Russ Grothman, Jack Olson, and Ruth Redinger—was soon providing hundreds then thousands of man hours of advanced technical training for field service engineers each year.

Courses were later made available even to the in-house technical employees of GE customers.

The new facility was located next to the Milwaukee airport and directly connected to a major hotel complex. Thus, students found it extremely convenient to attend courses at any time of year, even in the midst of a harsh Milwaukee winter. They also could fill up those long winter evenings with additional hours of self-study in the adjoining Institute labs. All they had to do was use a special key to open an access door from the hotel's bowling alley (really!).

The Medical Systems Institute immediately set a new, higher standard for the medical equipment industry. It was the first and largest dedicated technical training facility of its kind to be established by a diagnostic imaging manufacturer. It also launched GE Medical Systems on a leadership trajectory in professional technical education that continues to this day.

Repositioning for strength

Charlier was struggling with a full plate of issues from his first day on the job. In addition to launching an urgent effort to develop a remote control x-ray table, he also started work on a new product development plan affecting all the lines.

Strengthening the staff also received priority attention. He had already attended to the leadership issue in Belgium by bringing Joseph H. d'Adler-Racz over from Usines Balteau to run General Electric Medical, the name selected for the subsidiary in Liege (d'Adler-Racz would be succeeded by Jean DeLeeuw, GEM's marketing manager, in early 1971). Changes were more extensive in Milwaukee. Though fully confident of John McGown's ability to run the factory and with Austin West in charge of a well-managed field organization, Charlier saw the need to bring in new players for several other key staff positions. Over a period of time, a number of GE managers from outside the business were appointed, such as Carrol Houser in Human Relations, Chuck McMullen in Finance, Herb Hannam in Engineering, and, in anticipation of Austin West's pending retirement, Bob Stocking in Sales & Service. Several other key positions were filled through internal promotions.

None of these efforts was more important than developing a credible strategic plan for the business. Charlier soon had his entire staff engaged in this critical project and even accelerated the schedule when word was leaked that the entire business might be in play at Corporate.

At this time, General Electric's vaunted strategic planning process had not yet been implemented. So Charlier and his staff may have been blazing the future path for the company, though unwittingly. Their new plan was ready the following year and, after a trial run before the Milwaukee area employees, was presented to Reuben Gutoff, the Chemical & Medical Products Division chief, whose organization included Medical Systems, Plastics, Carboloy, Magnetic Materials, Specialty Materials, and several others. Gutoff was so impressed he arranged for Charlier to present the plan in person to the Corporate executive board at 570 Lexington, GE's New York headquarters.

The reception was somewhat cool, Charlier later recalled, perhaps because Reg Jones, then GE Senior Vice President & Chief Financial Officer, could not believe the U.S. was willing to spend more money for healthcare; perhaps because some of his lieutenants were secretly lobbying to sell the business. Vice Chairman Herm Weiss, for example, questioned why the plan presented no alternative strategy to growth. In other words, where was the option to sell Medical Systems?

"Nevertheless," Jim said, "the meeting was somewhat useful. At least, the question of the future of this business was still open."

Not long thereafter, Charlie Reed was promoted to a key position at GE headquarters in charge of exploring new technologies. Gutoff was named to replace him as Vice President & Group Executive of the Components & Materials Group.

When GE implemented its formal strategic planning process across the company, Medical Systems rewrote its earlier plan in the new format. The effort by Charlier and his staff must have had an impact, because the Corporate strategic plan designated Medical Systems as one of the company's two "strategic business units," along with the Plastics Department, giving them the right to insert "Business" into their official titles (e.g., Medical Systems Business Department). More importantly, the medical business was now being recognized, officially, as having an especially important role to play in GE's future growth.

Medical Systems had come a long way in a very short while from a prospective "disacquisition" to a GE star. And the good news continued to flow.

On June 28, 1971, the GE Board of Directors approved plans to expand the business in the Milwaukee area. Some 6 weeks later, the Medical Systems Business Department

top to bottom

Jim Charlier (in shade at center right) addresses Electric Avenue employees shortly after his arrival in 1969. (The Hotpoint plant in the background was later razed.)

Julien (Jim) R. Charlier

Charlier presents his 1970 strategic plan at an all-employee (and spouse) meeting in Milwaukee, September 1970.

was elevated to a GE division. The new organization included the former operations and added responsibility for various suboperations in the medical technology field. Included was the Medical Development Operation that had been set up in Schenectady about 3 years earlier and was being managed by a scientist-businessman named Walt Robb.

As further evidence that Medical Systems' standing with GE Corporate was in the ascendancy, the GE board elected Jim Charlier a company vice president in the spring of 1972. Another new corporate officer named at the same time was the general manager of the renamed Chemical and Metallurgical Division, that included GE Plastics, carbide cutting materials, industrial abrasives, insulating materials, and so on. This bright, hard-charging, young executive was destined to have a profound impact on Medical Systems and, indeed, the entire company in subsequent years. His name was Jack Welch.

Just over 1 year later, in June 1973, Reuben Gutoff was selected to head up GE's new strategic planning effort for the entire company, and Jack was named to replace him at the Components and Materials Group. Jack now had both a professional and a personal interest in the fortunes of Medical Systems.

Making tough choices

None of these positive developments was achieved without considerable effort and no small amount of sacrifice.

Preceding the Board's decision to allow the Milwaukee expansion, Corporate Human Resources insisted some way be found to convert the local incentive (piecework) wage system to a day work (time-based) wage system. The implication was that in the absence of an agreement to bring plant wage costs under control, either the expansion would be disallowed or the business might leave Milwaukee entirely.

Local leaders and members of the International Association of Machinists and Aerospace Workers were extremely upset by this ultimatum, since their only choice seemed to be between a likely overall reduction in pay for many of their production-

line workers or no job at all. Considerable invective was aimed at the proposal, but they ultimately had little option but to agree. At last the way was clear for GE Medical Systems to reach for its full potential, although the fallout from this issue would continue to affect the business for several years.

Similarly difficult restructuring decisions were being made in other areas of the business, notably in the field organization. In anticipation of Austin West's retirement in 1972, Charlier had recruited a bright, energetic executive with years of field management experience in one of the most demanding technical organizations in the world—IBM. This new leader was Bob Stocking, who would go on to create a legendary career during his two dozen years of service to GE Medical Systems, its employees, and customers.

Lessons in Leadership

Robert LaVere Stocking (1934–2004), a Michigan native, received his B.S. degree in mechanical engineering from Michigan State University in 1956. He then joined International Business Machines as a sales trainee and over the following 16 years served in various sales and sales management assignments. In 1972, he was appointed general manager of the GE Medical Systems Sales and Service Department. In October 1978, Bob Stocking became general manager of the Medical Systems Sales and Service Operation, when the function was divided into separate sales and service departments. His organization was elevated to GE "division" status in 1981, and he was elected a GE vice president in 1982. Upon his retirement in 1994, a permanent award was established in his name to recognize the outstanding GE field sales professional each year.

One of Bob's first and most urgent actions was to implement a new compensation plan for the field sales force. This was essential if the business was to succeed in all of its new product lines. The field sales reps were most comfortable selling what they knew

left

As announced in this 1972 issue of *GE Monogram*, the company's former quarterly employee magazine, Jim Charlier and Jack Welch became GE vice presidents at the same time.

top to bottom

Union and company representatives sign the 1971 agreement that cleared the way for GE's expansion in the Milwaukee area. Participating were (seated, l-r) Lodge 1916 representatives John Pegelow, Ray Hoffmeier, Gil Kamin, and George Lajsic; company representatives Gene Sheehan, Jim Feiereisen, William Kennedy, Larry Kludt and Jane Christie; (standing, l-r) union reps Cliff Guske, Gene Kolar, John Michalowski, Francis Vandenplas, and Bob Matthews; and company representative Pat Smith.

Bob Stocking's appointment to lead the Sales and Service Department was announced in *GEMS News*, March 17, 1972.

best and were extremely well compensated for it. They weren't particularly interested in sparing valuable time to "prospect" in unfamiliar markets on behalf of unfamiliar products. The predictable result was the nontraditional offerings were languishing.

The solution was the introduction of a quota-based compensation plan that required each field sales representative to reach a certain level of sales in each assigned product category. Otherwise, the rate of compensation for even those areas where quotas were met would be reduced. Once again, the howls of protest were predictably loud and long; some sales reps even left to join the competition. But Stocking, with Charlier's full support, stood his ground and made his plan work, because it was the right thing to do for the business.

Bob's second major action was to divide the field sales and service force into separate organizations, though both continued to report to him. This move had a profound impact, since it freed up the service business to become a major profit center in future years. Don Porter, manager of the former Installation & Field Service organization, was appointed to lead Service into the new era.

Other key Medical Systems Sales and Service Department managers Bob appointed to help implement his new vision for the field organizations included: Jim Magner, Western Region sales; Mike Moakley, Eastern Region sales; Austin West, National Accounts and Government Relations; Bob Moliter, Marketing Communications and Development; Len Grassman, Relations; and Jim Fleming, Financial Planning and Analysis. The way was now clear for a more focused effort to bring GE medical technologies to a more diverse and expanding customer base.

Expanding to Waukesha

The proposed expansion was to include a new headquarters and manufacturing center plus major upgrades at the Electric Avenue plant. Announcement of these expansion plans had been preceded by an extensive search to locate a suitable site. Potential locations were considered within the city and Milwaukee County, as well as adjoining suburbs.

A few weeks after approval of the new factory pay plan, GE announced that the new headquarters and manufacturing facility would be constructed along Interstate 94 in Waukesha County, a dozen miles or so west of Milwaukee. Following additional siting and planning work, the project was released to a major Chicago architectural firm for the actual design work.

When Reg Jones became GE president in early 1972 (then chairman and chief executive officer later that year), one of his first actions was to bring the Board of Directors to Milwaukee for a first-hand review of the business they were about to invest in so heavily. That May, the Board issued the final expansion go-ahead by approving the actual construction appropriation. Ground was broken shortly thereafter, and the fast-track construction process launched.

How GE Came to Town

L. B. (Buzz) Hardy is a fourth generation Waukesha native who began his career in the commercial and industrial real estate business in 1959. His path intersected with GE in about 1970 when a Wisconsin Electric Power Company (WEPCO) representative informed him a Fortune 500 company that wished to remain anonymous was searching for a large tract of land with good Interstate access. Buzz picks up the story:

"I had found some commercial building sites for several companies near the Waukesha airport and I-94. One man we bought them from suggested that I also talk to Roy Schaefer, who owned a 100-acre farm just across the expressway and I ended up buying that tract. Had Larson and Lee Larson owned a second, adjoining farm and gave me a purchase option. When Tom Traband from WEPCO approached us in 1969, I realized there was the potential for an even larger site.

"About 6 months of so later, Tom asked if I had anything to show him, and he came out with two men I later found out were from GE. It was the middle of winter, so I took them all around the site on snowmobiles and explained where I thought

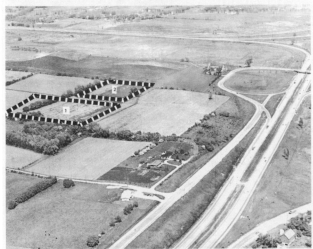

To Begin on Schedule at Waukesha Site

landscaped to add to the attractiveness of the facility.

The buildings will be constructed of concrete and glass and will be totally air conditioned and heated electrically. A special warm-tone glass being used on walls that face I-94 and route 16. Night lighting will provide a soft glow.

Inside, the manufacturing facility ll be a single story structure, interrupted only by a mezzanine floor manufacturing offices. Production flow has been carefully engineered and will include a unique system employing programmed carts that will carry parts and components to the proper assembly stations.

The office building is a two-story up-right "T" shaped structure. The main entrance to the facility will be through a glass-fronted lobby at ground level. The second floor rests on the relatively narrow lobby section of the first floor and on hills on either side of the entrance area. Interior design in the divisional head quarters building will minimize the need for internal walls. It will utilize modular furniture and strategic design ideas to isolate work areas but maintain an open appearance.

Reflecting on this expansion, Division General Manager Charlier noted "This is just one more step in the continuing efforts of the division to make this Milwaukee-based business the world leader in medical equipment field."

A BIRD'S EYE VIEW of the 436-acre Waukesha expansion site shows where the new facilities will be built in relation to the interchange of I-94 and route 16. This view is looking east with the interchange in the upper righthand corner. The dotted lines ind te the s and the placement of the buildings on the inal phase of construction. Number 1 is the manufacturing and engineering facility and number 2 is the division headquarters.

left to right

"Buzz" Hardy is the Waukesha developer who found the property for GE's 1973 expansion to Waukesha County.

An aerial view of the proposed site for GEMS's new headquarters and manufacturing center near Waukesha.

the limits were to give us the best chance of getting it annexed and all the utilities run out there. The nearest utilities at that time were in Pebble Valley, so we would have to run them under the expressway, renegotiate the interchange, and all those kinds of things. It was a huge undertaking.

"The visitors were very happy with the site and wanted to tie it up by giving us a substantial down payment for a 1-year option to buy. They had a fixed price per acre in mind, but we were apart by maybe $250,000 on the total value. I also didn't have all the parcels involved, so I asked for a week to digest their offer. During that week, I drove from Waukesha down to the Illinois state line, back to Waukesha, then out to Madison and back. I determined that ours was the only site of any size that had sewer and water available. They agreed to a fair price per acre with adjustments depending on how many of the 11 different parcels involved I was able to acquire. I spent the option year lining them all up for a total of 436 acres.

"A big concern was the annexation issue. The parcel was on the Pewaukee side of the expressway, and I had spoken to town officials about it. However, there was a substantial gap between our tract and the Town of Pewaukee's sewer and water plant, so I was concerned about having to go through other people's property. I had considerably more confidence in Waukesha and arranged a private meeting of the Waukesha Common Council—you could have secret meetings in those days—to consider an annexation proposal. We presented the unnamed client's plans, and the council happily agreed to annex and zone the property, as well as pay for extending water and sewer lines. In exchange, we guaranteed about $20 million in taxable improvements.

"When we filed for annexation to Waukesha, we ran into a real buzz saw. The Town of Pewaukee decided to hold two public meetings to discuss a potential lawsuit. We asked Jahnke & Jahnke, the town engineers, to study the potential school portion of tax bills in Waukesha and Pewaukee, about half the total then. They concluded that since the school rates were the same, everyone would benefit from the increased assessed values created by the development. The town chairman, who was a very close friend of mine, was also helpful by rebutting claims that our secret client might be a waste disposal company. When both meetings were concluded, the Pewaukee town board voted to withdraw their appeal.

"We still didn't know who the actual customer was, only that they were from the East Coast, because I had to call them in the Eastern time zone during the period of negotiations. It was actually good that nobody knew, because if even one landowner had pulled out in hopes of getting more by dealing with GE directly, it could have caused the whole deal to backfire. Their local attorney, Reuben Peterson, invited us to come to Milwaukee to discuss the project. We got to his office and were shown into the conference room. The only thing on the table was a copy of Fortune magazine with a picture of a light bulb on its cover. That was Reuben's way of telling us that his client was General Electric. They asked for a 45-day extension to await the outcome of the union vote at their Milwaukee plant. A few weeks later I saw an article in the Milwaukee Journal reporting that the union had voted something like 20 to 6 to change their wage system and the rest was history.

"We couldn't have picked a better partner for the Waukesha community. They have been just marvelous. I've had many wonderful relations with GE personnel such as Phyllis Piano who helped us start an organization called Finer Waukesha and played a big role in making it a success. Waukesha would have been a different community today without GE because, with the expressway, it was becoming a bedroom community. But the people they brought here joined the community and got involved in the schools and the not-for-profits right away. They're still doing it today. It was the biggest break we ever had."

★ Thursday, July 6, 1972

WAUKESHA FREEMAN

GE Plant Work Begins

Leveling work has begun on the site of the General Electric plant to be built at the intersection of I-94 and Highway 16 (above, looking southwest). Two buildings housing manufacturing, sales and engineering facilities are planned for the 436-acre site, with a combined space of 460,000 square feet. The offices should be ready by the fourth quarter of 1973, according to Julian R. Charlier, a GE vice-president.

(Freeman Photo by Earl Schneider)

top to bottom
This *Waukesha Freeman* photo from July 1972 shows heavy equipment leveling the site for GE's new headquarters and manufacturing facility.

By May 1973, the new Waukesha complex was rapidly taking shape.

New products, new opportunities

As mentioned earlier, one of Jim's major initiatives was to update and upgrade the product line. The first fruits of this effort were on display at the 1970 meeting of the Radiological Society of North America (RSNA). Still held in Chicago's Palmer House Hotel at that time, this meeting had long been the traditional stage where the imaging industry introduced its latest offerings.

GE Medical Systems' marketing communications team, led by Bob Moliter, Bob Filip, and John LaRocco, did not disappoint.

Foremost among the innovations from GE was the brand new Telegem™ 90 remote-control x-ray table, the premium system that Charlier had called for virtually from his first day on the job. Bob Mueller and his engineering group responded magnificently. This elegant unit was based on the popular Telegem 15 table that the Belgian subsidiary was supplying. Engineered and built in Milwaukee, the Telegem 90 allowed remote fluoroscopy, radiography, and tomography in a single exam room. With 90°/90° table angulation, a three-way tabletop and multidirectional tubehead angulation, it provided unprecedented versatility and efficiency. The Telegem 90 table received an enthusiastic welcome and remained a best seller for many years.

A string of additional GE innovations were on exhibit, including:

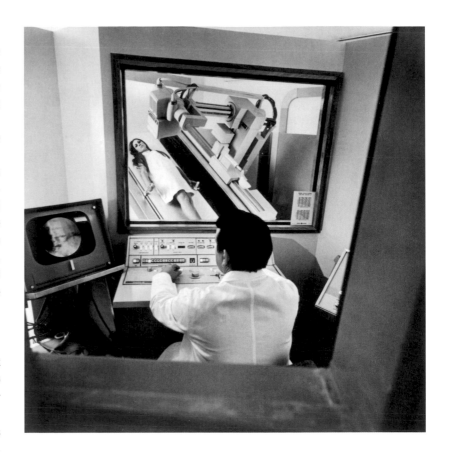

- Two new MSI™ generators, both featuring millisecond interrogation, instant initiation and termination of exposures, and photo-timing accurate to two milliseconds. They were the direct descendants of the solid-state generator technology pioneered by Don Graves several years earlier.
- The Fluoricon® 300 image intensifier that Bob Godbarsen and his engineers had designed used advanced solid-state electronics to maximize image clarity, brilliance, and information content. It was offered in a choice of single- or dual-field image tubes and also featured GE's new Cine 180 recording system.
- The new Sentry™ collimator anticipated proposed government regulations by automatically limiting the x-ray beam to reduce off-focal radiation. This feature not only minimized patient radiation but improved film quality.
- Another hit was GE's new vertical Bucky stand that increased the versatility and flexibility of general x-ray procedures rooms. This film-holder/positioner permitted off-table chest films, horizontal and vertical radiographs of the skull and spine, plus standing, recumbent or sitting views of the patient. They flew out the door.
- In addition to all the new offerings, GE's exhibit also featured a strong selection of proven performers, such as the Maxitome™ "dial-a-pattern" conventional tomography system; the Maxiray™ high-thermal x-ray tube line; the CMX-110™ battery-powered mobile x-ray unit; and many others.

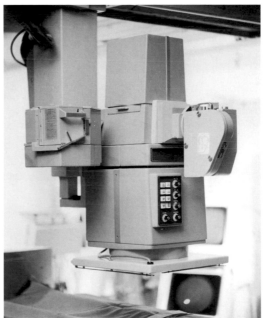

top to bottom
GE's Telegem 90 remote-control R&F system.

GE's Fluoricon 300 image system.

Not every new product at the show hit a home run. Though an imaginative new approach to solving the problems of film jamming and vibration, the Q-82™ rapid film changer (named for its developer, Joe Quinn) never quite caught on in the market and was abandoned a few years later. What made it special was its air-driven film advance mechanism that could change full size x-ray films at speeds up to 12 per second. Its daylight film magazine was loaded automatically and could hold up to 39 frames. A great idea, but the market simply wasn't ready for this "outside the box" product.

One of the biggest benefits of this exhibit was it announced to both customers and competitors that General Electric was in the diagnostic imaging market to stay and that it intended to be a leader. Equally important, it demonstrated to GE engineers, marketers, production line workers, and staff that they could meet a challenge and compete with the best.

GE's 1971 RSNA exhibit was equally successful. Among the important products

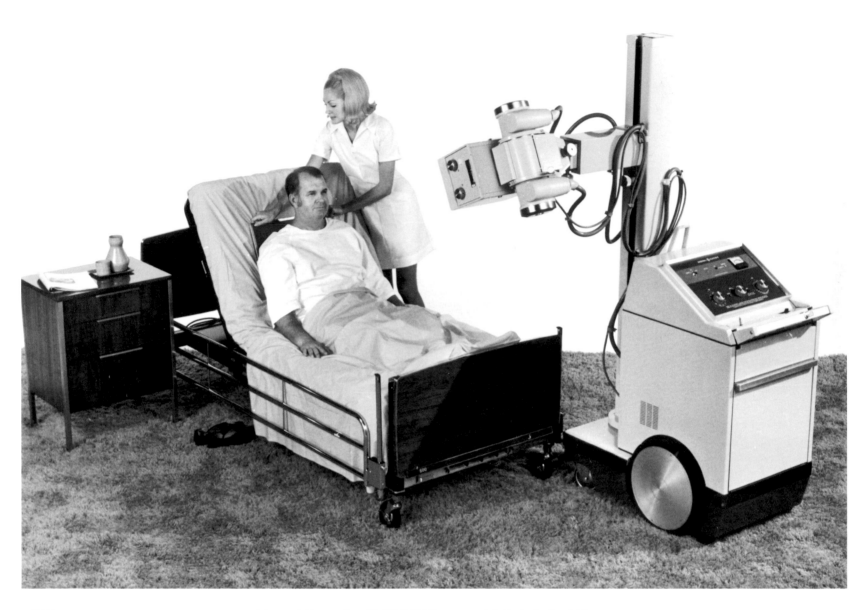

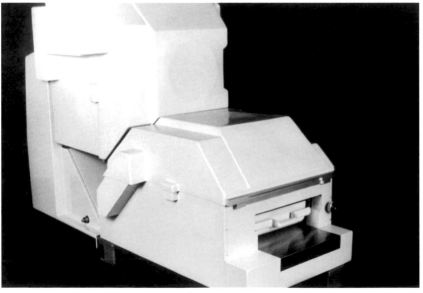

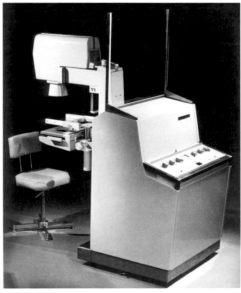

top
GE's AMX-110 auto/mobile x-ray system was one of the first models in the most popular line of self-powered x-ray units ever.

bottom, left to right
The Q-82 rapid film changer was a great idea ahead of its time.

The MMX II mammography system combined Xerorado-graphic and conventional film imaging capabilities.

introduced at that meeting was the MMX™ portable mammography system, GE's first dedicated unit for breast studies. As Jim Charlier said just after that meeting, "Most of the radiologists that I talked with made the same unsolicited comment: that they believe GE is now a leader in the radiological industry. Even most of our competitors recognized our leadership and congratulated us for our outstanding performance."

The buzz at Corporate also was positive, thanks to Charlier's foresight in inviting all eight GE regional vice presidents to the 1971 RSNA meeting to see for themselves what GE's newest division was doing. Their curiosity had been whetted by an extensive article on the business in the *GE Investor* magazine, as well as considerable positive discussion at an information meeting for shareowners earlier that autumn.

Following detailed presentations by Charlier, Austin West, Phil Read (the new biomedical section manager), and Bob Moliter, the group took an extensive tour of the technical exhibits, followed by lunch with Reuben Gutoff, group vice president. At the conclusion of the busy day, it was clear these influential GE executives were firmly in Medical Systems' corner.

By the way, another GE innovation at that meeting was the introduction of professional models as booth presenters, demonstrators, and hosts. Though several other exhibitors objected strenuously, show management said no rules had been broken and allowed GE to continue. The following year, virtually all of the major exhibitors had professional models in their booths, too!

Reaching for Europe

The first European X-Ray Congress (RADEX) was held in Amsterdam during the summer of 1971. This was the largest x-ray convention organized in Europe for many years, so the "home" manufacturers—Philips, Siemens and CGR—pulled out all the stops to make an impression. It also marked the first serious effort by GE Medical Systems to organize a first-class exhibit at a European venue.

This coming out event was important to GE's competitors, because it signaled they would have to factor it into their home market strategies in the future. It was important to potential European customers because it was their first real opportunity to get to know GE products, management, and sales personnel. It was important for GE, because it was a great forum in which to directly measure its product line and quality against the best Europe had to offer.

GE's first major foray into Europe returned real value in many ways. Even in those areas where clear competitive deficits were identified, the critical input gained in Amsterdam was extremely important in positioning the company and its products for a major win 2 years later at the huge International Congress of Radiology (ICR) in Madrid, Spain.

The Madrid ICR Meeting

In October 1973, the 13th International Congress of Radiology in Madrid, Spain, drew over 8,000 radiologists from around the world, including 1,500 from North America. GE was among the largest technical exhibitors with 3,800 square feet of space, its largest booth ever up to that time. Under the theme, "General Electric Means Performance In Any Language," huge crowds gathered throughout the 6-day event to review the wide range of GE imaging products on display, from advanced vascular procedures equipment to mobile x-ray units. Several new products made their market debut, including the Televix 90/15 table and Polarix mobile image intensifier from the Liege operation, as well as the Fluoricon-U vascular diagnostic system, Physiological Monitoring System, and a new patient table for the Neurotome from Milwaukee.

American-style marketing was also on display. Two highly visible billboards (each in English, French, and Spanish) were on the road in from the airport to welcome ICR visitors and urge them to visit the GE booth. Medical Systems also exclusively sponsored a special 500-page abstract volume of all the papers being presented

MEDICAL SYSTEMS NEWS

A LOOK AT MSD'S COMPETITION . . . INSIDE THE NEWS

Vol. 3 No. 42   General Electric Medical Systems Division   November 2, 1973

Waukesha Office Moves to Start Early in 1974

Moves into the new division office complex in Waukesha will get underway in late January and early February of 1974 for most headquarters operations, says David Schmidt, manager, plant and facilities.

A ceiling problem in the new building, created by drawing error, has now been corrected giving the early 1974 green light to the office moves, originally scheduled to begin later this year.

However, as a result of the recent creation of the X-Ray Products Manufacturing Dept., final planning of the moves for those activities has not yet been determined.

"A careful reevaluation is now underway to determine where those various manufac-
(Continued on page 4)

THE STORY WAS in the crowds that flocked around division demonstrations, like the Neurotome, at the 13th International Congress of Radiology in Madrid, Spain. More that 8,000 international radiologists viewed MSD's product performance at the six-day meeting, carefully comparing division equipment with major x-ray manufacturing competitors.

THEY HAVE LOTS OF GLASS. Construction men show perfect teamwork as they hoist huge window panel into place at division headquarters building at Waukesha. Move-in schedules for early next year have been announced for most engineering and office employees.

8,000 Radiologists at Madrid Find Exhibit Worth the Trip

MADRID, SPAIN - - - Medical Systems meant performance in more than 15 different languages as radiologists from around the world crowded division displays at the 13th International Congress of Radiology here.

The Congress, one of the largest international shows, met in Madrid for six days of meetings and equipment demonstrations by every major manufacturer of medical equipment for the worldwide market.

More than 8,000 radiologists, including 1,500 from North America, attended the Congress and each of them had a chance to see MSD equipment in action.

"I think that the real story of the ICR was in the massive number of radiologists who took the opportunity to view our demonstrations and find out about our equipment," says Bob Moliter, manager of Market Operations, Sales and Service Dept.

"Competitively, I would say that we significantly outdrew Siemens, Philips, Picker and CGR in customer traffic at our exhibit," he says. "Radiologists really took an interest in what we had to display."

And there was a lot for those radiologists to see under the GE logo.

(Continued on page 2)

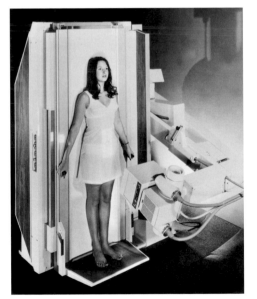

top to bottom

Visitors crowd around the Neurotome exhibit at the 1973 ICR meeting in Madrid. Within months, the Neurotome and its sister, the Omnitome, would fall victim to a superior new imaging technology called "computerized transaxial tomography"—CT.

Televix remote control x-ray system produced in Liege.

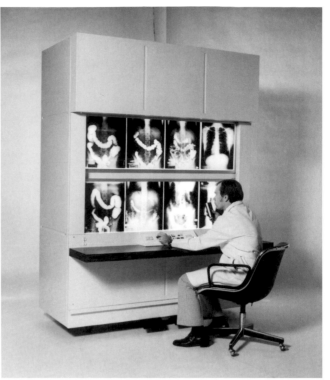

at the meeting, ran ads in the Congress daily paper, and distributed press kits to all the media.

"We significantly outdrew Siemens, Philips, Picker, and CGR," said Bob Moliter, Manager of Market Operations at the time. "The new products displayed the innovation of General Electric and our pride in new product development. It was truly an excellent show."

Jim Charlier launched another significant international outreach effort that autumn when he invited a number of key European radiologists and their wives to visit Milwaukee in advance of the RSNA meeting in Chicago. This program helped solidify and expand on the positive results from the RADEX conference by giving these important thought leaders another convincing demonstration of GE's expertise in imaging technology and commitment to serving the world radiology community.

While the radiologists toured the Milwaukee facilities for detailed technical and business briefings, their wives were being treated to their own activities, including tours of Chicago architectural treasures, special hospitality events, and even shopping expeditions. On the final evening, the European guests and their GE hosts enjoyed a gala dinner party at the Chicago Playboy Club. The visitors were truly impressed, since this level of hospitality was completely unknown in the Europe medical community at that time. Months later, they were still talking about their trip to the United States, which provided a huge boost to GE's still young image in the European marketplace.

Incubating better ideas

Besides the gains being made during the early 1970s in medical and dental x-ray, pacemakers, and patient monitoring, the company was also busily searching out new business opportunities in related areas of technology. Among the most promising areas were nuclear medicine, thermography, hearing conservation, membrane products, and an expansion of the supplies and accessories offerings in imaginative new directions.

GE's interest in the developing technology of nuclear imaging sprang from its desire to become a full-line supplier of imaging technologies to healthcare providers.

Nuclear imaging was one of the most promising new techniques of the day and used scintillation detectors to image concentrations of radioisotopes injected into the body. The idea was that the "uptake" in areas with active disease would be greater than surrounding normal tissue, resulting in a detectable pattern that could be analyzed and even diagnosed.

Though GE had a long history of leadership in x-ray tubes, TV pick-up tubes, and various other types of high-power tubes, it had no particular expertise in designing and manufacturing the scintillation detector tubes used by so-called gamma cameras. Since they were the fundamental technology of nuclear imaging, the company found it necessary to look far afield in order to enter this new market. In 1971, this search led GE to an enterprising high-tech Israeli company named Elscint that had developed credible expertise in scintillation cameras and displays. Since GE was looking for technology and Elscint was looking for access to the enormous U.S. healthcare market, a marketing agreement was in their mutual self-interest. Soon GE became the U.S. distributor for Elscint scanners and set out to establish a track record in nuclear imaging.

A subset of the nuclear diagnostics business was the Bone Mineral Analyzer. This technology was acquired from a small Wisconsin company called Norland Instruments and provided a quick, accurate method for assessing the density of bone, an especially important measurement in post-menopausal women who tend to lose calcium. The patient's arm would be positioned inside the small, tabletop scanning device and the measurement made. With that information, the physician could determine whether bone density was in the normal range or if a corrective therapy was indicated.

Thermography was another cutting-edge imaging technology being investigated as an alternative to ionizing radiation in detecting certain diseases and medical conditions. The concept involved a heat-sensitive detector that was used to scan the patient and produce an image of the relative distribution of heat on the surface of the head or body. The thought was certain diseases—breast cancer, for instance—would cause elevated blood flow to the affected tissue with a corresponding increase in

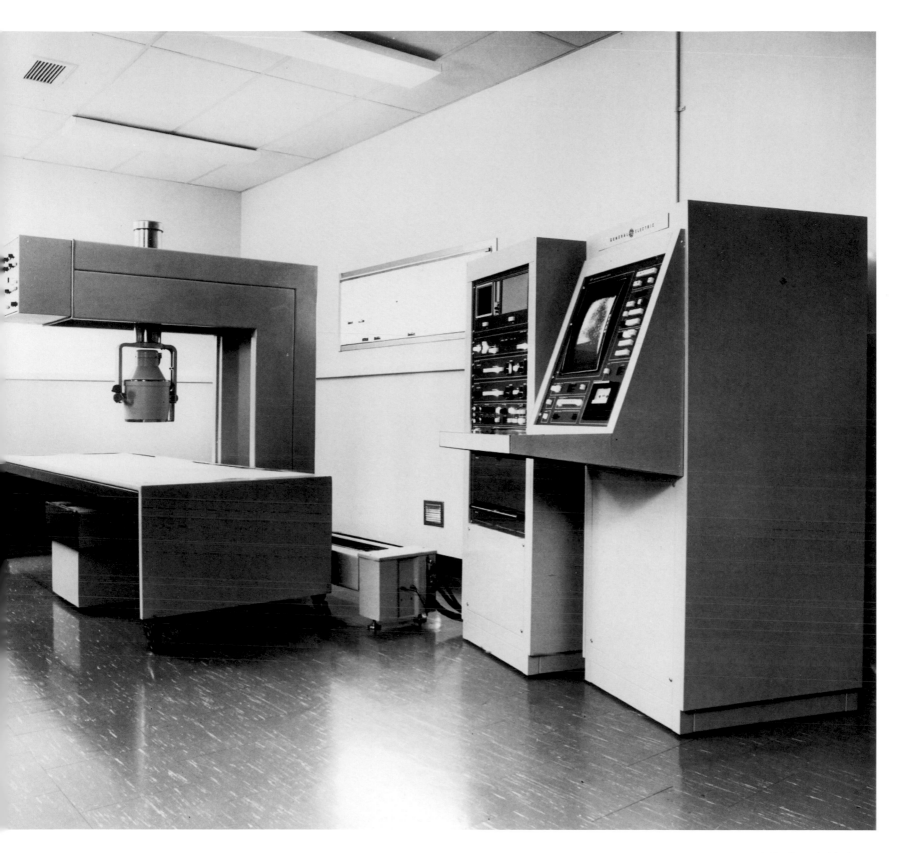

The MaxiScan whole body
scintillation camera was
one of GE's earliest models.

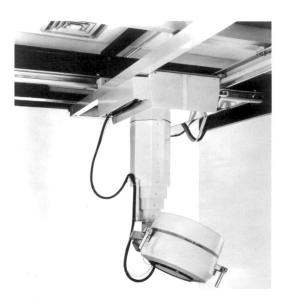

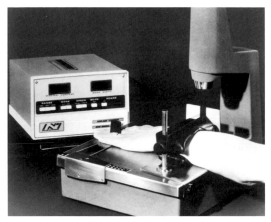

relative skin temperature. Similarly, an arterial occlusion might result in a bilateral temperature discrepancy in such areas as the head. The hope was a trained and experienced observer might learn to detect and interpret these variations.

GE got into thermography by purchasing a small producer that had a promising product but lacked the muscle to take it to market successfully. The new device, called the Spectrotherm 1000 thermography system, featured a high-sensitivity mercury cadmium telluride infrared detector that could detect and display temperature differentials as small as 0.2 C. Tim Hanson and his team launched it with a sustained marketing push over several years. However, the equivocal clinical results it and competitive units produced led to a lukewarm response from both diagnosticians and health insurers. For these reasons, GE eventually withdrew from the thermography business.

Dreams of a GE artificial heart

The least known of Jim Charlier's many "outside the box" initiatives was his dream of creating an artificial implantable heart. Invented in the early 1960s by Paul Winchell, a popular American ventriloquist, voice actor, and prolific amateur inventor, it was viewed by many as the ultimate therapy for terminal heart disease.

Jim began thinking about the artificial heart soon after his arrival in Milwaukee. He was convinced the implantable pacemaker alone would never yield sufficient growth to assure the future of GE's cardiosurgical business. An implantable artificial heart, however, could open up a tremendous worldwide market while burnishing the company's global image.

Success would depend on several factors: medical expertise, R&D resources, money, and time. Working alone in order to keep the rest of the business focused on more immediate needs, Jim addressed the first factor by interesting a well-known Houston heart surgeon in the idea. Next, he approached the GE Research & Development Center, but they weren't interested in such a project. Undeterred, Jim made preliminary contacts with several U.S. foundations and found some interest in possibly cofinancing such an effort.

"To pursue the project," Jim said, "I decided that we should prepare a specific strategic plan dedicated to the artificial heart and present it to the GE board of directors. But only after we had successfully opened our new plant and headquarters in Waukesha. Unfortunately, events did not give me enough time to act."

A particularly interesting marketing effort was the Peacekeeper™ personalized hearing protector that had been introduced to the industrial safety market in late 1970 by Walt Robb's Medical Development Operation (MDO). This device, based on GE silicone technology, was individually fitted to each user by pressing uncured silicone into the external ear canal and inserting a small tab to help extract it. After a cure time of several minutes, the Peacekeeper was ready for use. The big advantage of the Peacekeeper was the silicone would completely fill the external ear canals, totally blocking dangerous high-frequency sound waves and moderating excessive loudness. Yet normal speech could be easily heard even with the earplugs in place.

Several well-known Medical Systems' executives served in MDO during this period. Besides Walt, Jim Del Mauro had come to Ted Johnson's Health Safety Products Section in 1970 as the first salesman for the Peacekeeper product. Several years later, Jim and two colleagues, Pete Conners and Larry Sangermano, proposed to take the Peacekeeper business outside GE as a separate venture business. Their plan was thwarted when Johnson found another buyer for the entire business, so Jim moved over to the Metallurgical Products Department as Midwest Manager for Carboloy® carbide cutting tools. In 1975, Jim returned to Medical Systems after Jack Welch urged

him to interview for the top job in the newly created Eastern Region. He eventually became a GE vice president and served as general manager of the U.S. sales organization, the U.S. service organization and the corporate accounts group.

Rich Stevens came to MDO from the Silicone Products Department and later led the division's marketing support team under Walt Robb before serving as the Computed Tomography marketing manager. Rich was responsible for Health Safety Products advertising and sales promotion, including Peacekeeper hearing protectors. At the 1971 Indianapolis 500, he fitted several well-known racecar drivers with Peacekeeper earplugs, including Jackie Stewart, the Formula One champion. James Garner of "Maverick" fame, and an avid sports car racer, was also an early convert.

Though few people still remember the Health Safety Products Section, it was extremely imaginative in its marketing efforts. In addition to the Peacekeeper, it also offered several other hearing conservation initiatives to industry. One was the Hearing Van Service, a mobile evaluation service that assessed the hearing of workers at their job locations. Another was a program to develop improved hearing receivers. For example, in early 1972, some 60 AT&T telephone operators in Birmingham, Alabama, participated in the evaluation of various types of headsets. GE's improved product was introduced soon thereafter. Medical Systems sold the Health Safety Products Section to Marion Laboratories in 1973 for $1 million. As a condition of the sale, Marion also brought Ted Johnson over to continue managing the business.

From "films" to Filmamatics

Another cutting-edge project was based on GE's unique film technology in polymer and gas permeable membranes. Walt Robb had made his scientific reputation at the R&D Center in the mid-1960s by his work in developing these materials for medical analysis applications and even artificial lungs. Alvin Toffler, in his iconic 1970 book *Future Shock,* described Walt's work in some detail as another example of the fantastic advances being made in virtually every area of science and technology during this amazing decade.

In one of his experiments, Walt used a selectively permeable artificial membrane for the six sides of a small box. He then placed a hamster inside and submerged the box in water. The hamster survived a long immersion no worse for the experience; the membrane allowed oxygen molecules from the water to pass through the membrane

as a breathable gas. Thus, the hamster was in no danger of suffocating (though starvation may have been another concern!).

When Reuben Gutoff initiated the Medical Development Operation (MDO) in 1968 to find applications in the medical field that did not compete with GE Medical Systems, he selected Walt to run it. An early objective was to explore the "automated clinical laboratory" business. Unfortunately, large pharmaceutical companies had already bought up the best labs before MDO was formed. So Walt set his sights on the membrane business and soon won a $40,000 order from Technicon Instrument Company for their very popular Auto-Analyzer. Over the next few years, sales increased to around $3 million annually with excellent margins. In fact, when Walt Robb was transferred to Medical Systems in 1973, the profit of the renamed Medical Ventures Operation was as large as the rest of the division's businesses combined.

Among the earliest and most exciting applications for GE's gas permeable membranes was the GE-Peirce Membrane Lung. This device was primarily used to perfuse the blood of surgical patients requiring total support during such procedures as coronary bypass vein grafts. In 1971, it even maintained an adult female for 8 consecutive days, a huge breakthrough in membrane lung performance. Despite these great results, GE believed an artificial lung business was too risky, recognizing that a substantial percentage of patients on life support would not survive, and GE's deep pockets were all too inviting. The business was closed and no attempt was made to license the many GE patents in this area.

Bill Mathewson's cardiopulmonary support systems subsection had developed a related product—a membrane oxygen enricher for the home healthcare market. This business was sold to the project's chief engineer who formed a new company called Oxygen Enrichment, Inc. After being marketed for only a year or so, it was supplanted by newer technology.

GE's innovative pCO2 blood gas monitoring system also owed its success to membrane technology. Developed jointly by MDO, the R&D Center, and Bob Macur's blood chemistry engineers in the Cardio-Surgical Systems section (Roger Sergile, Joe Lai, and Dick Wrege), it solved a major operating room problem. Now, it was possible to continuously measure the partial pressure of dissolved carbon dioxide in a surgical patient's blood, eliminating the need to draw a blood sample, rush it to the lab, then wait for the results to return. This GE innovation displayed the information directly to the surgeon and anesthesiologist in real time.

Activities also were brisk in the area of supplies and accessories where Gene Lewis' X-ray Supplies Product Section was rapidly expanding its offerings. X-ray supplies had formerly been limited to those ordinary items an x-ray department needed to make use of its machines—film, barium, processor chemicals, light boxes, film sleeves, timers, and so on. Now the offering looked to satisfy the total needs of the department, whether by helping solve administrative problems or speeding the workflow. More than 2,000 individual items were listed in the 1972 x-ray supplies catalog, including some truly innovative new additions.

Foremost was the RAPORT radiological reporting system that linked a small computer with a CRT terminal, an optical scanner and a printer to speed the generation of examination reports. Depending on the study performed, the radiologist would select from among preprinted "mark-sense" forms corresponding to the anatomy examined (chest, abdomen, extremity, head, etc.) and check off a series of diagnostic descriptors of the examination findings. When findings were filled in, the form was inserted into an optical scanner, and the information correlated with prestored diagnostic phrases. The report would then be automatically printed out for final review and distribution to the referring physician. The tedious and time-consuming routine of dictating diagnostic findings into a recorder, transcribing the tape, and typing the

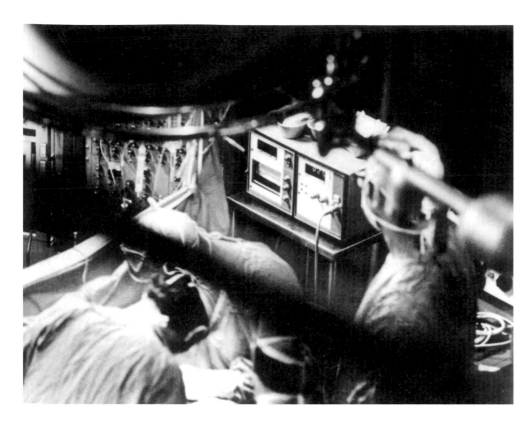

top, left to right
GE's on-line pCO2 monitoring system used permeable membrane technology to obtain in vivo measurements of arterial carbon dioxide with a disposable sensor.

RAPORT radiological reporting system speeded the distribution of examination results.

bottom, left to right
The compact Filmamatic film processor was easy to operate and could process all standard x-ray film sizes up to 14 × 36 inches in just 90 seconds.

The Changex chest radiography unit had an integral Filmamatic film processor.

opposite
GE-400 x-ray film processor.

report was totally eliminated, greatly simplifying and speeding the reporting process. The RAPORT project was led by Jim Schumacher who launched his distinguished GE marketing career with this product. He later held a variety of senior marketing positions, culminating in his leadership of the magnetic resonance marketing effort.

The biggest hit of the year, however, was the new Filmamatic™ automatic film processor. This remarkable little unit could be installed quickly and easily—no more difficult than hooking up a washing machine—and just as readily moved to a new location whenever necessary. Yet it could turn out completely finished 14×17-inch films in minutes.

The following year, this versatile unit was integrated in GE's new Changex™ chest radiography unit. This compact, floor-mounted system was designed to speed routine chest exams, the most common radiographic procedures at the time. The patient would be positioned in front of the adjustable film holder and the exposure made. The exposed film was then automatically sent to the Filmamatic processor and a fresh film automatically loaded in its place. No human intervention was required except to position the patient, periodically replenish the film magazine, and remove finished films from the processor.

The Filmamatic presaged a series of compact film processors from GE, such as the GE-400 and the Dentl-D-Veloper™.

All in all, GE's varied activities in these nontraditional areas of medical technology were a totally convincing demonstration of the imagination and innovation that have always been the hallmarks of General Electric and its people.

High tech, short life

Undoubtedly, the most dramatic new x-ray imaging products that General Electric introduced during the Charlier era were the Omnitome™ and Neurotome™ systems. However, they were fated to enjoy a very brief life span due to developments in a totally unexpected new area of medical imaging.

These complex positioners were engineering marvels, perhaps the ultimate expressions of remote-control R&F technology sophistication. Designed to facilitate advanced examinations of the brain and vascular system, they featured a double c-arm configuration in which the larger c-arm held an isocentric patient chair on one end and a smaller c-arm on the other. The latter c-arm mounted an x-ray tube and a combination film-holder/image intensifier on opposite ends. This entire mechanism was mounted horizontally to a wall fixture that permitted the entire assembly to be rotated.

The Neurotome was the somewhat less sophisticated of the two and specifically designed for advanced neuro studies, such as routine and special skull exams, pneumoencephalography, ventriculography, cerebral and arch angiography, and so on. The Omnitome could do all of that and more: cardiac catheterizations, coronary angiography, and routine visceral angiography. For the latter procedures, a special cantilevered examination table was rolled into position between the tube and intensifier.

The basic idea of the double c-arm design was to provide an almost unlimited choice of projection angles to get the best possible views of the anatomy of interest. This was a particular challenge in pneumoencephalographic studies, where a bolus of air was injected into the spinal canal then manipulated into the ventricles of the brain. The air was necessary to provide enough radiographic contrast to image the "shadows" of brain structures. Securely strapped in the examination chair, the patient could be rotated in virtually any plane to float the air bubble to its destination. The isocentric feature kept the area of interest in the exact center of the field of view no matter how the patient was turned.

Similarly, these complex motions were also used to assist the passage of an injected contrast material to illuminate the blood vessels of the brain, heart, and body organs.

As remarkable as their capabilities may have been, the Neurotome and Omnitome systems were living on borrowed time virtually from the moment they first appeared. That was because a new imaging technology called "computerized transaxial tomography" (CTAT) had recently been introduced in Europe and was quickly making its way to the U.S. The major advantage was this technique could directly visualize tiny contrast and spatial variations in brain tissue (and later other organs), and it could do so in just a matter of a few minutes while the patient sat in a stationary examination chair or lay on a table. Gone were the straps and extremely painful air injections.

The relative merits of CTAT (or "CT," as it ultimately became known) were obvious to physicians, patients, and manufacturers alike. In short order, these elegant engineering masterpieces joined the long list of x-ray curiosities that had their brief moments in the limelight and then disappeared forever.

Infrastructure improvements

The flood of imaginative new products and expanded services for which Jim Charlier had called had an impact upon facilities. We've already seen how the various biomedical initiatives had resulted in the construction of a new facility and how Dental X-ray had opened a new assembly plant. Ground had also been broken for the new headquarters and manufacturing complex near Waukesha. Meanwhile, an additional manufacturing location had opened in the nearby New Berlin Industrial Park in mid-1970. Among its various activities was assembling the first Panoramic 3000 dental x-ray systems. The Fluoricon 300, Rapid Accelerator, Rotor Controller, and Models 76 and 77 tables were also built there.

In later years, New Berlin would become the site for the CT engineering and manufacturing center and the first MR engineering and assembly facility. It also became home to Leon Janssen's Physical Distribution organization, which included Bob Pullen's Traffic and Transportation group and Charlie Yingling's National Distribution Center that relocated from Chicago in the early 1970s. Willy Dunham managed the warehouse for them. Also on hand at various times were Jim Knowlton's System Compatibility Assurance (aka "staging") operation, Ed Weaver's Export Commercial Services group, Phil Peck's Academic Research team, and various other smaller activities that also called New Berlin home.

Investments in the thriving area near the Milwaukee airport also continued. In August of 1971, 1 month after the Waukesha expansion was revealed, the company announced plans for a new 25,000 square foot biomedical laboratory and office building across the street from the biomedical manufacturing plant on Edgerton Avenue. The goal was to more closely integrate the marketing, product development, financial, and administrative activities with the manufacturing function. At the time, biomedical development operations were housed in Building 9-H (since demolished) at the north end of the Electric Avenue parking lot, while marketing and finance func-

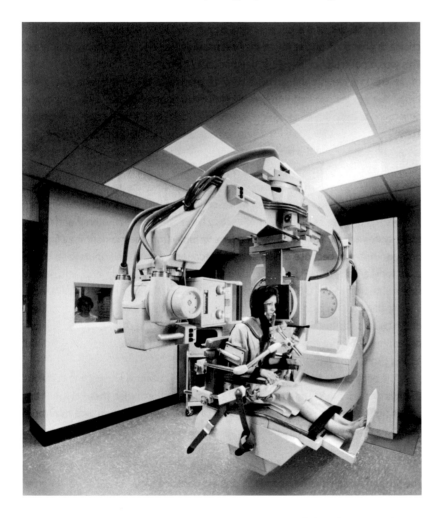

Perhaps the most complex radiographic system ever designed and manufactured by GE was the Neurotome positioner for imaging the brain and vascular system. It was soon supplanted by the arrival of CT scanners.

tions were in a leased facility at 60th St. and Forest Home Ave. By the time Phil Read's Biomedical Systems Section occupied the new facility at 315 W. Edgerton Avenue in early 1972, it also had a new name—the Cardio-Surgical Systems Section.

The main plant at Electric Avenue was also bursting at the seams. Cy Statt, manager of facilities planning and engineering, was making plans to free up 50,000 square feet of space to revamp manufacturing and relieve crowding until the new Waukesha facility came on line. The Edgerton expansion made Building 9-H available for other uses, such as personnel accounting, inventory control, and systems engineering. The acquisition of an additional 24,000 square feet at the Hotpoint plant (Building 5-A, since demolished) allowed the consolidation of all preassembly stock. This move made available 27,000 square feet of space in Building 3 (the main plant) to expand assembly, feeder, fabrication, and machining operations.

Shortly after these moves were announced, John McGown, manufacturing manager, announced planned changes at the Electric Avenue facility to make the future Waukesha expansion operable. The proposal was to convert Electric Avenue into a "master machine shop" for the new assembly site and add a separate machine shop to support the x-ray tube operation. Shifting the stock room to Building 5-A was the first step in implementing this plan.

The company was backing its plan with cash—an appropriation of $1.4 million to accomplish the first phase, plus cumulative appropriations of another $3.8 million through 1973 to add 50 new machine tools. It was estimated, at that time, the total appropriations for the master machine shop would grow to $8.4 million by 1976 for a total of 125 new machine tools and $13 million by 1980 for another 175 new machine tools.

Actions were also being taken to refine the organization. One of the most important was key personnel changes in the X-Ray Systems Product Department announced in February 1972. Al Scheideler continued as general manager with Cy Statt heading Manufacturing, Herb Hannam leading Engineering, Dan Paul in charge of Marketing, Tom Walsh managing Financial Planning and Analysis, Bill Kennedy running Employee Relations, and John McGown responsible for Department Integration Projects. Everything appeared to be set for a turnaround.

These various expansion activities and organizational changes conveyed a clear message. In return for the union's previous concession on the wage system issue, GE was delivering on its promises to expand the business in Milwaukee with massive investments in facilities, tools, and infrastructure. Medical Systems was here to stay!

As exciting as all these changes and improvements were, there was still a substantial price to be paid. With more new products being introduced into the factory at the same time it was being restructured, reorganized, and refitted for future needs, it was inevitable something had to give.

That something proved to be lengthening delivery delays. Products that once could be delivered in a matter of weeks now required months. Despite various corrective measures, the situation continued to deteriorate throughout 1972 and 1973. At its worst, a customer ordering a complex vascular system could expect to wait as long as 2 years for delivery. Not even loyal GE customers of long standing were willing, or able, to tolerate that kind of response.

The situation had come to the attention of upper GE management, of course. After considerable deliberation, the difficult decision was made to name a new management team in Milwaukee. First, Joe Williams was brought in from Aircraft Engines to solve the manufacturing bottleneck. He, in turn, assigned Bill Hawes the key task of creating a new materials management system capable of supporting a growing manufacturing program. Then, in December 1973, Walt Robb was named to take over as division general manager.

A new era had begun.

Vol. 1 No. 28   General Electric Medical Systems Business Department, Milwaukee   August 6, 1971

REAKING GROUND for the new biomedical office
uilding and development center to be built on Edgerton Avenue across from the present biomedical manufacturing facility is handled by these earth scrapers.

Second Major Plant Expansion:

BEGIN NEW BIOMED DEVELOPMENT, OFFICE FACILITY

top

The new GE dental x ray manufacturing center on Edgerton
Avenue was opened in 1972.

bottom, left to right

The headline in the August 6,
1971 edition of *GEMS News*
announced that construction
was underway at the site of
the new biomedical facilities
on Edgerton Avenue.

Working to overcome the
manufacturing backlog, super-
visors John Buckley and Ray
Hatch (left and center) check
Monitrol tables, while expeditor
Bill Barg prepares another for
final assembly in Waukesha.

Memories of My GE Days

Julien R. Charlier

I was the general manager of a small x-ray business at Usines Balteau. We specialized in a remote-control R&F table that we had designed and that had quickly become a hit in the fast-growing medical equipment market. Since the Balteau family lacked the resources to finance our potential growth, I persuaded them to sell us to a larger company. I visited more than 20 potential purchasers, including Westinghouse, Litton, ATT, Kodak, Philips and others, and finally reduced the choice to Siemens and GE.

Siemens was the world leader with a line of modern products and a good knowledge of the medical market. But their primary interest in our operation was to ease their penetration into French-speaking markets where a German company was not really welcomed at that time. Despite GE's basic and somewhat obsolete product line, I chose them because we could be their key entry to exploit the booming European market. Moreover, Walt Nelson was a decent man with whom I got along well. So I helped him to convince the Balteau family to sell to GE.

Following the acquisition, we had to change quickly from a European accounting system to the U.S. system. Our very small organization was soon submerged under GE audits, meetings, and bureaucracy. Nevertheless, we made our budget that first year. I recall a remark made by a GE director: "It is the first time in modern GE history that an acquisition beat its budget the very first year of its association with us." As a result, we got the right to rename our business "General Electric Medical."

After Reuben Gutoff became general manager of the Chemical & Medical Products Division, he decided to replace Jim Nelson in Milwaukee and tried to convince me to accept the job. I thought it was not a very good idea, as I felt ill prepared to manage such a large business and knew little of GE management methods and practices. I suggested that he instead appoint Walt Robb, head of the Medical Development Operation, and to promote me in his place. Gutoff refused, so I had no choice but to finally accept his offer.

I arrived in Milwaukee in mid-1969 in the middle of a nationwide GE strike. On my first day in the office, I asked to see the department's strategic plan and discovered to my surprise that there was none. So I quickly decided that my key priorities should be: 1) to improve the product line as soon as possible; 2) to strengthen the staff; and 3) to define with the staff our first real strategic plan. I first charged engineering to develop a premium remote control R&F system, then started working on a new product development plan and a credible strategic plan. Over a period of time, I brought in three outstanding associates: Carrol Houser in Human Relations, Bob Stocking in Sales & Service, and Chuck McMullen in Finance. To hire Chuck, I had to refuse the official candidate of Reg Jones, then GE's chief financial officer. I also made several internal promotions.

About this time, Stan Small, my first finance manager, informed me that the business would not meet its budget for the year or its target for 1970. I had the unpleasant task of giving Charlie Reed, our group executive, the bad news. He had a hard time swallowing it!

I learned that certain corporate executives were advocating the sale of the x-ray business because of GE's potential liability should our equipment hurt a patient. I thought such a sale was not in the company's interest, so I sped up the completion of the strategic plan to counter this alternative.

Reuben Gutoff was very excited when I presented the new plan to him in late 1970. He then arranged for me to present it to the Corporate Executive Board. I later discovered that this was the first time that a GE business had made such a strategic presentation to them.

The reception was somewhat cool. Reg Jones was doubtful about the willingness of the U.S. to spend more money for health care, while Herman Weiss expressed his regret that I didn't present any alternatives to growth. (His remark suggested that Corporate was already in contact with Boston Consulting Group and/or McKinsey on the subject of strategic planning since "alternatives" was then a key new idea in business consulting.)

Though I don't think that our presentation was a significant factor, GE did impose its formal strategic planning procedure a short while later. We rewrote our plan according to the new rules and reissued it officially. It is interesting to note that in all the presentations of our plan, I insisted that our goal should be to become number one worldwide in our market. This may have been the starting point for GE's later strategy under Jack Welch to be "#1, #2, or Out."

Our revised strategic plan still did not convince the board, so the long battle to be accepted as a growth business in the GE portfolio started. Successively, two review boards from GE headquarters were imposed on the division. We had many meetings; I spent time with each member to try to win them to our cause. Only Dr. Edward Kline, Corporate Medical Director, understood the medical market. To make our plan more palatable, we actually reduced our estimate of the potential of the health market in the U.S. and in Europe. We named the third edition "Best Bet." When the Corporate strategy consultants reviewed the plan at length, they became very supportive. I think their contribution was decisive. Finally we were officially designated a "strategic business unit." Gutoff was proud that the only two such GE "growth" businesses were in his division: Plastics and Medical.

As a result of our new status, Reg Jones, now GE President, brought the GE board to visit the plant and review our operations. That meeting was a success.

Phil Read, manager of the pacemaker business, called me one evening in 1971 to inform me that he had a quality problem. Several patients had died because of an acceleration of their heartbeats. We decided to recall several hundred pacemakers, replace them with new units, and reimburse cardiologists for the surgical procedures. It was a costly decision that *Time* magazine called "The Ultimate Recall." I had to inform Corporate. It was a blow to our business.

In the effort to beef up the product line, I wanted to engage the division in the CT scanner market, a new technology in x-ray diagnosis. We lacked the internal knowledge and resources to conduct a development program of our own, so our first contact was with Corporate Research. Their response was not encouraging; they had no time and no resources to devote to such a large project. So I decided to try to acquire the company that had originated the concept—an English firm called EMI that specialized in music publishing and recording, including the Beatles. I visited them twice for meetings with their executive board. My major argument was that they, with a single product, could not afford to finance the service organization needed to develop their market share. Though they had no knowledge of the medical business, they were convinced that they could succeed. So they refused to consider my proposal.

To prepare for the future, we needed a new plant. The old Electric Avenue facility was too small and lacked the right image for a business such as ours. Corporate Human Resources imposed as a condition for approval that we change from a piece-work wage system to a time-based wage system.

We had many meetings on this critical subject. Finally, John McGown, my manufacturing manager, declared he was sure we could implement the swap without losing productivity. My gut feeling was that we could not, but I had no rational argument to oppose his view. I discussed the issue with Gutoff, but he didn't think refusing was an option. When I warned him that our profits could collapse, he replied that it was not a major issue, since he was speculating in the silver market and thought that the profit from these transactions would offset any potential decline in our results. I felt I had no choice, so I reluctantly agreed. It was a major mistake. As I feared, manu-

facturing productivity collapsed and so did our delivery times and profits. We should have changed the wage system later, after moving into the new facilities and stabilizing the business.

In retrospect, I hope my contributions were somewhat useful to GE. I still remember a farewell conversation with a union representative who said, "You made a big mistake in changing our wage system. But you had a vision of our future and you put the business on the GE map, where it had not been before your arrival."

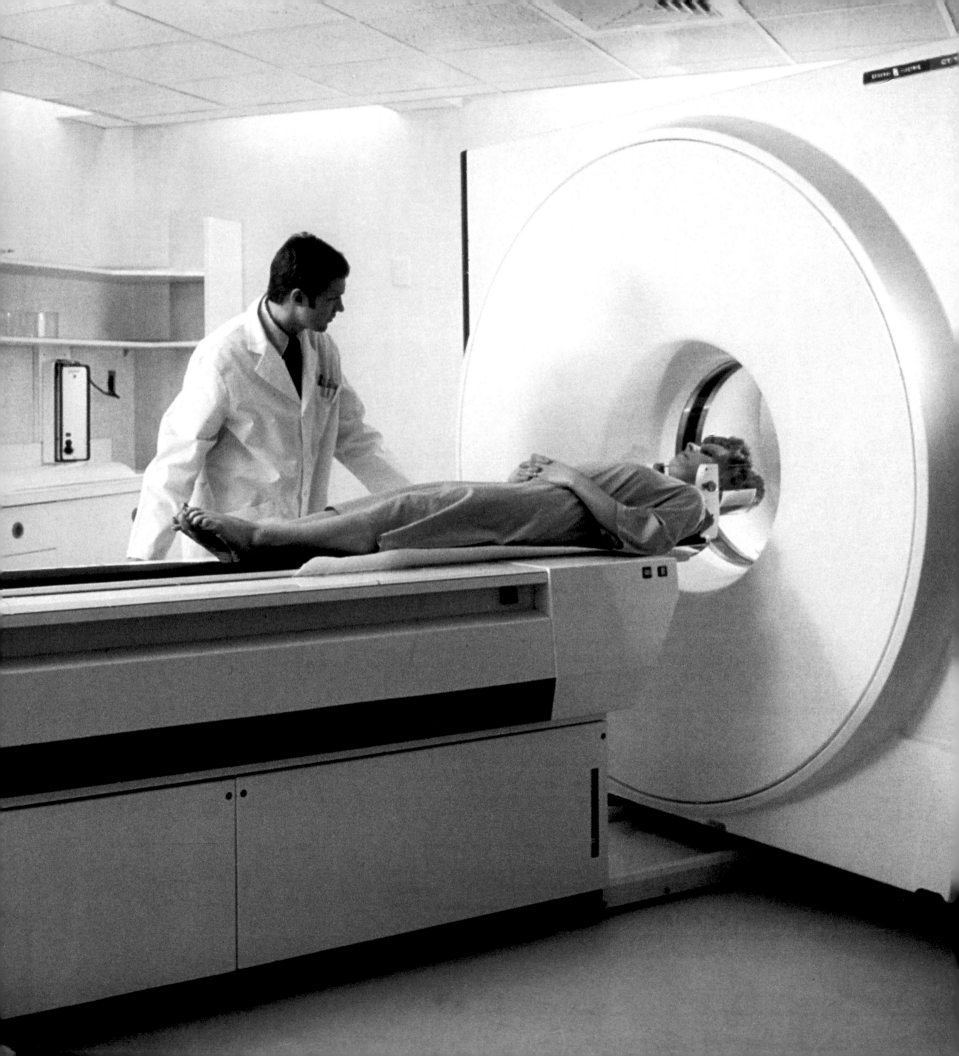

The Robb Era
1973-1986

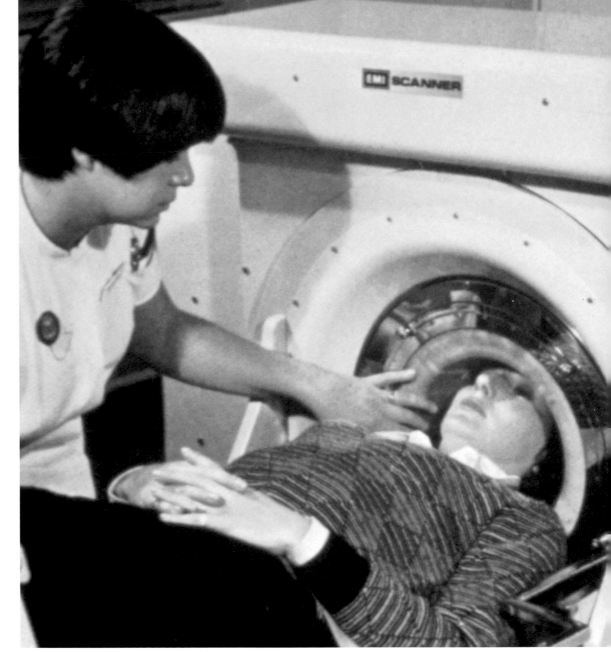

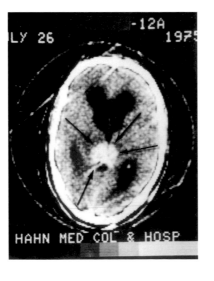

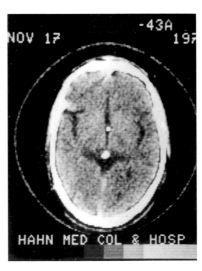

top left
Walter L. Robb

top right
The EMI Mark I computerized trans-axial tomography scanner revolutionized diagnostic imaging by making it possible to directly visualize tissue, even in the brain.

bottom
This pre- and post-therapy series from 1975 show a large tumor near the pineal gland (arrows left) and its disappearance (right) following treatment.

Walt Robb's tenure at GE Medical Systems began under difficult circumstances. The factory backlog was choking off timely deliveries, with a corresponding impact on orders and sales, though progress was being made.

The manufacturing operation had been established as a separate functional department reporting to its own general manager, Joe Williams, who had responsibility from order enry through manufacturing and delivery. Norm Gertz and Paul Sledzik headed Electric Avenue and Waukesha, respectively; David Schmidt was dispatched to Belgium to run the Liege plant; Bill Hawes focused on the materials management system transformation; Sam Koutas was brought in to enhance the labor-management interface; Les Waller led the organization and staffing work; and Leon Janssen took over physical distribution.

Robb assisted by eliminating many of the new products Charlier had put into production. However, it wouldn't be until the new Waukesha assembly center came on line late in the summer of 1974, and new production protocols fully implemented, that the bottleneck would be eased.

Lessons in Leadership
Walter Lee Robb (b. 1928) earned his B.S. in chemical engineering at Penn State and a Ph.D. at the University of Illinois. He was a scientist at GE's Knolls Atomic Power Laboratory and the Research Laboratory, where he won 12 patents for medical membranes. He founded GE's Medical Development Operation in 1968 and was appointed general manager of GE Silicone in 1971. He took over GE Medical Systems in December 1973 and was elected a GE vice president in early 1974. Walt launched the development of GE's fan beam CT scanner that eventually captured half of the U.S. market and a 1.5 Tesla magnetic resonance scanner that gained the leading market share worldwide. He led GE's R&D Center from 1986, until his retirement in 1993. Walt then served on the boards of 10 start-up companies, consulted widely, directed his Albany (New York) River Rats minor league hockey team, and traveled to exotic destinations with his wife, Anne.

Besides the manufacturing backlog, Robb and his management staff had a full plate of additional issues to digest. Foremost among them was what to do about this strange new phenomenon called "computerized trans-axial tomography" (CTAT).

Revolutionary stirrings
CTAT first appeared in the U.S. at the 1972 RSNA meeting in Chicago. EMI, its developer, had taken a small room off the exhibit floor where it briefed visitors on its new technology. Most were puzzled by what they saw, since the images were fuzzy, took nearly 5 minutes to acquire, hours to reconstruct, and required a machine costing several hundred thousand dollars. Besides, what did EMI know about diagnostic imaging? Didn't they produce Beatles recordings?

In fact, the evolution of CTAT from a research curiosity to a practical clinical instrument was largely due to Godfrey Hounsfield, an engineer at EMI's Central Research Laboratory. Working independently of several other early researchers, especially Allan Cormack at Tufts University (Medford, Massachusetts), and Bill Oldendorf at the UCLA Medical Center in Los Angeles, Hounsfield had constructed a prototype scanner in secrecy at the Atlkinson Morley's Hospital in Wimbledon (U.K.) in 1971. It was limited to brain studies because of its 4.5-minute scan time.

Footsteps of Pioneers
Godfrey Newbold Hounsfield (1919–2004) was born in Nottinghamshire, England and graduated from Magnus Grammar School in Newark. He served as a radar mechanic instructor in the Royal Air Force during World War II, then received a diploma from the Faraday House Electrical Engineering College in London. Hounsfield joined EMI in 1951, working on radar and guided weapons. He transferred to EMI's Central Research Laboratory at Hayes, Middlesex, where he became interested in pattern recognition. This work eventually led to the EMI Mark I scanner. Among his many awards and honors, Hounsfield was elected to the Royal Society in 1975, won the Albert Lasker Medical Research Award that same year, was appointed Commander of the British Empire in 1976, shared the 1979 Nobel Prize in Medicine with Allan Cormack, was knighted by Queen Elizabeth II in 1981, and received the Gold Medal of the American College of Radiology in 1986.

By that autumn, Hounsfield, along with radiologist James Ambrose, and their collaborators, had produced the first clinical CTAT image. It was a scan of a 41-year-old woman that clearly revealed a large cyst in the frontal lobe of her brain. Some 70 additional head scans were obtained the following winter—a remarkable number considering each took 2 days of computer reconstruction. When these results were announced at the Annual Congress of the British Institute of Radiology in London, the response was enthusiastic. More positive feedback resulted from Hounsfield's May paper at a neurosciences meeting in New York City and Ambrose's presentation at RSNA '72. Encouraged, EMI built five production "Mark I" units—three for U.K. customers, one for Massachusetts General Hospital in Boston, and one for the Mayo Clinic in Rochester, Minnesota.

Footsteps of Pioneers
Allan McLeod Cormack (1924–1998) shared the 1979 Nobel Prize in Medicine for his pioneering research in "computer assisted tomography." A native of South Africa, he received his bachelor's and master's degrees at the University of Cape Town, then went on to Cambridge University as a research student. He returned to Cape Town as a nuclear physics lecturer and became interested in a problem later known as CAT scanning. On a sabbatical at Harvard University from 1956–57, he was offered a position at Tufts University, where he spent the rest of his career.

He published his seminal research on CAT scanning in 1963 and 1964. Cormack received the National Medal of Science in 1990 and was posthumously awarded the Order of Mapungubwe, South Africa's highest honor.

It didn't take long for competitors to emerge. A dentist at Georgetown University in Washington, D.C., Robert Ledley, set out to develop a whole-body scanner. His prototype "ACTA" whole-body scanner was installed at the University of Minnesota in 1973. More credible was Ohio Nuclear, a company that had previously specialized in nuclear imaging cameras and computers. Their solution to the scanning speed problem was to add multiple detectors and multiple pencil beams (later, a small fan-shaped x-ray beam) to obtain several projections at once. Their "second generation" Delta 25 head-only unit and Delta 50 body scanner reduced scan times from about 4.5 minutes to around 2 minutes. The DeltaScan FS brought scanning times down to 18 seconds. They later tried to develop a unique version of "fourth generation" technology (stationary detectors and a revolving tube), but it proved too expensive to manufacture.

Solving the CAT puzzle

At first, Walt and his experts foresaw no danger, since the initial estimate was only 30 CTAT machines would be sold in the U.S. over 5 years. However, when orders for GE x-ray gear began to fall a few months into 1974 as hospitals diverted funds to the new technology, the issue took on new urgency. Walt assembled a panel of advisors in Bermuda to evaluate the threat. It included Jim Youker, chairman of the Department of Radiology at the Medical College of Wisconsin; Dave Reese, a neuroradiologist at the Mayo Clinic; and various staff members. Everyone agreed GE had to respond with its own CAT offering and do so soon. The question was how.

Unbeknownst to Walt, the R&D Center had already begun a CAT project of its own. Scientists there had been working on all-video imaging systems for Medical Systems, when they first heard about the EMI scanner. Several, including Lewis (Lonnie) Edelheit and Morry Blumenfeld, visited EMI's exhibit at RSNA '72 to find out what all the fuss was about. They began pushing hard to launch a CAT research project at the Center.

As it happened, the Mayo Clinic was working on its response to a pending "request for proposal" (RFP) that the National Institutes of Health was expected to issue for a "dynamic spatial reconstructor" for cardiac imaging research. Bob Hattery, Mayo's principal investigator (and, later, Mayo's CEO), approached the R&D Center to solicit their participation, and a team was set up in Rowland ("Red") Redington's Medical Diagnostic Systems Programs section. Unfortunately, when the RFP came out in 1974, it was for a whole-body cancer detection system, not a cardiac scanner. All was not lost, however, since this was when GE's concept of a fan beam coupled with a xenon detector was born.

On March 1, 1974, Walt Robb dispatched John Truscott, engineering general manager, and two of his top engineers, Tom Lambert and Bob Godbarsen, to Mayo to inspect the EMI Mark I in detail. They reported back they could have a GE prototype scanner ready in 18 months, and it would perform whole body scans in 1 minute. When Walt asked what the R&D Center had to say, he was surprised to learn no one had approached them. In fact, except for the all-video project launched by Jim Charlier, Milwaukee and the Center hadn't been involved in a joint project since William Coolidge had turned over his high-voltage x-ray tube to Victor X-Ray Corporation more than half a century before.

Me too" or "leapfrog"?

Walt phoned Art Bueche who responded, "We have been waiting for you to call!" He then told Walt about their concept for a "third generation" machine that would em-

ploy a rotate-only scanning motion in conjunction with a fan beam of radiation and a multielement xenon detector. Morry Blumenfeld, who was then the liaison scientist between the R&D Center and Jack Welch's Components and Materials Group, recalled a fateful meeting with Walt:

> We showed him the two different approaches—'me too' and 'leapfrog.' Walt didn't say anything and we thought this was going to be another meeting with no results. However, as he was putting on his coat, he said we should pursue the leapfrog approach, but we had to have a unit finished in 9 months!

To understand their relative merits, let's see how these two basic approaches differed. First generation and second generation translate/rotate scanners (EMI, Ohio Nuclear, ACTA, etc.) positioned the patient inside the gantry opening. This space was surrounded by a frame (concealed in a gantry) that held an x-ray tube on one side and two or more detectors on the other. To make a scan, the tube and detectors would "translate" by moving in parallel across the patient along the length of the frame while the first exposure was made. The frame would then "rotate" several degrees and the translation motion repeated in the opposite direction. This process continued until views were obtained from all around the patient, then these data were processed by computer and reconstructed into an image. First generation machines required about 4.5 minutes to acquire one scan; second generation machines about 2 minutes (18 seconds, ultimately).

GE's idea was for a third generation scanner that would mount an x-ray tube on one side of a rotating ring and a multidetector array on the other. As this mechanism spun around the patient, the tube would emit x-ray pulses in a fan-shaped beam sized to the length of the detector array. Each detector cell would measure the attenuation of radiation reaching it—and, therefore, the density of the issue through which

top left
The EMI Mark I revolutionized brain imaging.

top right
Morry Blumenfeld was a guiding force behind GE CT and MR for 35 years.

bottom
GE's third generation approach to CT swept the x-ray tube and xenon detector array around the patient in less than 5 seconds.

360° CONTINUOUS SWEEP

X-RAY TUBE — PULSED FAN BEAM — XENON DETECTOR ARRAY

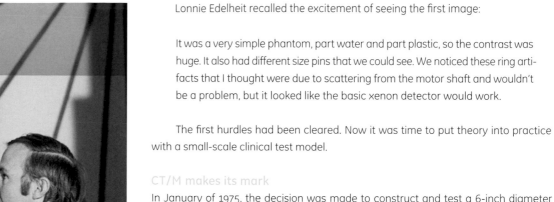

it had just passed. This "rotate-only" motion promised two major benefits. First, scanning time could be drastically reduced, perhaps to less than 5 seconds. Since this was well within the comfortable breath-hold time of most patients, high-quality images could be obtained without concern for motion artifacts. Second, faster scans meant more patients could be examined in a given period of time—no small consideration for hospital managers worried about paying for such expensive equipment.

Before the final design choice was made, Jack Welch and Walt Robb also debated the relative merits of third generation versus fourth generation, a promising approach that used a ring of stationary detectors around the scanner aperture in conjunction with an x ray tube that rotated about the patient. Walt held out for third generation and Jack finally acquiesced, though not before warning Walt, "You're betting your job!"

Launching the program

The detector was the first challenge presented by this complex, "fast track" development program. It had to be fast, accurate, reliable, and work when configured in an array of several hundred identical detectors. Next was the computer data collection technology and reconstruction software needed to handle the increased complexity and faster data rates. Key R&D Center players on the detector team were John Houston and Ray Wetten, while Don Puckett spearheaded the data acquisition system effort. The software talent (people such as Ed Chylinski and Gwynn Pearsall) was provided by the Center's Information Technology unit. Among the key non-GE players, Gabor Herman, a professor of mathematics at the University of New York at Buffalo, was instrumental in solving the challenge of the fan beam convolution.

The solution to the detector issue was ingenuous. The Center proposed an elegantly simple design employing a series of small metal plates spaced a couple of millimeters apart in parallel to the radiation beam. The volume and intensity of x-rays entering these spaces would be measured and the results sent to the computer for processing and reconstruction into a diagnostic quality image. The detector array was contained within a high-pressure chamber filled with xenon, an inert gaseous element that would provide a stable environment for detecting such tiny quanta. Just 9 months into the development program, and right on time, the Center proudly displayed a 12-element xenon detector prototype and demonstrated the reconstruction of a simulated image.

Lonnie Edelheit recalled the excitement of seeing the first image:

It was a very simple phantom, part water and part plastic, so the contrast was huge. It also had different size pins that we could see. We noticed these ring artifacts that I thought were due to scattering from the motor shaft and wouldn't be a problem, but it looked like the basic xenon detector would work.

The first hurdles had been cleared. Now it was time to put theory into practice with a small-scale clinical test model.

CT/M makes its mark

In January of 1975, the decision was made to construct and test a 6-inch diameter prototype with 125 detector elements. It was configured as a breast scanner because of the lower dynamic range requirement. That was important, because the only way to meet the aggressive schedule was to use off-the-shelf, analog-to-digital converters of limited power. The proposed device, named the CT/M (for mammography), was designed with a water bath to moderate the grazing x-rays and make it easier to measure the differences between x-rays passing through normal and abnormal tissue. Edelheit, who would go on to a distinguished career at Medical Systems and later return to the R&D Center as its director, was appointed to manage the CT/M project.

The prototype was delivered to the Mayo Clinic in October where it proved the validity of the GE fan-beam concept and the multielement xenon detector array. Meeting this aggressive schedule required exceptional efforts from everyone involved. Teams and individuals typically worked from dawn to dusk, often all night long, and most weekends. To keep peace at home, the Center paid for babysitters so spouses could get out of the house for necessary errands. Catered meals for the hard-working scientists and engineers were a routine courtesy.

above left
Walt Robb and Jack Welch share a "quiet" moment.

top to bottom
The CT/M prototype breast scanner was fabricated at GE's Automation Equipment Operation in Schenectady. Dave Barrett (left), an engineer from Milwaukee, checked the unit.

The CT/M begins its journey to the Mayo Clinic.

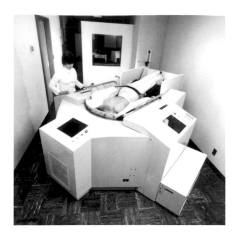

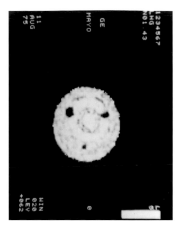

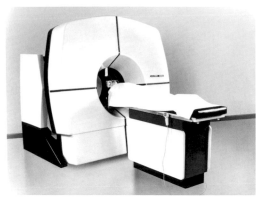

top left

The CT/M scanner, installed at Mayo Clinic, was the test bed for GE's innovative rotate-only approach to "fast scan CT" technology.

top right

An early breast image from the Mayo CT/M scanner.

left, top to bottom

GE obtained manufacturing and distribution rights to the Neuroscan head scanner which was renamed the CT/N. Intended to fill the gap until the CT/T whole body scanner became available, it was abandoned in 1976.

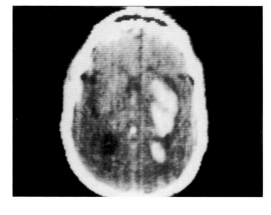

It was head images such as this CT/N view that created much excitement in 1975.

Phil Peck, posing here as a radiologist in a promotional photo, led the CT/N development program throughout its brief life.

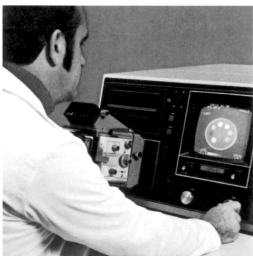

As the CT/M was being tested at Mayo, the first EMI 5005 body scanner was being installed there. Clearly, EMI intended to generate clinical images to support the unit's formal introduction in 2 month's time at RSNA '75, lending even more urgency to the CT/M project. Under the prodding of Al LeBlang, CT/M project controller, GE began making plans to unveil its program at the same event.

Since it still wasn't certain the third generation approach could be made to work, GE took out an insurance policy by completing a distribution agreement with a small Los Angeles firm that had developed a first-generation head scanner. Neuroscan Inc.'s device, soon renamed the CT/N (for neuro), would give GE something to market until a "fast scan" body scanner was ready. Phil Peck transferred over from engineering to head CT/N development. When it soon became clear Neuroscan wouldn't be able to meet the delivery schedule, a supplementary agreement gave GE certain manufacturing rights. Soon, the entire CT/N program was transferred from Los Angeles into Building 9 at Electric Avenue. For the next 2 years, a small software team comprised of Bob Chybowski and Bill Edens; system engineers Roger Sergile, Dick Rieke, and M. C. Mayel; and physicists Frank DiBianca and Lonnie Edelheit, pursued significant changes to the original system design. The CT/N was abandoned after 14 units had been delivered to GE, but many of the things learned were migrated into the CT/T development program.

Betting the farm

In the early summer of 1975, Bobby Bowen, the new CT engineering manager, and Red Redington met to draw up the specifications for a fan-beam body scanner. GEMS committed to develop it as soon as the R&D Center was able to demonstrate the xenon detector worked. This full-scale system was to have a scan time of 4.8 seconds and use a 301-element xenon detector array. It would also have sufficient data acquisition and computer capacity to handle a data rate 100 times that of the EMI Mark I scanner. Throughout that summer and fall, Art Chen, the Center's full-body project manager, along with Walt Berninger, ramped up development activities. Engineers from Milwaukee also played a role as Dave Barrett and a procession of others were dispatched to Schenectady to assist in the effort.

The GE program was announced on schedule at RSNA '75 in Chicago's McCormick Place. GEMS took a suite in the adjoining McCormick Inn and invited interested radiologists over for a detailed look at the program. The news quickly filtered back to the convention floor, and the suite was soon overwhelmed by a swarm of curious visitors. This led to an amusing sidelight, when show managers insisted GE shut it down as a violation of exhibit rules. In a matter of hours, Bob Filip, John LaRocco, and their exhibit house designed a new CT theater for the regular GE booth and had it operating when the exhibits opened the next morning. Amazingly, a number of orders for GE's proposed body scanner—the CT/T (for total body)—were booked despite the fact neither hardware nor clinical images were shown. This was an enormous vote of confidence in GE's technological prowess and a great morale boost for the scores of people who had been working so hard for so long.

In early 1976, the R&D Center began to produce body images on the CT/T prototype. The first human images were of a local physician who had been diagnosed with pancreatic cancer. However, the very first CT/T image was of a beef roast reluctantly provided by Pat LeBlang, Al's wife. (Years later, a leg of lamb would play a similar role during GE's magnetic resonance development program.) Encouraged by the initial results, GEMS sponsored a visit by some 200 radiologists to Schenectady on February 21, 1976. Walt and his marketing team were on hand to offer their guests the opportunity to put down a refundable deposit of $15,000 to reserve a spot when deliveries began. Several checks were written then and there.

The CT/T prototype was shipped to the University of California-San Francisco (UCSF) Medical Center in April 1976 for clinical evaluations. Meanwhile, Milwaukee was putting together its CT manufacturing organization. Bill Hawes was selected to lead the group, assisted by Frank Waltz and Al Teslik. A new building on Cleveland Avenue in New Berlin was found and GE's first CT (as the technology was now being called) plant went into operation in March 1976. The first images from a production unit were made that June. Orders were coming in so fast that planning for a much larger building already was in motion. The huge Ryerson Road CT center would be ready in a year.

Some consideration had been given to making the CT/M test bed scanner into a product. In fact, Lonnie Edelheit had moved to Milwaukee from the R&D Center in the spring of 1976 to help Bobby Bowen design production models. Bobby put Paul Mirabella in charge of building the CT/M in engineering, and one of the first production units was soon delivered to Dr. Chang at the University of Kansas. He used it to discover that contrast agents could help distinguish cancer from fibrocystic disease and published several scientific papers on his results. Altogether, 12 sets of CT/M parts were built before it was deemed unviable as a stand-alone specialty unit.

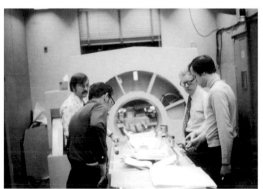

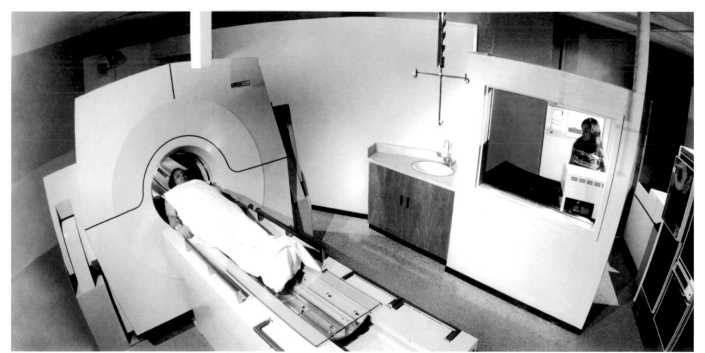

top
The crowds were large and enthusiastic when GE announced its entry into CT at RSNA '75.

middle, left to right
The Automation Equipment Operation (AEO) in Schenectady fabricated the CT/T prototype.

AEO personnel prepare to truck the CT/T prototype across town to the R&D Center for final assembly and testing.

Bob Godbarsen (second from right) worked with the R&D Center team to assemble and test the CT/T prototype.

bottom
The prototype CT/T scanner was installed at the University of California-San Francisco Medical Center in the spring of 1976 for clinical trials.

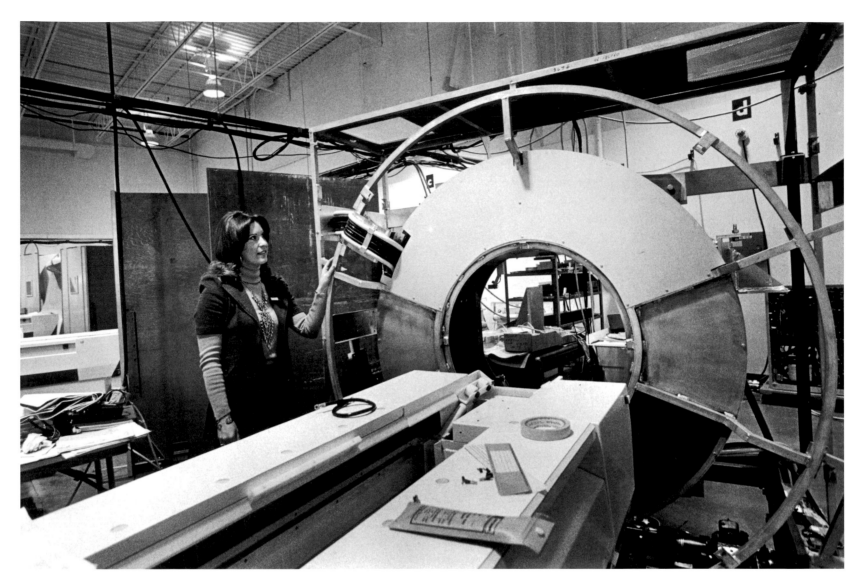

top
Early CT/T scanners were assembled at GE's first CT manufacturing facility on Cleveland Avenue in New Berlin, Wiscosin. It was soon replaced by the huge CT engineering and manufacturing center on nearby Ryerson Road.

bottom, left to right
The Ryerson Road CT plant was completed in February 1977. Checking the plans were (l–r) Chuck Thomas, operational planning manager; Ron Jervis, facilities engineering manager; and Tom Waldheutter, construction superintendent.

Lonnie Edelheit came to Milwaukee from the R&D Center in 1976 to work on the CT/M scanner.

"Ring" artifact crisis

UCSF had been selected as the CT/T clinical evaluation site, in part, because of its great experience with the very latest translate/rotate head-only and body systems. It also had an outstanding research staff in the persons of Hans Newton, Dave Norman, Al Moss, Henry Goldberg, Alphonse Palubinskas, and others. A major factor was UCSF's unique understanding of their role as a clinical evaluation site. "When Al LeBlang, Bobby Bowen, and I were visiting potential evaluation sites," said Morry Blumenfeld, "everyone else asked us what we wanted them to do. UCSF presented a full program of what they would do for GE. We were almost speechless."

Alexander Margulis, the UCSF radiology chair, also recalled that meeting:

They were visiting several potential evaluation sites including Cornell, Penn, and Massachusetts General Hospital. They asked me where I thought my department ranked nationally, and I told them that everybody said we were number 2. When they asked who was number 1, I said whomever they were talking to!

Morry and his colleagues had no trouble convincing Walt that UCSF was the right choice, and the CT/T prototype was soon installed in a converted research space there.

"Some people who were bypassed called Walter and said we put the machine in a dog lab," Dr. Margulis chuckled. "So he and Gene Lewis came out and saw it was a beautiful place. This was the first time I met Walter."

By May of 1976, the CT/T prototype unit was installed and running. It didn't take long for word of initial results to reach Milwaukee. And did GE get an earful! Those "rings" Lonnie had noticed on the first images from the CT/M prototype were about to become a very serious issue.

While the body scans produced by the CT/T prototype were quite credible, the head scans were considerably inferior to those from dedicated head scanners. GE had already taken 55 orders for the CT/T system by this time, but as word of its poor head images leaked out, cancellations soon exceeded new bookings. Bob Stocking and his top sales managers, assisted by the CT management team and even Walt Robb himself, visited every customer in the backlog to explain the problem and what was being done to fix it.

"Ring" artifacts were caused by a combination of factors, including the geometry of the fan-beam design. Sir Godfrey Hounsfield had famously predicted the third-generation approach would never work, because it was "three orders of magnitude more difficult than engineering could solve." (His remarks would be recalled by a huge banner hung along the back wall of the Ryerson Road CT plant: "They said it couldn't be done!")

Dr. Margulis remembered everybody was frustrated:

One day, my senior faculty came to me and said they wanted to replace the GE machine with a Pfizer stationary detector unit. In their presence, I called Walter and told him I didn't feel that GE had put enough of an effort to make it work. So he sent some of his best people to help us and, within a month, the scanner started working well. This episode was when Walter and I became lifelong friends.

GE scientists had been aware of the problem since it first appeared during the CT/M program. The R&D Center was convinced the problem was in the details of the computer; Milwaukee felt it was related to detector and calibration issues. Walt concluded that if the ring artifact problem was going to be solved, Medical Systems would have to do it themselves.

As Gary Glover, who was the mathematician-scientist in charge of the CT/T algorithm development program in Milwaukee, explained it:

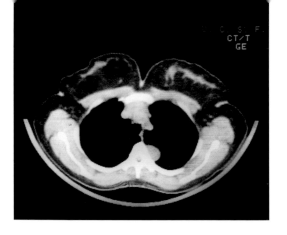

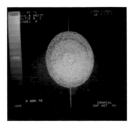

top left
An early body scan from the prototype CT/T scanner.

top right
A CT/T head scan from 1976 showing a typical ring artifact.

middle
Their shared CT/T experiences cemented a lifelong friendship between Alex Margulis and Walt Robb.

bottom
Gary Glover won the Charles P. Steinmetz Award in 1985 for his contributions to GE CT and MR.

Ring artifacts result from the fact each detector element contributes information uniquely to a thin annular region of the image. If you cast a ray from tube to detector through the image matrix, then spin the image relative to the scanner about the origin, that ray will leave an annulus at the radius corresponding to the detector angle from isocenter.

If all the detectors are perfect in shape, precisely aligned, and carefully calibrated with each other, there are no ring artifacts. However, any number of factors can cause one detector element to vary from its neighbors. For example, a difference in gain of just 0.1% between detector elements will show up as a ring. "Because the error energy is concentrated in a narrow ring, even small imperfections cause a noticeable ring in the image," Glover noted.

Al Grant, CT software manager, tasked Terry Griffie and Richard Lewis with developing a "ring fix" algorithm. At the same time, Gary Glover and others set to work revising and writing new algorithms in both projection space and image space to improve system performance. Dick Lewis had the honor of finally implementing the new algorithm that eliminated ring artifacts. This algorithm has never been published or patented to avoid revealing detail. As Glover later said, "A number of contemporary competitors were unable to solve the ring problem. People still ask me how we fixed it and I won't tell!"

The solution wasn't entirely software driven. A major effort was directed at improving the uniformity of the xenon detectors. The first model was a 320-channel xenon ion chamber that used 288 channels for the image and the remainder for reference calibrations. Each detector consisted of a center plate biased positively with chambers

on either side. If these tungsten plates were slightly skewed, vibrated, nicked, or had some other flaw, that channel would cause a ring. The substantially improved X1 detector was retrofitted to the units already in the field and all new production CT/T systems. This upgraded scanner was renamed the CT/T 7800 total body scanner (after its product data sheet page number).

In addition to the ring problem, parallel efforts were being directed at solving several other important issues, such as beam-hardening artifacts. Glover developed the so-called "matrix deconvolution" algorithm to reduce this problem, and Griffie wrote an efficient code to implement it. Meanwhile, new members were joining the CT/T software team, including Rick Altekruse, Bob Chybowski, and Bill Edens.

"This was an exciting, wonderful time," Gary recalled. "People were committed, because it was a delightful application of high-tech math and physics to a uniquely human problem. Everyone worked very long hours, because they felt good about what they were doing."

Glover won a GE Charles P. Steinmetz Award for technical achievement in 1985. He subsequently became a professor of radiology, electrical engineering, and psychology at Stanford University and director of its Radiological Sciences Laboratory.

The CON debacle

Through 1976, a total of 860 scanners had been sold in the U.S. and Canada. Healthcare payors were demanding something be done to control this "high-tech epidemic." The weapon of choice was a 1974 Federal law that required a government-issued "Certificate of Need" (CON) for the purchase of capital healthcare equipment costing more than $100,000. Though laxly enforced or totally ignored prior to 1977, the Carter Administration began to use it to rein in the galloping growth in healthcare costs that threatened to imperil the Medicare and Medicaid programs. CT scanners became an easy target. The immediate impact was a plunge in orders from 420 units in 1976, to 220 in 1977, and just 154 in 1978. A modest recovery began with 170 units ordered in 1979 and 290 in 1980, but it was 1981 before the market recovered to 1976 levels.

This downturn actually was a stroke of good fortune for GE, because it coincided with the ring artifact problem. By artificially restricting the market, the CON debacle severely decreased sales and revenues for the two leading CT suppliers of the day— EMI and Ohio Nuclear. Both were facing added costs in developing new second-generation models and meeting commitments to upgrade their first-generation units. Also, both had invested in staff and infrastructure improvements sized to the very large markets and very high growth rates they had anticipated. Therefore, the CON-driven market collapse had extremely serious financial consequences for them. GE was perfectly positioned when government controls eventually eased and a second, rapid growth spurt was unleashed. EMI, Ohio Nuclear (Technicare), Artronix, Syntex, Varian, Searle, OmniMedical, and others never recovered from this seismic dislocation of the CT market.

The first production CT/T scanner was installed at Miami's Jackson Memorial Hospital in the fall of 1976, quickly followed by units at Emory University in Atlanta, and Ross General Hospital in Marin County, north of San Francisco. Over the next year, 75 more went to customers throughout the U.S. and Canada; several were shipped overseas.

A key early installation was at the Milwaukee County Medical Complex (MCMC), where Jim Youker and his key lieutenants, Vic Haughton, director of neurological scanning, and Dennis Foley and Tom Lawson, co-section chiefs of body imaging, were eager to put the GE technology to the test. This unit was installed in a specially designed suite equipped and decorated by GE for use as a "show site" for prospective customers. In March of 1978, it became the first to be upgraded to the CT/T 8800 configuration with the high resolution X2 detector, associated electronics, and new covers. Later that

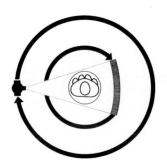

top to bottom

The engineering team responsible for the first production CT/T system included (l–r) Tom Lambert, Wes Klages, Al Grant, Bobby Bowen, Phil Peck, Pete Staats, and Dick Rilling.

This CT/T 7800 scanner graphic illustrated the rotation of the tube and detector around the patient.

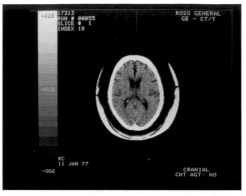

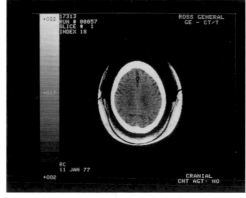

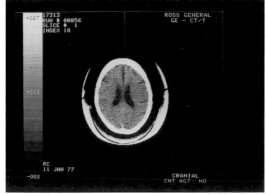

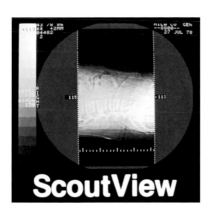

top, left to right
Head images produced by a
CT/T system installed at Ross
General Hospital in Marin
County, California. It was one
of GE's first three production
CT scanners.

Jim Youker (right), radiology
department chairman at
MCMC, discussing CT/T
images with John Truscott,
GE's engineering general
manager.

bottom, left to right
Dennis Foley, a radiologist-
researcher at the Medical
College of Wisconsin, was a
key clinical contributor in
the development of GE CT
and MR.

The ScoutView localization
feature produced radiograph-
like images by keeping the
x-ray tube and detector stationary while moving the patient
through the exposure field.

The CT/T 7800 scanner at
MCMC was the first to be
upgraded to the CT/T 8800
configuration. (The second
"T" was soon dropped from
the product name.)

year, it also received the first ScoutView upgrade, an imaginative feature developed by Frank DiBianca that allowed the scanner to make radiograph-like images for use in localizing the precise anatomy to be scanned. Ultimately, hundreds of guests—and thousands of patients—visited this very special facility.

The MCMC/MCW Connection

Though it ceased to exist in 1995, the Milwaukee County Medical Complex was the largest healthcare center in Southeast Wisconsin for many years. It offered a full range of general and specialized clinical services at Milwaukee County General Hospital and the adjoining Eye Institute, all backed by the academic research capabilities of the Medical College of Wisconsin (MCW) next door.

With such a medical powerhouse literally in its backyard, GEMS frequently used MCMC as a clinical research and development site. The benefits were enormous— research expertise, clinical capabilities, academic curiosity, proximity, and so on. There were substantial benefits for MCMC and MCW, too. As Alan Williams, then a young assistant radiology professor who was to become MCW's Chief of Neuroradiology and, later, Chairman of Radiology at St. Louis University, recalled:

"Vic Haughton and I were the neuroradiologists at the time the CT/T 7800 was installed. When word of the outstanding image quality spread, we were deluged with calls from physicians all over the Midwest wanting us to scan their patients. The terrific image quality provided by the CT/T 7800 and, subsequently, the CT/T 8800, gave MCW radiologists the opportunity to write and lecture extensively on topics related to the intervertebral disc, facet joints, pituitary gland, temporal bone, liver, kidneys, and so on. Vic and I co-authored textbooks on spine and cranial CT that were quite successful.

"There is no doubt in my mind that the collaborative efforts between GE and the MCW faculty were the 'making' of MCW in academic circles. MCW became one of the most highly regarded academic radiology departments in the United States. Jim Youker, the radiology chair, deserves a great deal of credit for cultivating the GE connection and recruiting faculty who were able to take advantage of the technology. Though I had not planned to stay in academic radiology, the excitement offered by the GE CT program at MCW got me started on an academic career that still continues."

CT "Continuum"

Although the head images resulting from the improved software and detectors were good, EMI and Ohio Nuclear were now promising even better head scans in their next generation scanners. So the CT engineering team under Bobby Bowen and the CT manufacturing team under Bill Hawes began to develop a higher resolution detector. The X2 detector increased the number of cells from 301 to 523 and was designed to be retrofitted to CT/T systems already installed. This was a totally new concept in the medical imaging industry. Customers now had protection against technological obsolescence.

Morry Blumenfeld recalled a meeting with Jack Welch:

After hearing the explanation of the concept behind the detector upgrade, Jack said, 'Do you guys know what you have done from a marketing viewpoint? This is the same as driving into the dealer in your 1976 Chevrolet, having him do some things under the hood, and driving out with a 1977 Chevrolet. We have got to give this idea a name.' Jack thought for a few minutes and said, 'Let's call it the Continuum!'

The Continuum upgrade was priced at $100,000 and included the X2 detector, a new data acquisition system, and a high-speed array processor. Though GE lost

money on every upgrade it sold at this price, its announcement in the autumn of 1977 brought in more orders. Customers were now confident the CT/T 7800 could be upgraded to the new CT/T 8800 configuration that had just been introduced at the American Roentgen Ray Society meeting in Boston. A series of free Continuum upgrades throughout 1977 and early 1978, such as improved tube cooling times, out-of-sequence reconstructions, and a new convolver board to speed reconstructions, added to GE's credibility. The major Continuum upgrade in 1979 was ReView™ retrospective image analysis that was provided at no charge to all CT/T 8800 users. The following year, GE changed out every system operator console with an updated model, also at no charge.

Meanwhile, CT engineering and manufacturing activities began to occupy the Ryerson Road facility that Joe William and Bill Hawes had brought on line in record time. In January 1977, a CT distribution agreement was implemented with Yokogawa Electric Works (YEW) of Japan. March brought an announcement by the Public Health Services Administration that the CT/T scanner had been approved for Medicare reim-

top to bottom

In early 1977, Walt and Anne Robb hosted a CT celebration banquet at the Mohawk Country Club in Schenectady for the combined Medical Systems and R&D Center teams and their spouses. At the head table were (seated l–r) Bobby and Ginny Bowen; Walt and Anne Robb; (standing l–r) Shirley and Roland "Red" Redington; Helen and Frank Schilling.

For 25 years, the Ryerson Road plant was the center of premium CT engineering and manufacturing.

Art Glenn (left), CT general manager, demonstrated an Optional Diagnostic Capability console to an interested visitor.

bursement. Also, a new CT detector production area was opened at Electric Avenue. In April, the first CT/T to go overseas was shipped to Japan. In May, the CT/T was honored with the Wisconsin Governor's New Product Award, the first of several to be won by GE. The first CT/T manufactured at Ryerson Road was shipped in July, even as the prototype CT/T 8800 system was scanning its first patient. The CT/T 8800 was introduced in September, the first CT/T for Germany was installed in November, and the 100th CT/T was shipped from Ryerson in December.

As 1978 began, GE had nearly everything in place to become the leader in CT (which now stood for "computed tomography," rather than "computerized tomography"). The final key element was added in March, when Art Glenn was selected to lead CT because of his considerable experience in managing large, high-technology projects at the Heavy Military Electronics Division in Syracuse, New York. It was a brilliant selection; Art would later lead GE's next high-tech medical imaging development program—nuclear magnetic resonance imaging.

Managing success

Glenn's first challenge was to reconcile customer demands with supply chain realities. The overwhelming success of the CT/T 7800 and the new CT/T 8800 was the proximate cause of the problem. The large installed base of CT/T 7800 customers was demanding Continuum upgrades even as orders for the CT/T 8800 were zooming. With a finite supply of Milwaukee-manufactured detectors and vendor-supplier data acquisition systems, it was impossible to fully satisfy both sides of the equation at once.

Art Glenn recalled the considerable efforts by many people to finesse this situation:

Lonnie Edelheit, who was establishing the new Applied Science Laboratory, and Bill Hawes, the CT manufacturing manager, co-chaired the effort to refine and speed detector production. They were detailed to Electric Avenue until the problem was solved. Also playing huge roles were the CT field sales team that tended to the customer base, and Jim Vincent, CT Program Control manager, who planned shipments to balance sales needs with site readiness.

Lonnie remembered this episode in similar terms:

That was one of the most interesting times in my career. It turned out the X2 detector was 10 times harder to build than the X1 detector. Bill and I spent full time for months at Electric Avenue fixing the design and manufacturing problems. The fact we worked so well together made a huge difference.

This issue was the harbinger of an even greater crisis just down the road. The rapidly expanding installed base, coupled with increasing patient volumes and new applications, put enormous stresses on CT x-ray tubes. As these critical components were worked harder and harder, failure rates ballooned. At the most desperate moment, there were only six CT tubes in reserve to support a large installed base and a rising volume of new shipments.

The tube problem was handed to Jerry Cote, manufacturing manager, and Bill Love, tube programs manager, who launched a crash program to identify the causes of premature failures and implement solutions. Bill Belcher oversaw many changes in manufacturing methods and materials, while Pete Shelley and his tube engineering team developed advanced new designs. Coupled with additional changes throughout the Tube Operation, the eventual result was the turnaround everyone was seeking. CT tube life grew from an average of only about 4,000 slices in 1980, to 12,000 slices in

1982, and to over 25,000 slices a few years later. Combined with an innovative "per slice" pricing system that had been implemented to protect users during the darkest days of the crisis, the tube business became a major profit center.

The key to sustaining these efforts was a $16 million investment in the Electric Avenue tube facility. This major upgrade and expansion included a new $3 million engineering and laboratory facility adjoining the Coolidge Lab, as well as numerous changes and improvements on and to the factory floor. Among them were new dehumidifying and air conditioning systems, suspended ceilings in critical process areas, the addition of new equipment and processes, improved material flow, a new wall dividing the machining and tube areas, and a new floor to replace the familiar wood blocks of the original WWII-era construction.

Meanwhile, the CT/T 8800 had become the most widely sought system of the day, winning nearly half of the U.S./Canada market and over one third of the global market. In August 1980, the 500th GE CT/T system was shipped; 3-1/2 years later, in March 1984, the *2,000th* GE CT system went out the door.

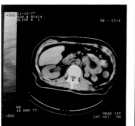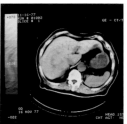
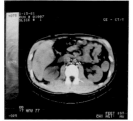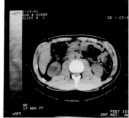

top to bottom
The CT/T 8800's X-2 detector brought unprecedented resolution to head and body imaging.

In April 1981, Jack Welch (center with striped tie) brought the GE Board of Directors to Milwaukee. Among their tour stops was the CT manufacturing center where Walt Robb (right) briefed the visitors.

Also on the Board's itinerary was a visit to headquarters where Russ Noll briefed them on the nuclear imaging business. *(Bottom two photographs are from* Medical Systems News.*)*

Even with a best seller in their portfolio, Art and his team were already planning the CT/T 8800's replacement. During his first year in the CT leadership role, he launched a study to determine what would be required to stay ahead of the competition. The conclusion was the CT/T 8800, as capable as it was, had a limited future. What was needed was a system with faster scanning speeds and higher resolution. That meant improved detectors with more detector cells, data acquisition system improvements in dynamic range and speed, a higher heat capacity x-ray tube, a more robust gantry design, and higher computational and data storage capabilities. In other words, an entirely new scanner.

By late 1978, the concept for the CT/T 9800 was in hand. It was initially conceived as a head-only scanner to avoid competing with the whole body CT/T 8800 but would be upgradeable to whole-body capabilities. Much of 1979 was spent fleshing out the technical details for what would be a 2-second, 360-degree device with a solid-state detector (a 742-element high pressure xenon detector would be used until the new technology was ready). The head-only version was soon dropped in favor of pursuing two whole-body models—a high-resolution system with more data acquisition system channels (and a higher price tag) and a mid-resolution system for general applications.

The R&D Center was called in to develop the solid-state detector. Their efforts were primarily focused on finding a new material that would efficiently convert the x-ray photons to light for optical detection at very fast speeds and with little or no lag time. Analogic Corporation, which was supplying the data acquisition system (DAS) for the 8800, would develop an improved DAS with a 1,000,000:1 dynamic range and operating 16 times faster than the current model. The Milwaukee team was charged with figuring out how to bring all these advances together in an integrated package that could be manufactured at about the same cost as the CT/T 8800.

On the software side, Al Grant's team set out to achieve the 16X increase in data transfer and processing rates. Though these new targets exceeded 95% of the prevailing theoretical disk storage transfer rates, Gary Glover wanted to double these rates for future capacity. Credit for meeting these goals using the current 8800 computer hardware went to Richard Toop at Data General, along with Rick Altekruse and Bill Edens at GE. The prototype unit was shipped to the Milwaukee County Medical Complex in May 1981 for clinical trials. After the usual birthing pains, CT 9800™ system (the second "T" had been permanently dropped from the GE nomenclature) was introduced at RSNA '81.

The engineering heroes of the CT 9800 project were many, beginning with Lonnie Edelheit, CT engineering manager. More than 100 Medical Systems engineers and technicians attended the delivery, including Dick Brandt, Bill Taylor, Ian Botley, Jim Kandler, Glenn McGriff, Gilbert Wu, Ron Abel, George Seidenschnur, Dennis Pritzkow, Neil Loomis, Robert Naubert, Ernie Waldron, Wayne Naleway, John Kramer, Jim Anderson, Dave Arnold, Bernie Sandler, K. C. Acharya, Sue Wallenslager, Jim Hajicek, George Holling, Gene Williams, and scores of others. On the manufacturing side, key players were Frank Waltz, who had replaced Bill Hawes as CT manufacturing manager, and Maurice Dake, CT quality control manager, who moved into this key position when Wes Ison was promoted.

Though the global CT market peaked in 1983–84, the lead GE had established was secure. Now, Art's exceptional management talents were urgently needed elsewhere. In November of 1983, Walt Robb asked him to lead the emerging nuclear magnetic resonance imaging business. Lonnie Edelheit took over at Ryerson Road.

The history of CT during the remainder of the Robb era was marked by both challenges and opportunities, but the path to the future had been clearly drawn. The emphasis would be on executing business plans and maximizing CT's contributions. The next big breakthroughs were a decade down the road.

top to bottom
Among the engineers contributing to the CT 9800 project were (kneeling) Glenn McGriff, Jim Kandler, Ian Botley, (standing) Bill Taylor and Dick Brandt.

Presentation of the "Vision in Medicine" award to Alex Margulis (2nd from left), UCSF radiology chair, and Red Redington (2nd from right), R&D Center program manager, for their contributions to "fast scan" CT. Others are Art Bueche (left), GE's chief technology officer, Walt Robb (center), and Roland Schmidt (right), R&D Center director.

A new diagnostic window

By 1975, it was clear GE's strategy of becoming a credible full-line supplier was going to require substantial investments in several key areas. For instance, while the 1971 distribution agreement with Elscint had produced some significant gains in nuclear medicine, a larger solution was needed. Under the direction of Al Fried, general manager of the Special Health Products Section, the answer was found close by. In January, GE announced a $3 million cash deal to acquire certain nuclear medicine products manufactured by Nuclear Data of Schaumburg, Illinois. GE finally had its own line of gamma cameras, processing systems, and related products. Though Fried's untimely death would deny him the opportunity to see the ultimate results of this acquisition, his farsightedness had set GE on a course toward success.

The nuclear products management team at this time was headed by Mike Woodard, product line manager, and John DeFeo, marketing manager. This dynamic duo rolled out GE's new product line at the 1975 Society of Nuclear Medicine meeting in Philadelphia. Over the next few years, several further moves were made to strengthen the offering, the most important being the acquisition of a small, extremely innovative gamma camera manufacturer in Hoersholm, Denmark. Led by Kai Lange, managing director, General Electric Nuclear Medical would be the source of world-class nuclear imaging technology for years to come.

top to bottom
The GE Nuclear Medical facility in Hoersholm, Denmark.

GE's MaxiCamera nuclear camera system.

Restructuring for progress

Walt was making significant changes to the organization itself. First, he implemented a "matrix" structure with separate engineering, manufacturing, programs (marketing and profit & loss), and sales and service departments. This arrangement vertically integrated technical resources through the various businesses so they could be precisely targeted on specific product needs. Next, he sold the Belgian subsidiary to the French x-ray manufacturer, Compagnie Générale de Radiologie (CGR). The reasons were many, including: 1) the increasing ability of U.S. operations to build "international" products; 2) the advantages of concentrating product development and manufacturing in one location; 3) the emergence of GE's Spanish subsidiary, General Electrica Española (GEE) as a reliable partner in Europe; and 4) a history of strained labor relations in Liege.

Walt also brought in a seasoned international marketing executive, Jim Finke, to restructure the International Sales Operation. Using the strong experience base developed under Bob Parkhurst, great results came quickly. When the books were closed on 1974, GE Medical Systems had set an all-time export sales record. Among the most significant deals were 3 Telegem 90 systems for Mexico; 17 GEE diagnostic x-ray systems for Colombia and 13 for El Salvador; 50 diagnostic x-rays systems for Iran; and an 80-bed installation of GE 3100-Series patient monitors for the Primero de Octubre Hospital in Madrid.

Supporting these record-setting activities were headquarters' export specialists such as Frank Patton, Rocky Koch, Dick Larsen, Janine Barré, Wendy Leitner, Don Iwinski, and Norm Berg, among others. Their efforts were recognized in the spring of 1976, when the U.S. Commerce Department awarded the division the President's "E-star" Award for excellence in exporting. At special ceremonies in Washington, D.C., Secretary of Commerce Elliot Richardson presented the award to a contingent of Milwaukee officials, including Walt Robb, Jim Finke, and Bob Parkhurst.

The "E" Award

The President's "E" Award was introduced in 1961 as a revival and adaptation of the WWII Army-Navy "E" pennants awarded to industrial plants for superior production. This was the first "E" Award to be presented to a GE component since 1963. GEMS would win another just 6 years later for "continued export achievements selling high technology medical diagnostic imaging products overseas," especially CT scanners.

Several days later, the nearly 150 Milwaukee employees directly involved in export activities were honored at a luncheon in the Waukesha plant. U.S. Senator William Proxmire spoke to the group and officially raised the "E" flag. Special guests included William Kidd, Wisconsin Secretary of Business Development; Waukesha Mayor Paul Vrakas; Harvey Raasch, chairman of the Wisconsin District Export Council; Edward Watson, Metropolitan Milwaukee Association of Commerce chairman; Gil Kamin, president of Local Lodge 1916, International Association of Machinists; and Ray Hoffmeier, Local Lodge 1916 shop committee chairman.

Another restructuring initiative with immediate and positive consequences was Walt's decision to "rationalize" the x-ray product offering. By concentrating on a proven core of standard offerings, while carefully introducing new and upgraded technologies where needs existed and as the manufacturing situation allowed, GE had begun to recover U.S. leadership in this key modality. For example, by the end of his first full year, Walt had the pleasure of joining with the x-ray and sales organizations in celebrating the shipment of the 2,000th GE battery-powered mobile x-ray unit.

X-ray innovation continued as Bill Zabriskie and his engineering team developed such innovations as the LAD (longitudinal angulation device), advanced RFX Table/Spotfilmer, and MPX line of constant-load x-ray generators. Many of these advances

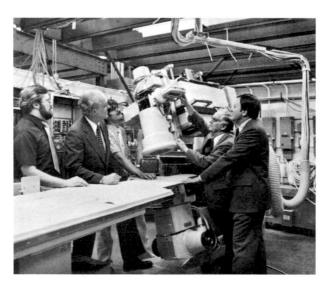

bore Bob Godbarsen's unmistakable imprint. In a classic instance of virtue rewarded, Bob, who was now the manager of advanced technology engineering, was selected to receive a 1977 Charles P. Steinmetz Award, a biennial honor for outstanding GE engineers and scientists. Among his many accomplishments, Bob was credited with developing image intensifiers that used x-ray pulse-width modulation to capture dynamic physiological events in real time, pioneering the application of three-field image tubes, and playing a key role in the development of the CT/T scanner.

A profoundly important event was the installation of a specially modified CT research system called "Radview" at Stanford University in July 1979. This program, directed by Stanford radiology and engineering professor, Bill Brody, investigated the utility of "computed radiography." What was learned would make enormous contributions to GE's successful effort to develop the technology that became known as "digital x-ray."

"Sound" investment

There was still a significant gap in GE's plans to become a full-line diagnostic imaging supplier. As part of the 1976 CT distribution agreement with YEW, the company was selling their low- and mid-tier ultrasound products in the U.S. and Canada. In addition to helping GEMS gain experience in the office-based market, this arrangement also allowed it to focus its energies on the premium end of the market. George Ward, who followed Al Fried as general manager of Special Health Products, chose Russ Thompson to lead the ultrasound business. One of their first projects was a water-bath ultrasonic breast scanner from Ausonics in Australia. After an equivocal clinical evaluation led by Dr. Barry Goldberg at Thomas Jefferson University in Philadelphia, this project was abandoned. (Ausonics would later became a part of the GE Medical Systems family when its then parent firm, Elbit Ultrasound of Israel, was acquired in 1999.)

More successful were several initiatives with the R&D Center. Dick Lawton was commissioned to assess the ultrasound market, evaluate the sophistication of the technology, and judge the market potential for a GE product. In addition, the Center launched a phased-array technology development program focused on cardiac applications. Dave Lederman and Axel Brisken led this effort in Schenectady, while David Sahn and Kai Haber of the University of Arizona conducted early clinical evaluations.

By the beginning of 1978, Russ Noll had taken over as the Special Health chief, Ed Voboril had replaced Russ Thompson as ultrasound program manager, and Paul Amazeen was the engineering program manager. Their imperative remained unchanged: to establish a viable ultrasound business as quickly as possible. The acquisition option bore the earliest fruit. Ed had known Ron Pizer, the owner of a small ultrasound firm in the picturesque mining town of Folsom, California, for many years. Electro-Physics Laboratories (EPL) was headquartered in the old opera house and their development lab in a Quonset hut out back. They had been struggling to gain a position in the radiology ultrasound market with an articulated-arm B-mode (static image) scanner. What EPL lacked was the marketing muscle to make the product competitive and the technical depth to develop future generations of ultrasound technologies—exactly GE's strengths.

In early 1979, for the bargain basement price of $1.5 million, GEMS purchased EPL to finally become a direct player in ultrasound. Now the challenge was to make ultrasound just as successful as GE's other imaging lines. An early move in that direction was to put a seasoned GE relations pro—Art Goldberg—in charge as the first plant manager to speed the EPL integration and smooth the overall transition process. Next, the facilities issue was solved by relocating the operation to a modern plant a few miles away in the Sacramento suburb of Rancho Cordova.

An immediate need was for real-time technology to complement EPL's B-mode scanner. That quest first led to a physician in Paris who had been working on an un-

usual Fresnel-focusing device. The advantage of this approach over the more usual time delay method was that Fresnel lenses are much less expensive to manufacture. So GE purchased the patent rights and dispatched a chartered aircraft to pick up the prototype unit in Paris. Though it was known the previous developer had been unable to get good performance from the Fresnel device, the feeling was "GE would make it better." Steve Flax and his colleagues in Milwaukee's Applied Science & Diagnostic Imaging Lab soon proved this assumption wrong, and the Fresnel project was cancelled.

To keep things on track, Ed explored several options to source a suitable real-time module, including an unsuccessful negotiation with Masa Sugita at YEW on their new real-time product. The final solution was to purchase an off-the-shelf real-time module from Aloka, a leading ultrasound supplier, and integrate it with the existing EPL B-mode product. Progress thereafter was swift-and GE's prototype was installed at the University of Kansas Medical Center in April for clinical trials. The Datason™ integrated real-time and B-mode digital scanner was formally introduced at the RSNA '79 meeting in Atlanta. It would help GE capture 10% of the U.S. market the first year with 122 units sold and transferred, plus another 45 orders booked.

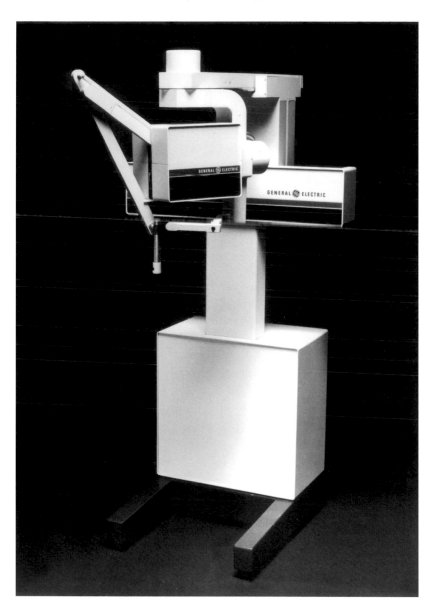

The Datason B-scan ultrasound unit.

Much of its early success was due to the physicians on the Datason Medical Advisory Board. They contributed many valuable suggestions regarding system design and performance, as well as remarkable clinical scans for display in the RSNA booth. These clinicians included Nabil Maklad of the University of Kansas Medical Center; Kai Haber of the University of Arizona at Tucson; Bill Steel of Detroit's Hutzell Hospital; Alan Dembner of Barnabas Hospital in Livingston, New Jersey; and Carlisle Morgan of St. Mary's Hospital in Richmond, Virginia.

In coming years, the ultrasound business would be headed by a series of strong, imaginative leaders, including Phil Griswa, the former CT sales manager, and Ken Leenstra. It would also benefit from a stream of innovative new products attuned to the needs of an expanding diversity of clinical users. The R&D Center's ultrasound project ultimately helped to solve the two major imaging limitations intrinsic to linear array scanners—image capture speed and transducer size—by perfecting a compact, phased array device small enough to see between the ribs and fast enough to stop heart motion. YEW also stepped in to help close the product gap by granting GE distribution rights to their new Dataline™ real-time linear array system. Even Analogic, an important supplier to the CT program, got into the act with a contract to help develop a phased array sector scanner.

The Datason system got a major boost at RSNA '80, when a real-time sector scanner module using a licensed mechanical sector scanner transducer was introduced. Progress continued at RSNA '81 with the introduction the stand-alone SRT™ system, a combination sector/linear real-time scanner. "The SRT scanner is a significant development in ultrasound technology," claimed Phil Griswa. "Now the diagnostician will have instant availability of both imaging modes with state-of-the-art image quality. Studies will take less time and yield optimum diagnostic results."

Existing products also were being improved. Advanced linear array transducers appeared in a variety of configurations for pediatric and small parts imaging, biopsy studies, and OB/GYN applications. The economical Datason S gave users the flexibility of linear array and sector real-time with the option to add static B-scanning at a later time. A new extended-reach B-scan arm for the Datason was introduced, while a new formatter for the popular Dataline unit allowed users to capture static views of its dynamic images.

A significant effort was made to enter the cardiology market with the 1982 introduction of the PASS™ ("Phased Array Sector Scanner") system. Though developed by Analogic, it made little headway against Hewlett Packard and Irex. It was finally phased out in favor of a new, dedicated cardiac system developed by YMS, the RT5000 system. YMS was also helping plug gaps elsewhere. Their RT3000 was a low-cost, combined phased array/linear array system for radiology and OB/GYN. Its lack of Doppler was corrected with the introduction of the popular RT3600 system.

As the Robb era drew to a close, GE was becoming a credible ultrasound player. Though much work remained to be done, a series of technical and strategic moves would eventually accelerate it along the path toward market leadership. Not bad for a business that began in an Old West opera house and a Quonset hut.

Tending to the field

Significant investments were also being made in the field sales and service organizations. Earlier, Bob Stocking had divided sales and service into separate, independent entities and implemented new compensation plans. A number of new district sales managers had been brought in. They understood the emerging high-tech nature of the business and how to train and motivate sales reps to meet the challenge. He picked two "new breed" sales executives for key region sales management assignments—Jim Del Mauro and Fred Espinosa. Jim would go on to head both the Sales and Service divisions as a GE vice president.

The growing sophistication of GE products demanded more specialized technical support for the field sales force. Bob responded by creating a staff of product sales specialists to assist in customer presentations and negotiations. Changes were also implemented at headquarters, where a support network was formed to provide immediate, comprehensive response whenever a field sales representative requested assistance. Product sales manager positions were established in all the modalities to help the marketing staffs introduce new products to the market and prepare the field sales force to receive them.

Other key initiatives were upgraded or implemented to assure the future availability of fully qualified leaders for the business, such as the Technical Marketing and Technical Sales programs. Bright young college graduates were identified and given a variety of challenging GE functional assignments on a concentrated schedule. Similarly, the "Women in Sales" program was implemented to give professional GE women the tools and experiences to become successful business leaders.

Winning in a high-tech market
The Technical Marketing Program (TMP) recruited young college graduates with technical degrees and developed them through a series of 6-month sales and marketing assignments in various GE businesses. Larry Sly directed the program at Medical Systems. Bob Stocking's commitment to creating a new kind of sales team through professional development led to this program having long-term impact on building future leaders in GE Medical Systems.

Patricia Brigman and Manning Philips started on the TMP program with two other trainees in 1975. After graduating, Patricia became the first applications specialist supporting computerized patient monitoring and then went on to significant marketing management roles in that business. She predated by a year or so the arrival of two other well-known applications specialists, Geraldine Barry and Diane LaValle, who brought their expertise to vascular x-ray.

In 1979, a star-studded TMP class of 11 started their 3-month training program at the Olympia Resort in Oconomowoc, Wisconsin. Among them, Beth Klein, Paul Stevenson, Dave Illingworth, Greg Perkins, Leslie Bottorf, and Paula Raskin all went on to important leadership roles in GEMS. Byford Smith led this class, supported by outstanding instructors such as Dan Merritt.

The 1982 TMP class included three GEMS legends—Scott Mathews, Tom Rheineck, and Dan Adams. Scott recalled, "My program ended up being modified mid-stream. I went from training in Chicago/Milwaukee to being pulled into an MR marketing assignment for Morry Blumenfeld to help with the first showing of the NMR system at RSNA."

The 1983 TMP class included Ted Opie, Brad Lamb, Rich Barr, Donna Hoh, and Cindy Schuster, among others. After spending their first 12 weeks in the field, they too traveled to Olympia Resort for intensive product and sales training. By this time, Jim Flynn and Austin Pacher were building their reputations as exceptional trainers and mentors to new sales candidates.

Substantial investments were also being made in the field service organization. Particularly noteworthy was the 1982 dedication of the $17 million E. Dale Trout Center, the Service Department's new 160,000 square foot home on the Waukesha campus. Named in honor of the legendary GE educator and radiation physicist, the Trout Center allowed Mike Moakley, service general manager, to consolidate his various Milwaukee-area operations into a single facility. It also provided plenty of room for GE's expanding x-ray equipment refurbishment business. Its most important function was providing parts support to customers around the world and featured an automated parts storage and retrieval system to keep track of the 35,000 types of parts on hand and speed some 2,000 daily shipments.

Tom Hoffman (left) and Austin Pacher were among GE's most accomplished sales training experts.

The E. Dale Trout Center, home to GEMS's equipment service business.

The entire September 8, 1978 issue of *Medical Systems News* was devoted to GE-100 festivities, such as "Up With People!"

An unexpected benefit of the Trout Center project was the creation of a 1.2-mile "nature trail" winding among the woods, wetlands, and original prairie grasslands adjoining the site. In a first of its kind program for GE, the two small lakes on the property were later used to breed and rear trumpeter swans. This cooperative effort with the Wisconsin Department of Natural Resources was successful in reintroducing this endangered species to the state.

MedFACS, another imaginative new Service business begun under Moakley, offered convenient, cost-effective, design-and-build solutions for customers who needed imaging equipment and the space to operate it. With design architects in each field service region backed by experts at headquarters, MedFACS could design and manage the construction of virtually any size project, from a simple room remodeling to a new building.

"GE-100"

Before getting too far ahead in our story, it's time to recall what was happening on the local scene. A good place to start is in 1978, with an event every employee at the time will still remember—the company-wide celebration of General Electric's 100th birthday called "GE-100." It was on October 17, 1878, when a group of farsighted investors decided to underwrite the Edison Electric Light Company with the then enormous sum of $50,000. By 1890, Thomas Edison had brought his various enterprises together in the Edison General Electric Company and, in 1890, merged them with the Thomson-Houston Company to create General Electric Company.

Now, exactly a century later, GE was an American industrial icon with a fantastic range of businesses—lighting, power generation and transmission, countless industrial products and components, housewares, home appliances, jet engines, aerospace systems, plastics, railway locomotives, earth-orbiting satellites and, yes, medical technology. It had also become one of the largest and most financially successful manufacturing firms in the world with some 300,000 employees and annual sales approaching $20 billion (not much more than GE Healthcare's current revenues but a very impressive sum three decades ago).

In his statement kicking off the centennial celebration, GE Chairman Reginald Jones observed:

> Now we begin our next 100 years.
>
> In many ways, the challenges we face are like those of the founders of the company—creating new markets, customers, products, and jobs; visualizing what we want to become; generating and allocating resources for maximum sustainable earnings growth.
>
> But we have new challenges today in this changing world. We are a diverse company that must contend with increasing worldwide competition, continuing international turbulence, expanding government intervention, a changing political climate, and slower economic growth. To maintain and grow our enterprise, we must make greater efforts to earn public understanding, approval, and support.

GE-100 activities continued throughout the year in each of GEMS's facilities and the various employee communications. One of many highlights was the September GE-100 Family Art Show that displayed the works of more than 175 employees and family members in the atrium of the Waukesha headquarters building. The biggest event was a huge birthday party for employees and their families at the Performing Arts Center in downtown Milwaukee. For most of the year, the official Corporate-sponsored celebration activity called the "GE Road Show" had been traversing the country, visiting every city with a significant GE population. Now, on the first weekend

in September, it was GEMS's turn to enjoy the fun, along with employees from other company components with offices in the area.

The centerpieces of the celebration were a show by the nationally known youth ensemble "Up With People!" and a high-energy audiovisual review of the company's history. These were followed by a gala cake and ice cream reception. A special local attraction was Walt Robb emceeing a TV-style prize show called "It's Your Choice!", which rewarded contestants with valuable GE merchandise for correctly answering questions about GE history. In a special drawing, Len Konkol, tool crib group leader at Electric Avenue; Waukesha tool and die designer, Henry Thomsen; and Robert Heinrichs of the local Power Systems sales and service operation, all won GE-100 celebration trips for their families to Disney World. George Nott won a separate drawing for field employees. Twelve others were honored with "Centennial Awards" for sustained outstanding performance and contributions to the business, including Thurston Ackerman, George Pokorny, John LaRocco, Robert Adams, Harry Hollington, Pat Cannestra, Harold Dalman, Bob Mueller, Morry Blumenfeld, Charlie Pascarella, Marion Duckwall, and Bob Parkhurst.

Community leadership

General Electric Company and its employees have a long tradition of charitable giving. Grants from The GE Foundation support special enterprises, while its "More Gifts . . . More Givers" program provides matching contributions to many local employee gifts. In Milwaukee, the Employee Civic and Charitable Organization (ECCO) was, for many years, a major tool to organize and increase the effectiveness of employee charitable giving. Managed and directed by employees, ECCO sought out and rewarded worthy local non-profits engaged in improving their communities.

GE charity has always targeted education. A 1982 cooperative project among The GE Foundation, GE Medical Systems, and Milwaukee Public Schools is an excellent example. This $50,000 initiative, called the Electronics Career Education Project, was designed to improve public school understanding of the role of high technology in society, encourage career interest in electronics technology, and heighten public awareness of the new occupational skills needed in a changing economy. It included the creation of an electronics technology specialty and an Electronics Technology Laboratory at James Madison High School, an upgrading of electronics equipment at Milwaukee Technical High School, and the establishment of an exploratory electronics career counseling and demonstration project at Webster Middle School. More than 30 GE engineers, scientists, and managers invested their personal "sweat equity" in the project by providing instructional and counseling assistance, plant tours and lab demonstration for students, and in-service training for participating teachers.

In fact, the personal involvement by employees in worthwhile local projects has also been a hallmark of GE community engagement. For instance, Medical Systems

has loaned some of is brightest executives on several occasions to help the Waukesha United Way organization meet its goals. The local chapter of the Elfun Society (a GE fraternal organization founded by GE president Gerald Swope in 1928; its name is a contraction of "Electrical Funds") "adopted" Milwaukee's Clarke Street School as the focus of its community improvement efforts.

Another great example of General Electric's generosity was a $100,000 GE Foundation grant to the Milwaukee School of Engineering that helped them establish a human factors laboratory.

The Minority Scholarship Program was established to encourage Milwaukee-area minority youths to pursue engineering and technical careers. It was open to graduating seniors, male and female, recommended by their high-school faculty, and placing high in competitive evaluations. The payoff was a multiyear scholarship to study engineering or other technical discipline at the college or university of their choice, plus a guaranteed summer position at GEMS throughout their schooling. These summer interns were a familiar sight around the business during the late 70's and early 80's. This program helped many young people launch extremely productive technical careers. In fact, Mike Barber, who became the chief technology officer of GE Healthcare and then vice president of Healthymagination, got his start at the Milwaukee School of Engineering, in part, because of a Minority Engineering Scholarship. (His future wife, Jackie, also won a Minority Engineering Scholarship, which is how they first met.)

GE community support extended to the arts. A $75,000 GE Foundation grant helped the Milwaukee Repertory Theatre provide physical access for the handicapped in its new "Powerhouse" theater facilities in downtown Milwaukee. At Walt's urging, the "Arts Support Program" was launched to encourage employees to contribute regularly and generously. Some of his top staff executives, including Ron O'Keefe, Lonnie Edelheit, Ira Miller, Frank Schilling, Bob Stocking, and Al Wilke, lent their influence by serving on the program's board.

Though the best known of all these arts support efforts was initiated shortly after Walt's departure, it owed much to the appreciation he helped to foster for the performing and visual arts. Called the "Arts in Community Education" (ACE) program, it was launched thanks in large part to a multiyear grant from The GE Foundation. Spearheaded by the Milwaukee Symphony Orchestra (MSO), the nationally acclaimed ACE program enhanced education for elementary- and high-school students through the integration of music and art into school curricula. Some three dozen ensembles, comprised of over 100 musicians from the MSO, plus many local cultural partners, visit these schools throughout the year providing arts experiences in support of both ACE and core curricula. Grade-specific concerts are presented frequently at Uihlein Hall, the home of the MSO, giving many of these students their first opportunity to hear a real symphony orchestra performing in a real concert hall.

Patron of the arts

Walt Robb's active, personal interest in the local arts scene led to a very special grant from The GE Foundation in 1985.

The Milwaukee Symphony Orchestra had been looking for new ways to share its musicmaking more widely. In addition to frequent state and regional tours, special performances at such venerable venues as New York's Carnegie Hall, and weekly broadcasts on its own international radio network, had given discriminating new audiences tantalizing samples of what the young ensemble, under its renowned music director, Lukas Foss, could do.

In the early 1980's, the MSO's board and its executive director, Bob Caulfield, began making plans to present the Milwaukee musicians to some of the toughest audiences of all with a tour of the major concert halls of Europe. Several anonymous donations had moved the planning forward; a booking agent was scheduling actual performance dates in England, Holland, Germany, and Austria. By 1984, however, the project was in peril, because not enough funding was yet in hand to pay for the very expensive process of transporting 90 musicians and their instruments around Europe for a couple of weeks. So when Walt stepped forward to present a major grant from The GE Foundation to cover the substantial budget shortfall, the bravos were sustained.

On March 1, 1986, the MSO departed for London and performed its opening concert in Barbican Hall 2 days later. Over the course of the next 2-1/2 weeks, the pride of Milwaukee played for sold-out houses in Hamburg, Hannover, Bonn, Amsterdam, Düsseldorf, Frankfurt, Wiesbaden, Stuttgart, Munich, Linz, and Vienna. When the exhausted, but exhilarated, troupe returned home, they were greeted by the headline in the local newspaper, "Milwaukee Symphony conquers Europe." In appreciation for GE's support, JoAnn Falletta, associate conductor, led the MSO in several special performances for area employees and their families.

Walt served for a number of years on the MSO board of directors and was vice chairman at the time he moved back to Schenectady. As a parting gift to the greater Milwaukee community, he, Anne, and their sons presented a major endowment to the MSO. The "Walter L. Robb Family Principal Trumpet Chair" is a fitting and permanent public recognition for a family that truly made a difference in their adopted hometown.

Jane Polin of The GE Foundation later said, "During my years as program manager and comptroller at The GE Foundation, GE Medical Systems was a favored GE business partner for community involvement. Walt Robb modeled civic engagement behavior for his team through his own active involvement with, and giving to, numerous local organizations, especially and notably the Milwaukee Symphony Orchestra."

Going global

With competitive products in every category and leadership products in many, the time was right for Medical Systems to take another look at the international marketplace. The CT/T scanner had already opened the doors to markets in Japan, Germany, and even Russia. One of the most satisfying early offshore wins was in the People's Republic of China, where a team from Milwaukee landed a $1 million CT order in February 1979. This high-powered group included: Ron Schilling, program manager for China and Japan; Art Glenn, CT program manager; Morry Blumenfeld, CT applications manager; and Dr. Alan Williams, radiologist from the Milwaukee County Medical Complex.

Schilling had pleasant memories of the GE team's victory:

GE was the last of nine CT manufacturers the Chinese interviewed and the first they placed an order with. They had studied the CT field for over a year and were impressed with GE's forthright presentation. This was one of the first GE products to be ordered by China directly and may have been their fastest order ever, coming in only 2 weeks.

Art Glenn said the Chinese doctors the group met all seemed anxious to make an arrangement with GE, perhaps because many of them had studied in the U.S. or visited before the revolution. He also noted they held GE's name in high regard because of the quality and reliability of its products. Their hosts proudly showed the group a pre-World War II CDX dental x-ray unit that was still in daily use at Beijing Medical University Hospital.

Another significant win was in Australia. Geraldine Barry, who had begun her professional career with GEMS in 1974, as a full-line sales representative in Los Angeles, had been selected by Bob Stocking to take over as the new sales manager for Australia and New Zealand in 1979. Her arrival "Down Under" was soon followed by GE's acquisition of Thorn EMI's worldwide medical diagnostic imaging equipment service organization outside the U.S. (OmniMedical bought the U.S. service rights), along with a factory in Radlett, England. The Department of Justice approved the $32 million deal on June 27, 1980. Though the Radlett plant was needed to supply replacement parts for Thorn EMI's huge installed base, it would only be matter of time until most of those systems would be obsolete. So employees at Radlett were greatly relieved when Al Grant, managing director, announced plans to bring in three new high-technology product lines: the

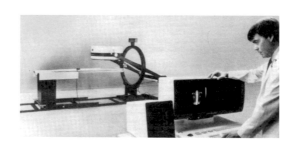

top to bottom

Dr. Guozhen Li, radiology chair at Beijing Medical University, proudly displayed her old GE CDX dental x-ray unit to Morry Blumenfeld during his 1979 visit. Dr. Li was known as the "grande dame" of Chinese radiology and became an honorary member of the Radiological Society of North America in 1998 and the European Congress of Radiology in 2001.

This factory in Radlett, England, was acquired as part of the Thorn EMI deal.

The Starcam system was among GEMS's first "global" products. Most of its components were manufactured in Denmark, but its digital electronics came from the Radlett plant.

advanced STAR computer-integrated nuclear medicine imaging system, the popular AMX-II mobile x-ray unit, and the multiformat camera for CT scanners.

Naturally, the agreement included Thorn EMI's former sales and service organization in Australia and New Zealand, where the English firm had been the dominant CT supplier. As Geraldine noted:

> At the time, there were no more than five EMI neuro scanners installed in the entire country. The customer base was aware of the ongoing improvements in third and fourth generation CT scanners and was clamoring for change. GE was in a position to became a player based on technological developments, upgradeability, reputation, U.S. market position, and, now, a strong local service structure.

Over the next few years, she virtually ran the table with the CT 8800, beginning with all five CT scanners put up for public bid in Sydney in 1980. Another four scanners followed in Melbourne, one in Tasmania, four in Adelaide, one in Brisbane, and four more in New Zealand. Besides product superiority and total support, GE's success hinged on Geraldine's credibility. She had visited the region on several earlier occasions, helping the former distributor turn over several GE heart cath and angio labs. So when she returned as country sales manager, she was already well known and trusted by many physicians who were soon to become GE CT customers.

An excellent example of the lengths to which GE was ready to go to satisfy its Australian customers was the unusual installation of a CT 8800 scanner in Sydney. The location was in the basement of a multistory building on Mac Quaire Street, the heart of Sydney's financial and medical specialist district. Not only were the building's doorways and elevator shaft too narrow for the scanner gantry, but the historic structure was protected by the Australian National Trust, which prohibited exterior modifications or defacements. The local GE service team, led by Geoff Turner, Australia/New Zealand service manager, scoured the country for the longest crane available to lift the gantry atop the 10 plus-story building then lower it to the basement through an interior light well.

Dave Sullivan, who had made his reputation as a full-line sales representative in Indiana, would later replace Geraldine when she returned to the U.S. to become the CT product sales manager in the Eastern Region and then was named the first woman to head up a U.S. sales district (St. Louis). Dave also went on to a stellar career leading the Australia/New Zealand sales and service team for many years.

On the other side of the world, Paul Bachand, general manager of GEMS's International Department, had set up the European Operation in Frankfurt, Germany. Under the leadership of several experienced European executives, including Rainer-Lionel d'Arcy and, later, Constantino (Costa) Barbavara, this new organization provided closer management of all marketing activities throughout Europe while taking the fight for share directly into the home markets of two huge competitors—Siemens of Germany and Philips of the Netherlands. With its own dedicated sales and service assets now in place, GE's move would force the European powerhouses to devote more of their resources to protecting their home turf.

In May 1982, GE's European efforts received a second boost with the addition of General Espanola de Electromedicina S.A. (GEMED) in Torrejon, Spain. Formerly a part of General Electrica Espanola, GEMED now joined the Medical Systems team. Tom Bray was named the first manager of the Spain Operation; Jose Maria Navarrete, the long-time manager of GEE's former medical electronics business, became director of the product management operation. (Jose also was appointed "Honorary Commercial Attaché" by then Wisconsin Governor Lee Dreyfus.)

The pieces were being methodically assembled for a concerted assault on Europe.

top to bottom
Aerial delivery of a CT 8800 scanner to the Mac Quaire Street Hospital in Sydney, Australia.

Geraldine Barry (left), Australia/New Zealand country sales manager, and several hospital personnel watch as the CT 8800 is lowered through the light well.

top to bottom

Walt Robb and his staff circa 1981: (l–r) Ed Voboril (Strategic Planning), Jim Del Mauro (Sales), Mike Moakley (Service), Ron Schilling (Japan/China), Frank Schilling (Programs), Art Glenn (CT), Walt Robb, Don White (Finance), Bobby Bowen (Engineering), Ron O'Keefe (Legal), Bob Stocking (Sales & Service), Jerry Cote (Manufacturing), Paul Bachand (International), Al Wilke (Relations), and Dick Sim (Special Health Products).

GE donated a pair of AMX mobile x-ray units to support the 1980 Winter Olympic Games in Lake Placid, New York. Art Marks (left), x-ray programs manager, and Leon Janssen, x-ray supplies manager, inspect one of the battery-powered units.

Stars in the East

The CT distribution agreement between GE and YEW had produced big results. By 1982, well over 100 CT/T systems had been sold in Japan, a remarkable number considering this was the home market for two of GE's largest CT competitors, Toshiba and Hitachi. In return, GE was selling significant quantities of YEW ultrasound gear in the U.S. The relationship had been so successful both parties were wondering if it might not be mutually beneficial to move it to a new, closer level. The answer came on April 20, 1982, when Walt Robb and Shozo Yokogawa, president of YEW, announced the formation of a new joint venture (JV) in medical imaging equipment. Named Yokogawa Medical Systems, Ltd. (YMS), it was GE's first medical joint venture ever.

The tough negotiations were led by Ed Voboril, GEMS's strategic planning manager, and Jerry Gould, president of GE Japan. Based upon its technology and experience, GE insisted on a majority stake in the proposed JV, while the YEW principals wanted a 50/50 partnership. As Ed recalled this event:

> We were all sitting at loggerheads in a conference room at GE Japan headquarters. I sketched out a picture of a CT scanner on a piece of paper with a 'Yokogawa Medical Systems' logo on it and a legend beneath that said 'GE equals 50.5%.' I slid the paper across the table to Shozo, and he nodded his head. That's how GE got its deal and YMS got its name.

Yokogawa won the right to name the JV's new president, Takashi Sugiyama, and GE appointed the senior vice president, Al LeBlang, who had been in Japan for a period of time representing Medical Systems at YEW. (Al and his wife, Pat, had moved to Tokyo on an initial 3-month assignment; they stayed for 10 years.)

Lessons in Leadership

Takashi Sugiyama (b. 1924) *grew up in Hyogo Prefecture (Kobe) and, after graduating from Tokyo University with a degree in electrical engineering in 1947, joined Yokogawa Electric Works. In 1969, Sugiyama-san completed a Ph.D. in engineering at Tokyo University and was appointed YEW's director of R&D 2 years later. He won the Prime Minister's Prize for invention in 1972, and the Shiju Hoshou Award, one of Japanese government's highest honors, in 1975. He joined YEW's board of directors in 1973 and was selected to lead its medical equipment business in 1976. "Tak" was appointed president of Yokogawa Medical Systems when it was established in 1982, YMS chairman in 1988, and chairman of Yokogawa General Research Center in 1993. He retired in 1995.*

YMS and its 333 employees hit the ground running. The Hachioji factory was soon churning out CT scanners for the Japanese market based on GE's proven technology and YEW's technical expertise in electronics. A substantial and growing installed base provided a steady stream of service revenue to further underpin the new enterprise. By the time YMS became fully operational on October 1, the 200th GE CT scanner had been installed in Japan. The new company had also begun distributing and servicing GE's advanced x-ray and nuclear medicine offerings in Japan and was providing advanced linear array ultrasound for distribution worldwide. YMS also was developing a strong line of low- and mid-tier CT scanners to augment GE's high-end products. First was the easy-to-use CT 8600 system that won Japan's most prestigious honor for product excellence. It was followed by the CT 9000 in 1984 and the CT MAX™ 2 years later.

YMS's remarkable technical achievements were recognized formally in the fall of 1987, when it was announced that Shinichi Kawase, general manager of the Engineering Department, had been selected to receive the Charles P. Steinmetz Award. This was

top, left to right
YMS logo.

Isao Matsumoto (left), YMS marketing manager, and Shinichi Kawase, Vice President and General Manager, YMS Development and Engineering, proudly display the Machine Design Award for the CT 8600 scanner.

middle to bottom
The CT Max 640 provided exceptional clinical performance in a compact package and was popular around the world.

Shozo Yokogawa, president of Yokogawa Electric Works, and Jack Welch, GE chairman, sign the 1986 agreement that gave GE a 75% share of YMS.

the first time such a prestigious GE award for technical and scientific achievement had been presented to an employee of a Japanese subsidiary company.

From such a strong technological base, growth was swift. To keep up with the expanding business opportunity, a new office complex was dedicated in Tachikawa in November 1985. This 95,000 square foot headquarters building allowed YMS, for the first time, to consolidate its multiple office locations. In the spring of 1986, Shozo Yokogawa and Jack Welch signed a new agreement that increased GE's stake in YMS to 75%. As a part of that agreement, Tak Sugiyama, YMS president, became a senior member of the Medical Systems Group staff reporting directly to Walt Robb. Otherwise, the management structure at YMS remained unchanged. The agreement also included the construction of a huge new manufacturing plant at Hino to open in the spring of 1989.

The complete acculturation of the two YMS partners was reached on December 1, 1988, when Charles P. Pieper, president of GE Medical Systems Asia, also became the president and chief operating officer of Yokogawa Medical Systems. After 6 momentous years at the helm of General Electric Company's most successful Japanese JV ever, Sugiyama-san was promoted to the new position of chairman and chief executive officer of YMS.

In 1983, emboldened by the fabulous success of YMS, Walt decided to see if that model could be duplicated in South Korea. The timing seemed ideal since GEMS had recently received its largest international order ever up to that time from the "Hermit Kingdom"—a $7.6 million deal for five CT systems and substantial quantities of x-ray equipment for Seoul National University. It was clear Korea had an appetite for advanced medical technology. The search for a partner soon led to the Samsung Group and, in November, the two firms announced their intention to establish Samsung Medical Systems Ltd. (SMS) to manufacture, market, and service medical equipment in the Republic of Korea. Following approvals from Seoul, SMS was inaugurated early in 1984. It initially assembled and manufactured GE-designed medical diagnostic imaging products, especially x-ray gear. With the completion of its own new plant, SMS quickly became a leader in Korea and a reliable source of quality imaging gear for distribution in other Asian markets. It continues today as an important link in GEMS's global supply chain.

Back to Europe

There was one more major move to be made on the international game board during Walt's tenure. That was the 1985 creation of an entirely new and expanded sales, service, and marketing organization to serve Europe, the Middle East, and Africa. General Electric Medical Systems Europe was headquartered in London and led by president and chief operating officer Vincenzo Morelli, former staff executive and manager of Corporate Business Development and Strategy at GE headquarters. A native of Naples, Italy, he was well equipped culturally and academically for his new assignment. He also had 7 years of practical experience with Boston Consulting Group in Europe and the U.S.

Vincenzo Morelli led GE Medical Systems Europe and, later, GE CGR.

In announcing the new organization, Robb noted, "This important organizational initiative is being taken to provide additional concentration of resources and business focus. It will be a truly European organization, largely staffed by Europeans, and its overall strategy will be driven by European requirements, strengths, and views."

Further strengthening its linkage with General Electric's overall activities in Europe, Paolo Fresco was appointed to chair the GEMS Europe board. Fresco was vice president and general manager of GE's Europe and Africa Operation, as well as president of GE Europe. Jack Welch would later tap him to become a GE vice chairman before he returned to his native Italy as president of Fiat.

To provide the primary interface with Medical Systems, Bob Stocking was appointed vice chairman of the GEMS Europe board. Other key appointments were Walt Jones, who moved from his Western Region sales manager post to become the vice president of sales and service, and Crist Cunico, manager of international service, who was named operations vice president and general manager of GEMED in Spain.

"The most exciting aspect of this effort is that it demonstrates the confidence Medical Systems has in our joint abilities to get this job done," Morelli commented. "The challenge is enormous, but I'm convinced we will stand up to it."

GEMS Europe was soon to be overtaken by events no one could have foreseen in the fall of 1985. Less than 2 years later, Jack Welch would negotiate a deal that profoundly altered the public appearance of both General Electric Company and one of its principal European rivals. At the same time, it would transform Medical Systems into "the American company with a European face" it had long sought to become. The full story of the GE-Thompson S.A. deal that brought Compagnie Générale de Radiologie (CGR) into the GE family will be told in due course.

X-ray by the numbers

Among the technologies that came to maturity during this period, one of the most exciting was the application of digital techniques to standard radiographic and fluoroscopic imaging. CT had convinced diagnosticians that computer images could be trusted for even the most difficult decisions. Now, several firms, including GE, were working hard to apply digital technology in other areas. GE's ScoutView positioning feature on the CT/T 8800 scanner had introduced digital techniques into conventional x-ray imaging in 1978, but it lacked sufficient contrast and spatial resolution for diagnostic studies. What was needed was a modified approach that would allow the full utilization of the intrinsic dynamic range present in radiographic and fluoroscopic images.

Phil Peck, the new Digital X-ray Programs manager, and his Milwaukee engineering team of Mike Harsh and John Celek were studying two approaches:

1. Scanned projection radiography (SPR) used the CT fan beam and detector to scan the patient and convert the transmitted x-rays into digital signals (i.e., the "Radview" system at Stanford mentioned earlier).
2. Digital fluorography (DF) converted the video signal from a conventional image intensifier/TV system into digital signals (i.e., a special research system also installed at Stanford).

The Stanford program, which was directed by Bill Brody, soon yielded important clinical results. Early Radview images demonstrated enhanced image contrast resolution beyond that possible with x-ray film. Combined with its dynamic contrast range capabilities, Radview was uniquely capable of locating lesions, disease masses overlapped by obscuring tissue, and soft tissue detail that could not be visualized by conventional film. Subtraction imaging could isolate and enhance small contrast objects at all image brightness levels:

- Temporal subtraction enhanced differences between two images made at different times; and
- Energy subtraction revealed differences between images made at two energy levels.

By mid-1980, results were so encouraging the strategic decision was made to give the DF program an early introduction at RSNA '80, even though hardware development was still in the conceptual stage. This urgency was driven by the finding of an expert clinical panel that the potential for digital was so great it posed a significant threat to the core x-ray business. This aggressive upscheduling of the digital x-ray program was aimed at having a viable product ready for introduction in 1982. To that end, a dedicated digital x-ray engineering facility called Design Center West was established at Rancho Cordova and staffed by half a dozen newly hired digital design engineers. Design work was launched on January 1, 1981, and the first clinical evaluation system was shipped to Stanford University in September. Prototype units for Mayo Clinic and Froedtert soon followed. With these successes, the new Digital Fluoricon® 3000 system was officially introduced a year ahead of schedule at RSNA '81.

Accolades for the DF 3000 system rolled in. The first was the Wisconsin Governor's New Product Award in June, followed by *Industrial Research* magazine's "IR-100" award that recognized it as one of the 100 most significant technological advances of 1982 (the R&D Center won five IR-100 awards that year). Walt Robb accepted the honor on behalf of the business at formal ceremonies in Chicago's Museum of Science and Industry. In the audience were William Collins, senior systems engineer; Stephen Riederer, senior physicist; and Tom Lambert, digital radiology products engineering manager, all key contributors to the DF 3000 project.

GE's second-generation digital fluorography product—the DF 5000—was introduced at RSNA '84. The upgraded product incorporated further improvements suggested by the clinical research work performed at Stanford University. Now, GE was embarked upon the road toward the digital future in all of the imaging modalities.

Dr. Brody, by the way, was to continue his stellar medical and academic career by subsequently becoming chairman of radiology at Johns Hopkins University and

radiologist-in-chief at Johns Hopkins Hospital, provost of the University of Minnesota's Academic Health Center, and, in 1996, president of Johns Hopkins University. Following his retirement in March 2009, he was appointed president of The Salk Institute in La Jolla, California. He also serves on GE's Health Advisory Board, a panel of health experts charged with advising the company on its efforts in this field, evaluating progress, and making regular public reports.

"PACS"

PACS ("picture archiving and communications system") became a popular concept with the appearance of digital imaging modalities. The idea was to use the latest advances in digital storage technology to archive and manage the huge volume of digital images being generated by these new diagnostic tools. GE's involvement can be traced to the mid-1970s when Joe Marion, who had been delegated to explore PACS, established a collaborative relationship with Sam Dwyer at the University of Kansas Medical Center. The acknowledged "father of PACS," Dr. Dwyer's interest had been spurred by the fact he could only view images from the hospital's two GE CT/T 7800 systems on the specific unit that had scanned the patient. This was highly inefficient and wasted valuable scanning time.

"What Sam wanted was a method for centralized viewing and storage," Marion recalled. "He was working with NCR to develop the concept, and we picked up on it as an opportunity to develop a new feature for GE CT."

In January of 1978, the Independent Diagnostic Center (IDC) for the analysis of CT images was introduced as a Continuum advance. This free-standing unit included data handling capabilities, so image reviews were possible at any time. Doctors could magnify regions of interest, perform distance measurements, annotate images, simultaneously view segments from two or more images, outline areas according to CT number values, and much more.

"The IDC meant radiological consultation was no longer limited to one clinical site or a static film image," Marion noted. "It also provided a paradigm for our expanding efforts in creating PACS solutions for other modalities, especially computed radiography."

The next major PACS event came in 1983. IBM approached GE about a healthcare customer in Denver who wanted to manage their diagnostic images digitally. IBM knew digital text and information systems but not imaging, so they suggested GE partner with them in a joint project that resulted in the Integrated Diagnostics System (IDS). Ed Barnes, who was now GE's multimodality systems project manager, explained, "The IDS allowed diagnostic images and information in one hospital to be transmitted, in digital form, to other clinics and hospitals."

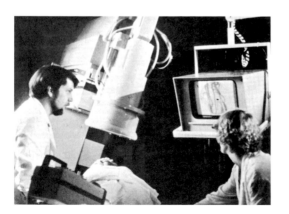

top to bottom

The Digital Fluoricon 3000 system was cited in the IR-100 award as "a revolutionary breakthrough" in x-ray imaging.

Wisconsin Governor Lee Dreyfus presented the 1982 Governor's New Product Award for the DF3000 system to Tom Lambert at ceremonies in Madison. Also attending were Lt. Gov. Russell Olson (center), and Gary Keys and Eli Benarie from GEMS.

right

The Digital Fluoricon 5000 digital system, introduced in 1984, strengthened GE's technological leadership in digital fluorography.

"Integrated diagnostics" (or PACS) was seen as one way to help control the soaring costs of high-tech health care. "Integrated diagnostics focuses on the imaging portion," explained Marion, now the multimodality marketing manager. "It could revolutionize the way hospitals communicate diagnostic images and related patient information by linking digital imaging modalities for the purposes of centralized communication, image display, analysis, and archive."

A significant milestone was reached in 1988, when CT 9800 scanners at Milwaukee County Medical Complex and Froedtert were linked to a radiology workstation and a viewing station for referring physicians. Later that summer, MR systems were added to the network, along with more workstations both inside and outside the two radiology departments. Dr. Dennis Foley, coordinator of the digital imaging section, predicted, "In the future, we could review images and information from a remote site, such as another hospital, clinic, physician's office, or home. Two radiologists could review the same information at once, greatly improving everyone's efficiency."

Perhaps the most exciting aspect of this project was the move it signaled toward diagnoses from high-resolution electronic displays, rather than conventional x-ray film. As Marion explained:

> This is the first time we have set out to design workstations specifically for referring physicians, rather than radiologists. We want to give them a user-friendly solution that allows them to easily review, compare, and manipulate the imaging information from their patients. PACS doesn't provide new information, but it makes it much faster to access and analyze the information already there.

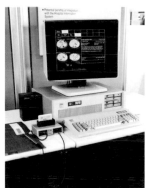

top, left to right
Walt Robb (left) and Doug Strait, IBM's PACS development manager, exchange congratulations at RSNA '85 on the public debut of their joint program.

The GE-IBM PACS workstation display at RSNA '85.

bottom
Dr. Dennis Foley (seated) and the GE team that developed the Integrated Diagnostics System, including (l–r) Jennifer Cranfill, Dave Piccirillo, Joe Tuttle, Joe Block, Terry Pope, John Mahoney, Peter Kendall, and Trish Layzell.

Déjà vu all over again

The warm embrace between Medical Systems and the R&D Center engendered by the CT development program was about to be renewed.

The new challenge was "nuclear magnetic resonance," a phenomenon first recognized in the early 1930s by the distinguished Dutch physicist C. J. Gorter, then described and measured by Isador Rabi of Columbia University in 1938. However, it remained for Felix Bloch of Stanford University and Edward M. Purcell of Harvard University to successfully demonstrate magnetic resonance for the first time in 1946. For their work, they shared the 1952 Nobel Prize in Physics.

Briefly, nuclear magnetic resonance (NMR) is a method of gaining chemical information using the magnetic properties of atomic nuclei. In the presence of a strong magnetic field, naturally spinning atomic nuclei can be made to precess or "wobble" about their axes of rotation and generally line up in the same direction. The rate of precession is characteristic of the type of nuclei in the sample. By then applying a pulsed RF excitation signal at right angles to the static magnetic field, the equilibriums of the nuclei are perturbed, inducing a signal that can be detected by a receiver coil. These data can be used to calculate the chemical composition of a sample (spectroscopy) or create a distribution map of hydrogen protons (imaging).

Though Bloch and Purcell were credited with the first demonstrations of NMR, their work was still a considerable distance away from what we know as MR imaging. That advance would be credited to Paul C. Lauterbur, who discovered the possibility of creating two-dimensional pictures by introducing gradients in the magnetic field, and to Peter Mansfield, who used gradients to develop a useful imaging technique and showed how fast MRI could be achieved. Their separate work was jointly recognized when they received the 2003 Nobel Prize in Physiology or Medicine.

Footsteps of Pioneers
Paul Christian Lauterbur (1929–2007) grew up in Sydney, Ohio and attended Case Institute of Technology (B.S. in chemistry) and the University of Pittsburgh (Ph.D. in chemistry). He joined the State University of New York at Stony Brook in 1969, where he set up an NMR lab. During a sabbatical at Stanford University, he became interested in biomedical NMR through his contacts with Syntex and Varian. In 1985, Dr. Lauterbur moved to the University of Illinois, where he organized and directed the Biomedical Magnetic Resonance Laboratory during the remainder of his career. In addition to the Nobel Prize, his many awards include the Gold Medal of the Society for Magnetic Resonance in Medicine (1982), the Albert Lasker Clinical Research Award (1984), National Academy of Sciences (1985), National Medal of Science (1987), the Gold Medal of the RSNA (1987), and the Gold Medal of the European Congress of Radiology (1999).

Dr. Lauterbur's interest in nuclear magnetic resonance extended back to his first job as a laboratory researcher with Dow Corning's Mellon Institute. While working on theories of rubber elasticity and elastomer testing, he began to learn about NMR spectroscopy and study its potential for investigating the structures and various physical properties of materials. Even after being drafted and assigned to the Army Chemical Center, he continued his research upon discovering an NMR spectroscopy device no one else knew how to use. He briefly returned to the Mellon Institute while completing his Ph.D. at the University of Pittsburgh and was then recruited to the State University of New York at Stony Brook, where he did his Nobel Prize winning research.

Lauterbur's key discovery was the idea of introducing gradients in the magnetic field to determine the origin of the radio waves emitted from the nuclei in the sample being studied. He described this work, including the first NMR image, in his seminal 1973 paper in *Nature* entitled "Image formation by induced local interactions: Examples employing nuclear magnetic resonance." But it remained for Peter Mansfield and others to actually conduct the research necessary to convert Lauterbur's idea into a practical clinical imaging tool.

Footsteps of Pioneers

Sir Peter Mansfield (b. 1933) is a native of Lambeth, South London, and studied physics at Queen Mary College, London, where he graduated with a B.S. in 1959, and a Ph.D. in 1962. After a 2-year appointment as a research associate in the Physics Department of the University of Illinois, he was appointed lecturer in physics at the University of Nottingham and remained there until retiring in 1994. In addition to the Nobel Prize, Sir Peter holds the Gold Medal of the Society for Magnetic Resonance in Medicine (1983), the Royal Society Wellcome Foundation Gold Medal and Prize (1984), the Duddell Prize and Medal of the Institute of Physics (1988), the British Institute of Radiology's Silvanus Thompson Medal (1988), and the Gold Medal of the European Congress of Radiology (1995). He was elected a Fellow of the Royal Society in 1987 and knighted by Queen Elizabeth II in 1993.

Mansfield also had a long-standing interest in NMR. His first experiment in this area was in the late 1950s, when he developed a portable, transistorized, NMR spectrometer to measure the earth's magnetic field. It was at Nottingham University where he conducted the work that led to his Nobel Prize. Mansfield's key findings were published in a 1973 letter in the *Journal of Physics,* entitled "NMR diffraction in solids," in which he suggested the use of gradients for spatial encoding (i.e., imaging). He also was credited with discovering how fast MR imaging could be accomplished by developing the echo planar imaging protocol.

Early NMRI efforts

Lauterbur's group was credited with the first instance of NMR imaging (NMRI) actually demonstrating pathology—a 2D projection of a mouse with a tumor. (It was eventually published in *Physics in Canada* 1976:32:33.11.) By 1974, NMRI experiments were also underway at the University of Nottingham in England and the University of Aberdeen in Scotland. The Aberdeen researchers, in trying to image a mouse that wouldn't keep still during an extremely long acquisition, observed a large signal change after its neck was fractured.

From this humble start, additional objects and body parts were soon to be imaged by various researchers using a variety of approaches. Following the first 2D-resolved NMR cross-sectional images of animals by Lauterbur, *in vivo* scans of Paul Bottomley's wrist were made by Waldo Hinshaw in Professor Raymond Andrew's group at Nottingham and published in *Nature* in 1977. Images of the first human thorax were reported by Raymond Damadian and Larry Minkoff that same year. The first human head image followed from Hugh Clough and Ian Young at EMI the next year.

In the 1970s, four independent NMR imaging research groups arose in Great Britain, the center of activity in the field. There were rival groups at Aberdeen University (Prof. John R. Mallard and Dr. James Hutchinson), Nottingham University (one headed by Prof. Peter Mansfield and a second by Prof. Raymond Andrew and, later, Dr. Bill Moore), and the EMI group in collaboration with Hammersmith Hospital in Wembley (Prof. Robert Steiner and Dr. Graeme M. Bydder). Their rivalry was muted by the lack of interest from the traditional physical and chemical societies in which these investigators were based. This created a "united we stand" attitude among them, prompting frequent friendly visits. Paul Lauterbur from Stony Brook also came. Radiology was still trying to digest CT, so it simply ignored NMR imaging.

Each of these groups focused on developing its own approach to a viable NMR imaging technique. Lauterbur was credited with the method of obtaining projections by applying a gradient during detection. Peter Mansfield's group was credited with selective excitation by applying a gradient during excitation. Bill Edelstein, a post-doctoral fellow with Jim Hutchison at Aberdeen, was credited with the spin warp method that applied phase-encoding gradients between excitation and detection. It was the combination of all three of these methods, one for each dimension, that forms the basis for most MR imaging today.

By about 1980, Bill Moore and Neil Holland from Raymond Andrew's group at Nottingham, as well as the EMI-Hammersmith group, had NMRI scanners suitable for imaging the human head and were studying patients. Aberdeen had a whole-body, vertical-bore, low-field scanner. Siemens, Philips, and Technicare all had head scanners that were producing very credible human head images. These activities came together at a landmark NMR imaging meeting in Winston-Salem, North Carolina, in the autumn of 1981, where the Society for Magnetic Resonance in Medicine was created.

The first commercial NMR scanner in Europe was a Picker-EMI unit installed at the University of Manchester Medical School (Prof. Ian Isherwood and Dr. B. Pullen) in 1983.

Contributions were also being made by Jay Singer and Larry Crooks at the University of California at Berkeley. Dr. Crooks moved to the University of California-San Francisco Medical Center where, in a subsequent collaboration with Pfizer (later taken over by Diasonics), he developed the multiecho, multislice technique and implemented it on a 0.3T superconducting system. Oxford Instruments in England was developing higher field, wide-bore superconducting NMR spectroscopy systems for larger animals but also could accommodate human limbs. Their first TMR ("topical magnetic resonance") system used surface coil localization and a magnet whose high-order gradients could be adjusted to create a local "sweet spot" for spectroscopy.

Soon, the first production NMRI scanners began to appear. Several of the big imaging companies—Picker, Siemens, and Philips—were losing market share in CT, so they accelerated their NMR development efforts and began testing at luminary evaluation sites. GE, on the other hand, had little interest in NMR, because CT had become a major success story for Milwaukee.

"Frankly, the last thing we needed at this time was another new modality," Walt Robb explained, "but when EMI announced it was about to install an imager at Hammersmith Hospital, we knew we had to learn a lot more about it."

In fact, Walt visited Raymond Damadian at his facility on Long Island in 1978. Dr. Damadian had published a 1971 paper reporting NMR could distinguish tumors from normal tissue *in vitro* using NMR relaxation times and had won a U.S. patent on this technique in 1974. He then formed FONAR ("field focused nuclear magnetic resonance") Corporation to produce an NMR scanner and proudly showed Walt his first machine, *"Indomitable,"* along with a few images. Walt was unimpressed and turned his attention to other matters.

Attracting success

The R&D Center had been interested in NMR spectroscopy for several years as a possible method of measuring energy metabolism; several steps had already been taken to start a research program. By 1980, Red Redington had begun to recruit the necessary talent, starting with Paul Bottomley, a recognized expert from Raymond Andrew's imaging group at Nottingham who had recently moved to Johns Hopkins to perform localized cardiac NMR spectroscopy. Next came Bill Edelstein of spin warp fame from Aberdeen.

The Center's initial interest was in localized spectroscopy. It was seeking funds to develop a whole-body NMR system to study phosphate metabolism in the living human heart. Since Medical Systems had no interest in NMR, Red and his team were relying on corporate assessed funds to support their efforts. They needed a high-field, high-homogeneity, superconducting magnet with at least a 1-meter bore to accommodate the human torso. The target field was 2.0 Tesla (a unit for measuring high magnetic fields), though 1.5T would be acceptable. The two leading suppliers of the day, Oxford Instruments and Intermagnetics General, both bid for the contract, though neither had ever built a magnet of such size. Oxford was chosen with delivery anticipated in late 1981 or early 1982. With at least a year to wait, the team decided to build a low-field imaging system that would eventually be needed anyway for localized spectroscopy.

"When Bill arrived from Aberdeen, he wasn't sure if spectroscopy was going to amount to much," recalled Bottomley. "He was more interested in working on NMR imaging. I also believed imaging was the more likely of the two to succeed."

Now, they had their opportunity to put their convictions to the test.

The acquisition of Thorn EMI in the summer of 1980 gave GE an opportunity to examine the EMI 0.1T system that had been built by Ian Young and his technical team in cooperation with Hammersmith Hospital. Young, who later became a professor and senior research investigator at Imperial College London, had just published an important paper in *The Lancet* demonstrating the effective application of NMRI in the diagnosis of multiple sclerosis. The question was whether GE should gamble on EMI's technology in a bid to get to market faster, or stick with the Schenectady program. Walt opted to go with Red Redington's crew and gave them $100,000 to purchase a 0.12T resistive magnet. They immediately set to work developing a prototype imaging system.

MR magnet nomenclature

Permanent: *A conventional magnet made from ferromagnetic materials (e.g., steel alloys containing rare earth elements) with a constant, static magnetic field. Permanent magnets are relatively weak; one powerful enough for imaging could weigh as much as 100 tons.*

Resistive: *A type of air or water-cooled magnet using copper or aluminum wiring and that is activated by a continuous electrical current. It can produce field strengths of up to .2T, sufficient for proton imaging.*

Superconductive: *A magnet that uses cryogenically cooled, superconductive wiring and is self-sustaining once it has been activated. Depending on the design and application, it can generate field strengths from .2T (whole body imaging) to 14T (chemical shift measurements) and beyond.*

By mid-1982, GE's NMR development program had evolved into a two-tiered effort:

1. Internal: The R&D Center program focused on determining the required field for optimum image quality, exploring advanced whole body spectroscopic applications, developing advanced magnet designs and components, and conducting research on siting and shielding concepts. The 1.5T superconducting magnet central to this work had finally arrived from Oxford Instruments and was installed in a specially constructed wooden lab on the Center's grounds. Soon, R&D Center researchers achieved major milestones with the first human images at this field strength and the first *in vivo* [31]P (phosphorous) spectra of human tissue.

In addition to Bottomley and Edelstein, the primary investigational team now included John Schenck, who helped Edelstein on the gradient coils; D. Vatis on RF antennas; Otward Mueller and Scott Smith, who helped Bottomley with the NMR coils and spectrometer; Bill Leue handling computer and interface; and Howard Hart minding the magnet. Dave Eisner was the senior technician for the project, assisted by Ray Argersinger and Joe Piel.

The decision to go with the 1.5T superconducting magnet, a unit five times more powerful than anything else then available, was not taken lightly. Many of the

top
Launching A Billion Dollar Business: The Milwaukee MR development team got together for a commemorative photo during a visit by Red Redington. Pictured are: (seated l–r) Red Redington, Pete Staats, Mark Riehl, Sandy Wiley, and Morry Blumenfeld; (standing l–r) Tom Wilkerson, Dave Barrett, Al Ruskowski, Bob Dobberstein, Jim Vincent, Bob Lijewski, Christene Imrich, Larry Long, Brij Khandelwal, Felix Wehrli, Tom Kurey, Lee Gray, Clyde Krumrai, James McFall, Harold Dalman, Joe Maier, and Ed Stevens. (Among the key people not present were Gary Glover, Norbert Pelc, Linda Lillybeck, Steve Engle, Bruce Gamble, and Skip Kerwin.)

bottom
Red Redington (left) and Bill Edelstein from GE's R&D Center examined images made by the 0.12T GE research magnet at Hospital of the University of Pennsylvania.

most prominent clinicians and researchers of the day were claiming a 0.15T magnet was strong enough; most competitors had announced plans for units in the 0.15–0.3T range. But higher field strength was needed for whole body spectroscopy. What remained to be seen was if it also would be suitable for whole body imaging.

Meanwhile, in Milwaukee, the engineering team led by Gary Glover and Norbert Pelc, and assisted by such people as Larry Long and Tom Pionke, was busy developing clinical research systems and conducting precision product design activities. A 0.3T superconducting magnet was installed in late summer at the new NMR laboratory on Lincoln Avenue in New Berlin and soon was imaging patients under the supervision of radiologists from the Medical College of Wisconsin. More magnets of various field strengths were on order.

Morry Blumenfeld, the first NMR program manager, was directing local activities. He had already hired physicist Felix Wehrli and soon added Linda Lillybeck to help keep the program on track.

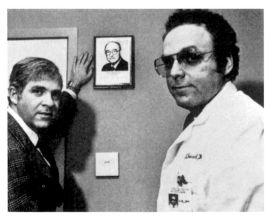

top to bottom
Dr. Herbert Kressel, director of the NMR facility at the Hospital of the University of Pennsylvania, explained the purpose of the GE clinical research magnet to a news reporter.

HUP's NMR Learning Center was named in honor of Art Bueche, the late GE research director. Morry Blumenfeld, NMR programs manager, and Dr. Kressel view his commemorative photo.

2. *External:* General implementation and application development activities were centered upon partnerships with clinical sites. The original 0.12T resistive system developed at the R&D Center was shipped to the Hospital of the University of Pennsylvania in 1982, where Herb Kressel and his team explored its capabilities. GE's first clinical NMR installation was also special, because it was part of the "Arthur M. Bueche NMR Learning Center," named in honor of the late director of the R&D Center. (Incidentally, Britton Chance, a biophysics professor at Penn, who was involved in the R&D Center's NMR spectroscopy project, received one of the early "large bore" magnets suitable for imaging a human limb.)

Several additional units were soon placed at other eminent research institutions, including a 0.15T magnet for Yale University School of Medicine, a 0.3T system for the Medical College of Wisconsin, and a 1.5T unit for Duke University Medical Center. This range of magnet types and field strengths permitted a comprehensive exploration of the clinical utility curve and ultimately confirmed GE's decision to go with the high-field 1.5T magnet.

Going public

Though GE's NMR development program was hardly a secret, there was a great deal of proprietary research and design work to be completed before an actual product would emerge. Loyal GE customers were anxious to learn the details of GE's program, since they wanted to choose a system that would put them on the leading edge of technology. Aware of GE's significant success in CT, they anticipated similar results in NMR but were torn by the fact several other manufacturers were already offering systems. How long could they wait to choose a scanner? Would GE be able to duplicate its huge CT win?

GEMS went public at the 1982 RSNA meeting. Morry, Linda, Joe Vacca, Felix Werhli, Scott Mathews, and a host of other technical, marketing, and sales experts were on hand to demonstrate the software. Jack Welch and officials from the R&D Center were also in attendance. Though no hardware was shown, GE did address many of the issues surrounding NMR in a series of educational posters and displays, including a jaw-dropping selection of early research images that were made all the more remarkable because of predictions NMR imaging would not be possible at high field strengths.

"We got the message across that it's premature to buy clinical units," Blumenfeld explained in a post-meeting interview. "We feel it is better to wait to purchase an NMR system until it can be determined it won't be obsolete in a year or less."

Morry's warning was driven by the fact FONAR, Technicare, Picker, and Diasonics were taking orders. GE launched an intensive customer education program to help stem the rush that included an "NMR primer," educational videotapes, and even an NMR teaching program for personal computers. A particularly effective companion effort was a series of seminars conducted by Les Alt of the International Department.

High-field perils
The RSNA '82 exhibit would have been even more impressive but for a near-tragic accident at the R&D Center that reminded everyone a 1.5T magnet required special care and handling.

The week before RSNA, the large RF amplifier powering the 1.5T system burned out while making images for the show. A replacement was located in Milwaukee and urgently air freighted to Schenectady. The deliveryman happened to arrive while Paul Bottomley and Bill Edelstein were at lunch, so he went directly into the magnet room through the outside doors.

As he wheeled the dolly past the magnet, it was suddenly swept into the magnet bore, crushing the deliveryman's hands in the process. Not wanting to quench the magnet with so little time left before RSNA, Laddie Stahl, Red's NMR project supervisor, gathered the team to see what could be done. Their solution was to attach

top left
The Signa MR system was introduced at RSNA '82. Jack Welch (left), GE chairman, was on hand for a personal briefing by Art Glenn (right) and Morry Blumenfeld. In the background is Pete Staats, MR engineering manager.

top right
Oops! The replacement RF amplifier and its trolley were firmly stuck to the 1.5T superconducting magnet. The ropes and slings were attached to winch them free. *(Photo courtesy of W. A. Edelstein)*

bottom
Now What?? A high-level conference was convened outside the magnet room to plan a solution. Participating were (l–r) Dave Eisner, Laddie Stahl, Paul Bottomley, and Howard Hart (partly obscured). The straps were anchored to the small tree on the left. *(Photo courtesy of W. A. Edelstein)*

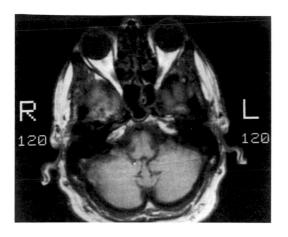

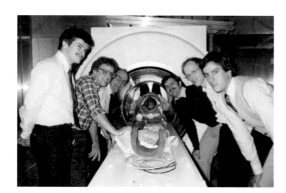

heavy straps to the dolly and a large tree near the door and winch it free. After considerable effort, the plan succeeded. Unfortunately, the Dewar was ruptured and the magnet was inoperable until the following January. Nonetheless, the existing images and spectra had the desired impact on the RSNA attendees.

A big breakthrough came on February 1, 1983, when Bottomley resumed high-field experiments using a special head-imaging coil of his own design. With Howard Hart's head in the slotted tube resonator, Paul began an imaging sequence and was astonished to see one fantastic image after another appear. "I was ecstatic," he said. "Since there was no one else around, I dragged in the cleaning person to take a look."

These images, along with companion spectra, were published the following July in *The Lancet* and set off a storm of excitement and criticism. Competitors circulated rumors GE's images were "fake," complained "they can't do whole body imaging," warned "the increased RF power is hazardous," and even claimed the work had been "rejected as unscientific." The R&D Center team ignored them and continued making better and better high-field images.

The good news kept accumulating. In Waukesha, the new 200,000 square foot NMR engineering and manufacturing building was quickly rising on its site north of the headquarters building. When Oxford Instruments rejected a proposal to form a joint venture, GE decided to build its own superconducting magnets at a 160,000 square foot facility in Florence, South Carolina. After an investment of $31 million, it opened in 1984. Carl Cliche and his team shipped their first 1.5T magnet to Milwaukee in December.

The next helping of good news was the October announcement of GE's purchase of Nicolet Magnetics Instrument Corporation (Fremont, California), a manufacturer of NMR spectroscopy instruments and small-bore NMR imaging devices. Soon thereafter, Art Glenn was appointed general manager of NMR programs. Morry Blumenfeld, who had shepherded NMR from infancy to adolescence, became the product general manager. "I am particularly grateful for the depth of technical leadership and the sustained efforts of Morry Blumenfeld who has managed the technical design of our NMR system for the past 2 years and has refined it into a superior system," Art said.

The Signa® 1.5T MR system was formally introduced at RSNA '83. Since it already had gained "pre-market approvable status" from the FDA, GE could aggressively solicit customer commitments. During the next year, a total of 14 investigational Signa MR systems were shipped, the first going to the Hospital of the University of Pennsylvania in October and the second to Milwaukee County Medical Complex shortly thereafter. The first international shipment went to Villejuif Hospital in Paris.

GE MR was on its way around the globe.

Quenching fires

Not all was sunny skies and calm seas, however. A nagging image artifact called "quadrant shading" was worrying everyone. In essence, two quadrants of the image were bright, while the two diagonally opposite were dark. Though the causes were well understood, how to engineer a solution wasn't so obvious. Walt convened a high-level meeting to discuss what to do. On hand were Red Redington and Bill Edelstein from the R&D Center, Art Glenn, Gary Glover, Norb Pelc, Morry Blumenfeld, Jim Vincent, and several others.

The problem was the RF antenna inside the magnet was designed to excite in a linear fashion, while the nuclei required a circular polarization to resonate. Although linear excitation does result in a rotating component, RF penetration problems in the body at high field strength result in the quadrant shading artifact. Everybody agreed if a way could be found to provide a circularly polarized excitation field with a coil that would fit inside the magnet, the problem might be solved. However, the engineers didn't know how to design such a coil.

After considerable discussion, Dr. Edelstein announced he could design such an antenna and have it ready in 2 weeks. Just 10 days later, he showed images from his new antenna completely devoid of quadrant shading artifacts. Not only that, his solution had the added benefit of allowing the Signa scanner to use all the power transmitted from both series of polarizations, which increased the received signal from the patient by a factor of 1.4.

The crisis was over and Bill Edelstein was the hero of the hour.

Other problems appeared as customer deliveries of the Signa system began, especially concerns about the size, fragility, and power of 1.5T superconducting magnets. These factors made them especially difficult to install in existing hospital facilities due to access restrictions and the need for magnetic shielding. At the UCSF Medical Center, for instance, there was no room available in the main building, so the Service Division's MedFACS group squeezed a preengineered structure onto a narrow shelf between the back of the hospital and a steep bluff face. It took two 60-ton cranes to lower the magnet from the top of the bluff down to the MR building. A big challenge was also overcome at the Mayo Clinic. Large slabs of marble covering the building's exterior were removed and the wall penetrated to provide access to the third-floor imaging suite. After the 7-ton magnet was hoisted into position and iron shielding installed around the scanner room, the wall was repaired and the marble reattached. The building and the Signa survived none the worse for the experience.

Space was an even greater issue in Japan, where YMS was finding it a challenge to sell the full-size Signa scanner. Although Japanese radiologists recognized it as the leading product on the market, many hospitals simply lacked sufficient space for the larger 1.5T magnet and the iron shielding it required. As a result, Toshiba, Hitachi, and other national manufacturers were gaining share with their smaller 0.5T systems. YMS wanted a smaller unit of its own, preferably with a self-shielded magnet. So it had undertaken a mid-field MRI development program completely independent of Milwaukee. Art objected, especially since he had brought Mike Kapp on board to head up a clandestine 0.5T scanner development project in Milwaukee. Walt resolved the conflict in early 1986 when he approved the YMS project. The result was the hugely successful MR Max system launched at RSNA '87.

Ramping it up

It was during this period the profession and industry agreed to drop "nuclear" from the name. That word was creating needless anxiety among the uninformed and had even caused a public protest at a meeting in Cleveland. Thereafter, the preferred term was "magnetic resonance imaging" or "MRI." NMR was exclusively reserved for industrial and scientific spectroscopy.

A significant milestone was the dedication of the new MR Center on May 30, 1984. A large crowd of dignitaries and employees were on hand, including Wisconsin Governor Tony Earl; Waukesha Mayor Paul Keenan; R&D Center director, Roland Schmitt; and GE Technical Systems Sector executive vice president, Jim Baker. The highlight was sealing a time capsule containing an assortment of artifacts to be opened 63 years hence, on May 30, 2047—the 100th anniversary year of the arrival of GE X-Ray Corp. in Milwaukee.

On April 25, 1985, the Signa system received its long-sought "premarket approval" from the FDA, making it the first high-field, whole-body MR system to achieve this key milestone.

Plaudits were flowing in from every quarter. The Industrial Designers Society of America chose the Signa to receive its "Industrial Design Excellence Award." Seth Banks, manager of industrial design and human factors, led the team that developed the prize-winning design. Other key contributors were Christine Fletcher, Hal Halvorson, and Herb Velazquez. Seth also credited the many engineers and programs people who helped design the Signa scanner.

A total of 26 Signa systems were shipped in 1984, 89 in 1985, 106 in 1986, and 141 in 1987. That is when Art became vice president and general manager of the Defense Systems Division in Pittsfield, Massachusetts. During his 4+ years with MR, GE's worldwide installed base grew from 0 to 348 systems, and its share skyrocketed to an estimated 65%. Not too shabby for a business that didn't exist just a few years before.

Burt Drayer, radiology chair at Mt. Sinai Medical Center in New York City, who was at Duke University and, later, the Barrow Neurological Institute in Phoenix during this period, stated:

> The persistence of GE in developing the 1.5 Tesla MRI system as the standard was very important. The concept that you needed a faster and more accurate image was absolutely critical, and the decisions GE made were absolutely vital to the development of MRI. By constantly trying to achieve a better and better product, they forced all the other vendors to create better products of their own to compete.

left to right
Wisconsin Governor Tony Earl sealed the MR Center's time capsule as GE vice president Jim Baker (left) and GEMS public affairs manager Chuck Willsey (rear) watch.

The entrance to the Magnetic Resonance Center on the Waukesha campus.

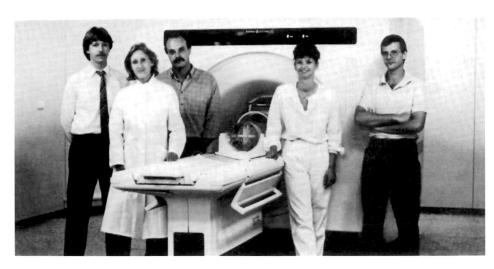

top to bottom

Workmen carefully lowered the second Signa clinical MR system into its new home at Milwaukee County Medical Complex in September 1984.

The University of Herne received Germany's first GE Signa system. Shown are (left to right) Wolfgang Mertens, supervisor; Dr. Eva Herbe, radiologist; Helge Bohn, service engineer; Birgit Moellenhoff, technologist; and Manfred Berger, service engineer.

opposite, bottom

The first Signa MR system in Australia was installed in 1986 at a private clinic in Sydney.

Mirroring the CT Continuum, new features and capabilities were being added to the Signa system. Perhaps the most important during this period was the Fast Cycle Option, a feature that allowed users to reconstruct clinical images faster than ever before. New imaging techniques included fast scanning, cardiac cine imaging, respiratory compensation, and phase-contrast angiography. Another significant GE first was the delivery of an investigational mobile MR system to NetCare, a health care consortium in the Minneapolis-St. Paul (Minnesota) area. It was the first high field MR system in the world to be operated in a truly mobile environment.

A major vote of confidence came when the National Institutes of Health (NIH) selected GE to design, construct, and equip an *in vivo* magnetic resonance research facility on its suburban Washington campus. It consolidated all NIH MR research activities of a biological nature into one of the world's foremost MR research facilities. The $5 million contract included a Signa high-field whole-body system, plus two chemical-shift imaging systems for small animal research manufactured by Fremont.

So the new MR business was rapidly accelerating as it entered 1986, the final year of the "Robb Era." The 100th Signa system had been shipped in late 1985; a cumulative total of 207 would be installed worldwide by the end of 1986. The first Signa system in Germany, which replaced a Siemens unit, was installed at the University of Herne in Bochum. The first two MR systems ever in Australia were Signas—one at a private imaging clinic and the second at the prestigious Royal North Shore Public Hospital, both in Sydney. Signa scanners also could be found in Japan, France, Italy, Saudi Arabia, England, and Monaco.

"Back to the future"

In the late summer of 1986, after an eventful 13-year reign, Jack Welch chose Walt to head up the R&D Center as Senior Vice President, Research and Development. Thus, he became only the sixth leader of this renowned institution, taking his place among the distinguished GE scientists who literally invented the concept of industrial research. Walt, who had begun his remarkable 42-year GE career at the R&D Center's Knolls Atomic Power Laboratory in 1951, would go on to serve with high distinction in this vital post until retiring in 1992.

So, another era was about to begin with the arrival of a bright, young executive who had come to Jack's attention during a series of tough assignments. Over the next decade, John Trani would have a profound influence on GE Medical Systems and its growing role in the worldwide medical equipment marketplace.

Walter L. Robb

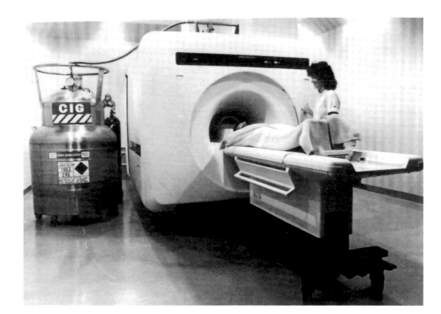

The Trani Era

1986-1996

John Trani had established a solid track record in several GE businesses, most recently managing a challenging turnaround situation at the Mobile Communications Division in Lynchburg, Virginia. Jack Welch admired John's passion for making the numbers and was convinced a hard-charging businessman was just what Medical Systems needed.

Trani took over on September 1, 1986, soon after a Boston Consulting Group review that rated GEMS against its major competitors. In the plus column, they found leadership technology in several of the major imaging modalities, a strong research and engineering team, an expanding worldwide marketing presence, a phenomenal field sales and service organization, and dedicated people. On the minus side was an $80 million cost disadvantage versus Siemens, the #1 competitor. Trani, himself, perceived a lack of clear internal processes relating business objectives to project execution.

In the first instance, the immediate challenge was to develop a game plan to overcome the cost competitiveness problem. To solve the second, a new operating mechanism was needed that would allow progress to be closely and continuously tracked.

Lessons in Leadership
John Michael Trani (b. 1945) holds a B.S. in aerospace engineering, M.S. in industrial management, and M.S. in operations research from Brooklyn Polytechnic Institute, as well as an M.A. in finance, strategy, and policy from New York University. Following several positions in engineering, financial analysis, and on Wall Street, he joined GE's air conditioning business as business development manager in 1978 and became General Manager, Audio Electronics, in 1980. He was appointed Vice President and General Manager, Mobile Communications Division, in 1984, then moved to Medical Systems as Senior Vice President and Group Executive 2 years later. He became President and CEO, GE Medical Systems, in 1992. The Stanley Works named him Chairman and CEO in 1997, and he served there until his retirement in 2003. He has been a director of Allied Waste Industries, Inc. (now Republic Services) since 2007, serves as a director of Goss International and Arise, Inc., and is a special advisor to Young America Corporation.

"Deverticalization"
John's most urgent initiative was to address the cost deficit. Under the banner of "Focus 80," he created a series of cross-functional project teams to find and quantify opportunities to remove costs. This was the opening salvo in his campaign to deverti-

cally integrate the business ("deverticalization," if you will), the first in a continuum of strategies to improve quality and increase cost productivity.

Vertical integration was an industrial management relic of the 1960's, when it was believed controlling every step of a process was necessary to assure its outcome. For instance, at Medical Systems, heavy machining was still being performed at Electric Avenue even though there were scores of highly skilled machine shops nearby that could do the same work with comparable quality at far less cost. Dozens of other examples were found in all areas of manufacturing, from wiring harnesses and printed wire boards to electrical and mechanical subassemblies. By deverticalizing manufacturing, substantial savings could be achieved by outsourcing nonvalue-added work.

Focus 80's cost reduction goal was actually $81 million, an enormous sum at the time. Making it even more challenging was John's warning to his team leaders he would only accept recommendations that were firmly grounded in reality. With this message ringing in their ears, the Focus 80 teams dispersed into every corner of the organization. Though their recommendations weren't always easy to implement

John M. Trani

nor applauded by those affected, Trani didn't shy from doing what had to be done, beginning with the toughest measure of all. On January 30, 1987, he announced plans to begin purchasing electrical and mechanical components from outside suppliers. As a consequence, about 20% of the Milwaukee-area manufacturing jobs would be eliminated.

"We have a strong and historically successful business and intend to keep it that way," Trani explained. "Our manufacturing costs are very high and, despite the best efforts of our employees, we were not successful in reducing them enough."

Most of the 650 hourly and 150 salaried workers affected were in 4 of the 14 area plants: the Electric Avenue components manufacturing operation, the electrical components assembly facilities at 300 and 315 W. Edgerton Ave., and the printed wire board plant in New Berlin. John Kelly and his 15-member Focus 80 team studying the sourcing issue found outside suppliers could produce electrical and mechanical parts for as little as half the cost of fabricating them internally. They calculated savings of $10 million annually.

Phyllis Piano, Communications and Community Relations manager, said, "We anticipate about 65% of these targeted components in terms of dollar value will be purchased from outside vendors based in Wisconsin. Most of the others will be in the Midwest, and all will be in the U.S."

Though the job reductions were painful, everyone understood the rationale. Rich Michalski, the local business representative for the International Association of Machinists and Aerospace Workers, acknowledged the company had treated his members fairly. "They've communicated their intentions very clearly and have committed to help out in whatever way they can."

That support included a generous severance package providing income extension aid; medical and life insurance for 1 year; up to 50% of pay and benefits for older employees until they qualified for early retirement; $7,500 in tuition refund benefits; company retraining programs; and job placement assistance.

Within 18 months, this change began yielding the anticipated savings. Additional efforts in the coming months included the development of a common computer architecture for CT and MR (the "Genesis" program), a new MR magnet design, an improved CT data acquisition system, the TARDIS MR software upgrade, a worldwide factory rationalization effort (including closing the Rancho Cordova ultrasound and Danish nuclear facilities), organizational streamlining, and dozens of similar projects.

"The basic challenge was to get people to make commitments," Trani recalled. "Many business objectives are very easy to state but extremely difficult to execute. In order to assess execution, you have to be able to measure it against a plan."

Or as one of John's favorite adages had it, "If you measure it, it will get better."

That's where Bill Buchholtz made his mark. An experienced finance manager, Bill put together a process that allowed Focus 80 activities to be tied directly to the profit and loss statement. His key tool was a standard "program monitor" the project leaders used to describe their activities, schedule, status, costs, and benefits. With such a consistent approach and tracking system, according to Bill, it was relatively easy to monitor each project:

John conducted monthly meetings at which each project leader would review an updated program monitor, and the finance representative would provide the latest costs and benefits. Because some of the projects were related to the same process or product, the individual project leaders also had to make sure their activities were appropriately linked.

An excellent example of the impact of this process was the Electric Avenue operation where over 8,000 parts were ultimately outsourced. That outcome was preceded by an enormous effort to analyze each make-versus-buy decision, identify competent suppliers, furnish the technical data they needed to fabricate high-quality parts, schedule the phase-in/phase-out process, and all the rest of it.

"Though it was difficult for employees to accept the loss of so many jobs, they responded magnificently," recalled Buchholtz. "Productivity at Electric Avenue actually increased during the outsourcing process, and no critical part shortages developed."

By the end of 1990, Focus 80 had helped eliminate $90 million in annual costs—real dollars that now were available for reinvestment in new products, infrastructure improvements, and so on. In fact, deverticalization, combined with various other initiatives, ultimately gave GE Medical Systems the lowest cost position in the diagnostic imaging equipment industry. The lessons learned through Focus 80 were key to developing a global restructuring process that effectively communicated and tracked project information across many different regions and cultures.

Growing the team

Several months before Trani's arrival, GE and Johnson & Johnson (J&J), the huge health care products firm, had announced preliminary plans to transfer the inventories and service contracts of J&J's medical imaging subsidiaries to GEMS. Included was their Technicare subsidiary that manufactured CT, MRI, digital x-ray, and nuclear imaging equipment; and J&J Ultrasound. Their decision to abandon diagnostic imaging was driven by financial and competitive realities. J&J had already approached several prospective purchasers without success, so it turned to GE to see what might be done to assure continuing customer service support.

As Bob Stocking, Sales and Service vice president, explained at the time, "GE has assumed warranty and post-warranty service responsibility for Technicare and J&J Ultrasound equipment. Our commitment is to provide those customers the same outstanding service for the life of their equipment as we do to our own."

To meet these obligations, arrangements were made to assure the availability of replacement parts. In addition, nearly 800 Technicare/J&J Ultrasound service technicians and engineers were hired by GE and became valuable contributors on the GE field service team.

J&J soon closed Technicare's CT and x-ray manufacturing operations, though GE continued to successfully market the Gemini™ nuclear scanner system. J&J Ultrasound was renamed ECHO Ultrasound and sold to Interspec, Inc.

CT in a whole new light

The big news in technology during this period was the new HiLight® detector for the CT 9800 Quick scanner. Officially introduced at RSNA '87, this industry-leading, solid-state detector had been under development for 8 years at the R&D Center. The first few years had been spent testing ceramic materials to find the one best able to efficiently and rapidly convert x-ray photons to light. It also had to be relatively easy and cost-effective to manufacture in volume. Medical Systems handled the overall design and subsystem integration tasks.

"GE's unique detector material stops virtually all the x-rays entering the detector, making it more efficient and resulting in brighter, sharper images," explained Mac Kaiser, general manager of CT marketing. "It provides uniform light output and minimizes 'afterglow,' allowing the detectors to be sampled every 2,000ths of a second."

The first CT 9800 Quick with the HiLight detector went to the Milwaukee County Medical Complex, where Dr. Tom Lawson and his radiology colleagues put it through its clinical paces. "The HiLight gives a more predictable response," Lawson soon reported. "With other materials, the more you bombard it, the poorer the response gets. The ceramic material is more heat stable and responsive. You can see smaller structures with increased clarity, because there is increased low-contrast detectability."

The existing detector manufacturing area at the Ryerson Road plant now was swamped with work. Separate, dedicated facilities were needed urgently. Fortunately, space was available at Electric Avenue as a result of the just completed Focus 80 outsourcing project. Plans were approved for a $7.5 million, 14,000 square foot (1,300 meters²) HiLight detector facility; construction began the following March. This mini-factory within the Electric Avenue plant was, essentially, a sophisticated chemical production system with extensive safety and environmental controls.

"The new CT HiLight detector and this facility reflect GE's continued growth in the CT marketplace and will help sustain employment in the Milwaukee area," commented Bill Love, Manager, Tube Engineering and Manufacturing.

Today, the HiLight detector continues to provide the imaging power behind GE's line of industry-leading computed tomography products. Every ounce of the ceramic material from which it is made is still produced at Electric Avenue.

Reorganizing for results

Trani was putting his stamp on the business in other ways. In early 1987, he announced a restructuring of several components as a part of his effort to rationalize GEMS's organization, operating mechanisms, and facilities worldwide. The major change was the creation of new marketing, technology, and manufacturing management organizations:

- The Medical Systems Marketing Division, under Bob Stocking, centralized all marketing and product planning activities for x-ray, nuclear imaging, ultrasound, CT, service, and financing. (MR continued to report to Trani.)
- Engineering and technical resources were assigned to Bobby Bowen's Technology Operation.
- Production was centralized in the Manufacturing Operations under Bob Smialek.

This new structure also eliminated the Sales and Service Division. Instead, its two constituents were each upgraded to "operations" reporting to Trani. Jim Del Mauro and Mike Moakley continued in their respective sales and service leadership roles. Jim also assumed sales management responsibility for the Asia Pacific-Latin America Department.

John saw all these moves as a part of his overall plan to remake GE Medical Systems on a global basis. "Our objective is to position this business as the highest quality, most cost-efficient supplier in the diagnostic imaging industry," he stated. "The new GE Medical Systems now emerging will be a stronger partner in healthcare than ever before."

Bombshell in Europe

The global status of GE Medical Systems was about to receive a huge and unexpected boost.

When Jack Welch was elevated to the GE chairmanship upon Reginald Jones's retirement on April 1, 1981, he set out to restructure the company. His first headline-making move was the January 1983 agreement to sell Utah International to Broken Hill Proprietary of Australia for $2.4 billion. Another stunner was the $6.28 billion purchase of RCA in 1986, the largest non-oil acquisition in U.S. business history up to that time. The Radio Corporation of America had been established as an independent company in 1932, when the U.S. government decreed it should be separated from GE due to antitrust concerns. (RCA's GE roots are still commemorated each time the familiar three-note musical motif is played by the NBC chimes—"G-E-C.")

Jack's next bombshell truly made Medical Systems a major player on an international scale while transforming General Electric.

In the summer of 1987, Welch was in Europe to attend the European Congress of Radiology and celebrate GEMS Europe's second anniversary. Already, Vincenzo Morelli and his team had tripled orders, more than doubled sales from $85 million to over $200 million, and turned a $22 million net loss into a profit. Jack also had been invited to the Elysée Palace in Paris to receive the Legion of Honor from François Mitterrand, President of France. Among the guests was Alain Gomez, chairman and CEO of Thomson. The two knew each other well and soon began to talk about a possible deal. Alain wanted GE Consumer Electronics; Jack wanted Thomson's medical equipment business, Compagnie Générale de Radiologie (CGR), plus $800 million in cash. Both were to get what they wanted.

Jack's interest in Thomson-CGR was driven by the need to add scale to GEMS. Earlier, he had asked Vincenzo to prepare a study on how to change the competitive landscape in Europe. It concluded what was needed to accelerate expansion was a large service infrastructure and installed equipment base. CGR was a good candidate, since it had a well-developed service organization, a large installed base of equipment, and produced conventional and digital x-ray, CT, MR, and nuclear imaging. CGR also had a strong line of radiation therapy and simulator products (CGR MeV), but its major technological strengths were in diagnostic and digital x-ray, especially mammography. The Senographe™ line was, and remains, the world's "gold standard" for breast imaging. Also, Jack had a healthy admiration for CGR's former chairman, Serge Roger, whom he had first met during their 1975 negotiations over the Liege operation. Though Roger had left the business several years before, it was largely because of his efforts that Thomson-CGR was now such an attractive acquisition prospect for GE.

"Paolo Fresco called to ask me to rush to Paris that same afternoon to flesh out the tentative deal Jack and Alain had just agreed to," Vincenzo remembered. "They wasted absolutely no time!"

During the coming weeks, Vincenzo and a host of others, especially Al Cerruti, the senior GE finance executive dealing with international tax and M&A issues, worked countless hours getting the details of the deal down on paper. Later that summer, Jack and Alain signed an agreement in principle to pursue the proposed deal. Now, the various governmental agencies with jurisdiction had to be convinced.

"This is a unique opportunity to enhance the participation of GE's medical equipment business in a growing and very competitive worldwide market," Welch explained at the time. "Consumer Electronics will now become part of a true worldwide consumer electronics business."

(It's interesting to recall Thomson was named for Elihu Thomson, the English-born electrical engineer who merged his Thomson-Houston Electric Company with Edison General Electric Company in 1892 to form GE. The next year, Compagnie Française Thomson-Houston was established in Paris and eventually evolved into Thomson S.A.)

Getting it together

Since the French government owned Thomson, it took some time to secure the necessary signoffs from Paris. The U.S. government also took a hard look at the proposed agreement to make certain it wouldn't violate antitrust laws. Joe Handros, GE's deputy general counsel, and Ron O'Keefe, GEMS's general counsel, held many meetings with the U.S. Department of Justice to smooth the process. However, the issue was cast into doubt in early December when a letter was received from the Justice Department stating, in part:

> This is to confirm my informing you yesterday that the Antitrust Division's legal staff investigating this proposed transaction is recommending, with support from the Economic Analysis Group, that the Division take appropriate action to prevent the consummation of the above-identified transaction.

Turgid prose, perhaps, but clear in meaning. Despite assurances from GE and Thomson, the U.S. government was concerned this merger would adversely affect domestic competition. However, they agreed to consider counterarguments. For several weeks, GE and Thomson management were on tenterhooks until a Department of Justice official announced: "I have been authorized to inform you that the Antitrust Division of the United States Department of Justice has no current plans to initiate a court challenge to the proposed transaction between your respective clients."

At last, the deal was on.

Meanwhile, anticipating a favorable outcome, GE and CGR had conducted the first high-level, integration-planning meeting. Several important decisions were made:

- The proposed holding company was named General Electric CGR and given responsibility for Europe, the Middle East, and Africa.
- Jean Ségui and Vincenzo Morelli were appointed managing directors.
- GE CGR was assigned responsibility for marketing, sales, and service in its area for all products manufactured by GEMS and CGR.
- GE CGR would phase out CT and MR design and manufacturing.
- GE CGR would become the "center of x-ray excellence."

Decisions also were made to continue an enhancement program for Thomson-CGR's existing CT and MR customers and ongoing MR clinical research programs at the Buc research center near Versailles and several leading French hospitals.

"While some of the equipment might change, we are firmly committed to continuing to provide European research radiologists with the opportunity to experiment and contribute to the advancement of medical imaging science in all technologies," Ségui promised.

Cultural shocks

In its long history, CGR had experienced many organizational changes. Marc Pelon, who later became GE Healthcare's OTR (order to remittance process) international general manager, personally witnessed several of these events, first as a world-girdling service engineer, then as a sales representative, and finally as an area and region sales manager in France. He had joined CGR upon leaving the military in 1971 and spent the next 5 years flying around the globe as a service engineer. At that time, CGR was a small company but had a lot of creativity. "The market was booming and margins were very high, so we had the ability to invest a lot of money to create new products," Pelon said. "Engineering was getting more than 10% of total sales and trying to invent a new product every year."

One of the most exciting areas was mammography, where CGR had established an international reputation based on superior technology. It also had a respected line of conventional and advanced x-ray systems, plus good CT and digital angiography offerings.

"Father of the Mammogram"

Emile Gabbay joined CGR in 1960 as a young engineer and earned more than 50 patents during the course of his long and fruitful career. His signature accomplishment was the role he played in launching the field of mammography, where his revolutionary x-ray tube design made it possible to image soft tissue with unprecedented resolution. But it almost didn't happen.

"I was involved in the development of a crystallography tube. One of the first devices intended for the University of Strasbourg had been sent mistakenly to the Strasbourg University Hospital where Dr. Charles Marie Gros was working. Seizing this opportunity, Dr. Gros, who had long been interested in breast radiography, tried the tube with numerous wax models and ended up adopting it, thus creating a mammography system.

"The pathological images obtained by Dr. Gros were published in 1968 and were a resounding success. They revolutionized the world of radiology. We consequently perfected the equipment that gave birth to the first mammography unit and sold and installed more than 1,000 units in the U.S. between 1969 and 1973."

Until his retirement in 1994, Gabbay perfected a stream of improvements that have helped keep Senographe mammography systems at the forefront of technology to this day. Among his many honors, he received the 1991 GE Steinmetz Award in recognition of his contributions to the field he literally helped create. His proudest achievement was becoming known around the world as "the father of the mammogram."

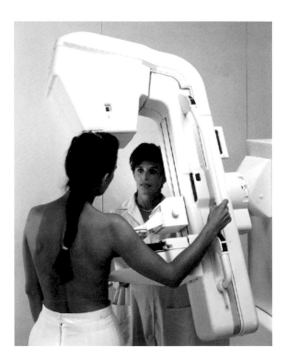

In 1975, CGR's status as an independent and innovative company changed abruptly when it was acquired by Thomson S.A., the huge defense electronics firm that had been nationalized by the French government just a few years before. The cultural shock was huge. Thomson's senior management was mostly former military officials who believed in a tightly organized, highly structured, hierarchical organization.

"We immediately saw the structure become overstaffed with many players, very little empowerment of the employees, and the loss of a lot of creativity and flexibility," Pelon remembered.

As a small, independent company, CGR hadn't achieved significant organic growth in the years immediately preceding the acquisition. Now, backed with Thomson's cash, it launched a series of actions to drive new growth and expand its international market presence. Over the next dozen years, Thomson-CGR progressed in several areas, including mammography, vascular x-ray, and interventional radiology. Now, they were about to be tested again.

Views from France

Though the challenge of bringing two proud competitors together was enormous, progress was steady despite the occasional cultural stumble. The attitudes of former Thomson-CGR employees varied from excitement to anxiety. Marketing and sales personnel tended to perceive it positively, since they would now have more and better products to sell, especially CT and MR. Another plus was access to the huge U.S. market where, except for mammography, CGR had been a negligible factor.

In the engineering, technology, and product development areas of the business, concerns were intense. As a former CGR MR engineer explained, "On the one side, we were very excited, because we were joining a big American company that was very strong. On the other, we were worried about what we were going to do. What would be the future?"

In France and Europe, generally, a concerted communication campaign helped to allay the concerns of former CGR customers. The integration coordinating committee had already addressed many of the major issues. So by the time the merger was completed, customers knew they would get the same high level of support they had received from Thomson-CGR.

Jean-Yves Burel, who was Thomson-CGR's director of sales and service for the Paris region at the time of the merger (and, later, Vice President, Hospital and Health-care Solutions at GE), vividly recalled the tenor of the times:

> Leading medical professors with whom we had special relationships initially greeted this merger with some disappointment and skepticism. CGR was the crown jewel of French medical technology and French universities were our partners in the development of new equipment and new techniques. They feared this research work would be concentrated in the United States, and they would be left out. Timely and focused communication reassured these loyal Thomson-CGR collaborators they would continue to play an important role in the future.

Nonacademic customers were quicker to grasp the benefits of the merger, especially the opening of the French medical equipment market to all competitors. "They understood the benefits they could derive from more intense competition in terms of technology, product and service quality, and, naturally, economics," Burel explained.

Francis Bailly, who became the new Sales and Service vice president for France, viewed the challenge as seamlessly integrating the various parts of the new organization:

> My number one objective was to consolidate the French operations, which were very substantial. Furthermore, there were now two organizations that sold and serviced very similar products. We, therefore, needed to make a merger within the merger to bring the GEMS and CGR teams together within GE CGR. They soon came to know and respect each other.

Another symbolic but extremely practical move came later in 1988, when the former headquarters of GE Medical Systems Europe at Shortlands, Hammersmith, London, were disbanded. Vincenzo Morelli, who had become the sole CEO following the departure of Jean Ségui, moved to GE CGR's new headquarters on Rue Camille Desmoulins in Issy-les-Moulineaux, a southwestern Paris suburb within sight of the Eiffel Tower.

top left
The METROMAX mobile CT scanner was among GE CGR's most notable early successes. A CT Max scanner was mounted in a specially modified city bus manufactured by Steyr-Daimler-Puch of Austria. Completely self-contained with on-board power and film processing, it could be dispatched wherever needed. A second METROMAX (shown being loaded at the Cologne airport) was loaned to the Soviet Union in December 1988 in response to a huge earthquake in Armenia, joining one purchased earlier by the Ministry of Health.

bottom left
Because the road system in Armenia was disrupted by the earthquake, patients were airlifted to Yerevan for care. The two METROMAX units rotated among the eight hospitals in the area, providing around the clock service for several weeks. The CT Max scanners worked flawlessly throughout that period, convincing Dr. Turnevoy, Chief CT Radiologist of the USSR, to later order dozens more.

above
This photo from an early 1989 edition of *GEMS World* shows GE CGR's new headquarters (circled, lower right) in southwest Paris. The Eiffel Tower can be seen in the distance.

"Travaux en cours" ("Work ahead")

From day one, Morelli and his staff were focused on facilitating the cultural transformation. Perhaps the biggest aspects of this process were about values, leadership, and people development. How do you define goals and objectives? How do you communicate? How do you bring transparency to the process of evaluating and promoting employees? How do you grow the team?

Helping lead the integration were contributors from both sides, such as Alain Rohaut and Toby D'Ambola from Human Resources (HR); Philippe Westercamp, who moved from finance to lead the engineering team; and Jack Price, the x-ray business leader who was first to lead teams on both sides of the Atlantic. Changes weren't accomplished overnight nor did they flow in only one direction. Indeed, an important early lesson was that the cultural transformation of the acquiring company is as important as the company acquired.

"One of the important things Morelli did was organize a big management meeting," a long-time employee said. "We had never had such a meeting before and we loved it. That was the starting point of our cultural transformation from a company managed by engineers to a company managed by businessmen."

This meeting was held in Luxembourg City less than 5 months after the merger. Its "Go For One" theme reflected GE CGR's mission to become one team, achieve $1 billion in sales by 1989, and aim at being number one in Europe within a decade. In his opening remarks, Morelli noted Thomson-CGR was the largest foreign acquisition ever made by General Electric and demonstrated the company's commitment to the medical equipment business and Europe. "Our goal," he stated, "is to build a powerhouse here in Europe by creating a single company culture within General Electric CGR and a unified image of superior technology and service."

"Route défoncée" ("Rough road")

Despite the best efforts of both partners, inadvertent gaffes sometimes complicated the acculturation process:

- *Some were offended by the "Go For One" team sweatshirts distributed at the Luxembourg City meeting.*
- *Soon after the merger, GE imposed its financial control system to bring GE CGR in line with corporate practices. French financial-reporting requirements and procedures were incompatible, so the system was in shambles for months.*
- *GE managers plastered English-language posters throughout the plants and offices to the great annoyance of their new French colleagues. GE management mottos—"Speed, simplicity, and self-confidence," for instance—weren't popular.*
- *When a high-ranking U.S. manager demanded that wine be removed from the menu of the GE CGR cafeteria, it took hours to convince him that such a move would have risked a general strike!*
- *Misunderstandings weren't all in one direction. One of GE's great frustrations in the early days was trying to teach the lessons of the marketplace to a former state-owned concern accustomed to government subsidies, guaranteed markets, and a leisurely working pace.*

As Vincenzo Morelli later acknowledged, "I think there is trauma in every acquisition. We tried to avoid the impression of imposing a victorious culture, on a vanquished culture but nobody has discovered the perfect formula for cultural integration."

The question everyone was asking was what role GE CGR would play in the company's future plans. In his Luxembourg City remarks, Trani stated, "There is a total realization that GE CGR must be a full-functioning entity on a worldwide basis, not merely a sales,

top
GEMS's willingness to invest in its new French partner was demonstrated in numerous ways, including a new European Data Center at Issy-les-Moulineaux. Attending its early 1989 opening were (l–r): Dave Bearman, GEMS finance manager; Vincenzo Morelli, GE CGR president; Marc Onetto, GE CGR's information systems manager; Edward Skiko, GE's vice president of information technology; Takao Murakami, information systems manager at GEMS Asia; and Jeff Ehrlich, GEMS Americas information systems manger.

middle
The combined GE and CGR teams were a major presence at the 1989 meeting of the International Congress of Radiology in Paris. This was GE CGR's first appearance at this quadrennial event.

service, and marketing organization in Europe."

He cited several examples where substantive changes already were being implemented, including a one third reduction in the U.S. x-ray engineering staff; a one fifth reduction in the U.S. x-ray new product programs budget; designation of GE CGR as the primary supplier of a major portion of the x-ray product line; and implementation of an exclusive vascular and cardiac digital imaging program in Paris. He also announced plans to move the LC and LP cardiac positioners to France, along with the "Druid" image review station being developed for future digital radiography systems.

He concluded his remarks by making several personal commitments to help GE CGR become a full-functioning and equal partner in GE's global organization:

I pledge that your North American colleagues will deliver $65 million in GE CGR equipment orders in 1988; that we are going to help GE CGR build a world-class x-ray operation by spending more than $250 million to restructure operations and the balance sheet; that we will invest in other areas that you think are necessary to grow your market share and help you be competitive in every market; and that we will invest in your personal growth and development by providing opportunities for you to move around the world in a variety of roles.

Backed by this strong pledge of support, GE CGR set out upon the road to the future. Though the journey would be difficult as unneeded plants were closed, product lines pruned, and employment reduced, thanks to the hard work of thousands of employees, it would become the full and equal partner John had predicted.

Spreading the message

In Milwaukee, all of these events had created considerable anxiety among employees. Trani decided to call them together at the MECCA Auditorium in downtown Milwaukee on February 17, 1988, to explain what was going on and why. Over 3,200 employees attended this first "state of the business" review to hear the details of his vision for GE Medical Systems. For over an hour, John discussed every aspect of the business with startling candor. The core of his message was the strategies GEMS was pursuing to achieve its overall mission of becoming the unquestioned worldwide leader in diagnostic imaging:

Globalization: With international markets growing twice as fast as the U.S., the opportunity for significant growth was offshore.

World cost competitiveness: In an era of slow growth and consolidation, cost competitiveness on a worldwide basis was essential. He said Focus 80 was already making a difference, and its lessons would be applied everywhere.
Installed base growth: John explained equipment service was an important source of revenue and net income.
Maintain technical preeminence: Technology leadership was critical, particularly in CT and MR where GE held a huge share lead.
Growth: Finally, he stated new growth was essential. Already, areas such as PET systems, lithotripters, and new opportunities in cardiology were being explored.

As it happened, GEMS was conducting its first worldwide business meeting literally next door the same day. So John was quick to take his message of change and growth to the more than 800 people attending from every corner of the earth. His concluding remarks at both sessions shared the same theme.

This is a great business with a terrific future. Yes, we are getting bigger and more global. The next few years could be the most rewarding that Medical Systems has experienced. But we must make a commitment to quality, a commitment to customer satisfaction, and a commitment to making an adequate profit. Let's work together to make GE Medical Systems the unquestioned worldwide leader in diagnostic imaging.

above
John Trani gathered some 3,200 Milwaukee-area employees in the MECCA Auditorium for the first of his annual business reviews.

left
The theme of GEMS's first worldwide business meeting was "Over the Top and Beyond," suggesting the challenge—and opportunity— for the greatly expanded global organization.

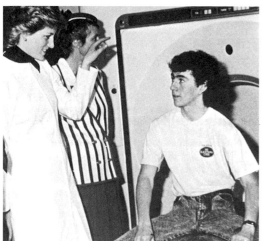

top to bottom

Several participants in the first-ever GLP session (Faro, Portugal) test their teamwork in an "Outward Bound" exercise. Crewmembers included (front, l–r) Jack Price and Paul Mirabella; (middle, l–r), Marc Onetto, Dave Bearman (standing), Norio Tanaka, and Bob Hubert (partially hidden). (Person in rear not identified.)

This photo from a mid-1987 issue of *GE SCAN*, the newsletter for GEMSE employees, shows the Princess of Wales admiring the new CT 9000 HP CT scanner at Stoke Mandeville Hospital in Aylesbury (U.K.). It was the first sold outside Japan.

Ram Charan, one of the developers of the Global Leadership Program.

Stretching for global reach

The new GE Medical Systems Asia organization, announced in early 1988, mirrored the earlier creation of GE Medical Systems Europe. Headquartered in Tokyo, it consolidated GEMS's Far Eastern resources under a single operating authority, a significant departure from the way the business had previously addressed these markets.

"Our strategic objectives are to gain a leading position in the Japanese market, achieve total integration with our U.S. and European organizations, and develop winning product and marketing plans for each of the key Asian Pacific markets," commented Chuck Pieper, President and CEO, GEMS Asia.

These integration plans received another boost in late 1988 when Pieper was coappointed YMS president. This was a remarkable development, since it was uncommon for a foreigner to become the chief operating officer of a Japanese firm. Reactions were positive, since the move strengthened YMS's role as the cornerstone of GE's Far East activities and broadened its opportunities to design and develop leading-edge technologies for the global market.

Top-level attention also was paid to integrating the business on a global basis. Trani had consulted with Noel Tichy, a well-known management professor at the University of Michigan and a former program manager at GE's Management Development Institute, to develop a new approach to globalization. The result was the Global Leadership Program (GLP) that kicked off in June 1988, with the first "Global Leadership Workshop." It brought together John's staff with some 55 high-level managers from GE CGR, GEMS Americas, and GEMS Asia—the three business "poles"—to find ways to foster integration, trust, and teamwork.

Four eminent educators and business consultants, with the help of Toby D'Ambola, HR general manager, and Craig Saline, HR staffing manager, created the GLP curriculum. They included Michael Brimm, from the Institute of Business Administration in Fontainebleau, France; Ram Charan, Columbia University; Hirotaka Takeuchi, Hitotsubashi University in Tokyo and Harvard University; and, of course, Noel Tichy.

The major product of the first workshop was the creation of teams to tackle urgent integration projects. "You are the leaders of this business," Trani told them, "and I'm counting on you to share best practices to make these projects work, because they are keys to establishing GE Medical Systems as a truly global business."

GLP was a test case for how General Electric Company could begin to globalize all of its domestic-oriented businesses. Other GE businesses and companies later duplicated it.

"I think the most important event was John taking the initiative and getting the support of GE Corporate," commented Charan. "Globalization gave the company more flexibility than its competitors in terms of where you manufacture and where you sell."

Another key lesson it provided was developing a global leadership "gene pool." By the time John left GE in 1997, his team included a large number of Japanese, Asians, and Europeans in top positions. "That was a huge globalization win," Charan stated, "because rational decisions could be made about designing products in one pole, manufacturing them in a second, and selling them in a third. The key was addressing the cultural issues first in order to help everyone work together."

The GLP process was a transformational tool that taught people from around the world how to deal with each other to develop solutions to real business problems. As the program evolved, participants were given 6-month assignments in other poles. They would meet several times to assess progress, extract best global practices, and receive coaching from the professional faculty. GLP continued to flourish under the direction of Marc Saperstein, who followed D'Ambola as Global HR general manager, and provided GEMS a source of culturally sensitive managers capable of thriving in a global environment.

Participants in Global Service Process Operating Council meetings came from every corner of the world. Attending this session at the Healthcare Institute were (in alphabetical order): Hideya Akasaka, Dan Asbrock, Bob Babcock, Bret Barczak, Wendall Barr, Justin Boswell, Acao Chong, Greg Davis, Guy de Montmarin, Sonia Dubreuil, Tom Dunham, Bill Farrow, Olivier Faugere, Tom Franks, Reinaldo Garcia, Craig Gemmill, Frank Goebel, Beth Goodhew, Charlene Grabowski, Mark Grabowski, Crystal Hanson, Bryan Heaney, Christina Ho, Richard Hulseberg, Leon Janssen, Juan Zhao, Peter Kakanson, Steve Kellett, Dan Kerpelman, Jose Klein, Brigitte LaCroix, J. B. Lee, Ellen Lindop, Bridget Marnocha, Gary Massie, Ron Mauer, Larry McWhirter, Jeff Moore, Edith Peterson, Rene Prunier, Nadia Romano, Jean-Marc Segura, Rick Shanks, Minoru Shinozaki, Mike Shiota, Mark Ship, Travis Simpson, J. T. Smith, Mark Smith, Walter Storch, Mike Swinford, Michio Takakura, John Taylor, and Hideo Watanabe.

As Tichy described the transformation:

GLP provided the human glue that made globalization happen at Medical Systems. You had three companies and three cultures that had no business getting along in those days. So cracking through those barriers and building personal, social networks was really important. It truly helped create a global business before just about anybody in the world did it.

Yoshiaki Fujimori, who was running the nuclear imaging business at the time, was in the second wave of GLP participants. "This was in my first year at GEMS, and I got to know the top 200 leaders of the business within 1 year," he said. "GLP was absolutely a powerful tool. . .an amazing program that was the major impact in my GE career."

GEMS's Group Operating Council (GOC) institutionalized globalization at the highest levels. All the top managers from around the world would meet on a quarterly basis at some international location outside the normal experiences of most attendees. In addition to business sessions, the group would take time to explore the culture by visiting local landmarks, experiencing unique cultural traditions, and calling on customers. The GOC spawned various functional operating councils that met frequently via videoconferencing to share best practices worldwide. Examples included the Global Service Process Operating Council, Global Technology Council, and the Global Information Technology Council.

In February 1989, GEMS Asia (GEMSA) held its first-ever sales conference to spur globalization and integration. Held in Kuala Lumpur, Malaysia, this 5-day event brought together over 100 sales and service managers, agents, and distributors from across GEMSA's huge geographic expanse to learn about team building, networking, products, and each other. Under the theme "One Team—One Goal," they covered all the usual subjects, plus a large helping of globalization. As Chuck Pieper observed during his opening remarks, "Our strategy is localization and internationalization. Localization means we have to win in each country and every modality. Internationalization means we have to be a key supporter for the overall business. We intend to do both."

Globalization and integration initiatives were also being implemented on an individual basis. The 10^3 Program, for instance, assigned up to 10 people from each pole to limited-term assignments in other poles. The objective was to foster integration by giving individuals an opportunity to learn how other poles operate, build working relationships with people from other countries, and increase cultural understanding.

A similar approach was the Global Exchange Program that let executives "walk in each other's shoes." Ren Shibata, Vice President and General Manager, YMS Marketing, was among the first to participate when he traveled to the U.S. in 1988 to take up consecutive assignments in Ultrasound and X-ray marketing. "Having Ren here is a real

asset, because his knowledge of the people, culture, and language helps get things done much faster," said Paul Mirabella, General Manager, Ultrasound Marketing.

Ren's experience was so valuable YMS added a second senior manager to the program. Norio Tanaka had been with YEW since 1963 and became involved with diagnostic imaging equipment when the CT distribution agreement was signed in 1976. He played an important part in the introduction of the RT3000 ultrasound scanner, the first product to be jointly developed by YEW and GE, and had a major role in the introduction of the Signa MR system in Japan. On arriving in Milwaukee to manage CT mid-tier marketing, he observed:

> There is an ocean between us, but the bridge has been built. We just have to cross it. The exchange of people between poles gives them the best chance to really understand globalization. The more people who participate, the smaller the gap between us and the closer we are to becoming one totally united team.

Several Japanese executives followed Ren and Norio on rewarding assignments in Milwaukee, including Junichi Osawa (1991–92), Masa Takaya (1992–94), Mitsuru Maekawa (1992–93), Yoshihiko Watanabe (1993–94), and Nobuhiko Ito (1994–95).

Housekeeping

In April 1988, Jack Welch brought the GE Board of Directors to Medical Systems for their first visit since 1981. This time, the occasion was the annual shareowners' meeting at the Waukesha Expo Center. In addition to touring the various new facilities they had been asked to approve, the Board also found out what John and his team were doing to make GE "the unquestioned worldwide leader in diagnostic imaging." As expected, they were dazzled by what they saw and heard.

This Board visit came a little too early for a look at the latest addition to the Waukesha campus. That summer, GEMS broke ground for a new $1.5 million fitness center, a 15,500 square foot (1,450 meters²) facility being constructed in response to employee requests for a place where they could exercise on a regular schedule regardless of the weather. Opened in early 1989, it provided an indoor running track, weight-training equipment, space for group exercise, men's and women's shower and locker facilities, and even an outdoor deck.

Another gratifying development was the selection of Mike Wilson, Manager, Manufacturing Quality Assurance and Regulatory Compliance, to receive the 1988 Gerald L. Phillippe Award. As chairman of the board for the Employees Civic and Charitable Organization, Wilson had led the effort to raise over $1 million for Milwaukee- and Waukesha-area charities. He also served on the Executives Council of the Hunger Task Force of Milwaukee; the Board of the Waukesha Chapter of the National Association for the Advancement of Colored People (NAACP), along with his wife, Lilly; and volunteered as a science mentor at Clarke Street School, an Elfun Society project.

above left
Ren Shibata (second from left), the first high-ranking YMS executive to participate in the Global Exchange Program, in an ultrasound strategy meeting with (from left) Bob Marinelli, cardiology product marketing manager; Bill Phillips, cardiology product marketing specialist; and Paul Mirabella, ultrasound marketing general manager.

above, top to bottom
Construction of the Fitness Center on the Waukesha campus is underway in this mid-1988 view.

The Fitness Center remains an important employee health resource.

Mike Wilson, winner of the 1988 Gerald L. Phillippe Award, with his wife, Lilly, also a GE employee.

Elfuns Mike Balistreri and Mike Wilson present a $10,000 GE Foundation check to students at Clarke Street School. Principal Diane Neicheril and Jackie Patterson of the Milwaukee Urban league watch.

One of Trani's most personally satisfying achievements was in reaching out to the minority community, both within the business and local area. Though a number of minorities, such as Joe Cleveland, had already achieved positions of high responsibility at GEMS, John recognized much more remained to be done. So when the local minority leaders expressed concerns that downsizing actions not impact GE's diverse employees unfairly, John invited representatives from the Waukesha NAACP chapter, the Urban League, and other groups for a frank discussion of the restructuring and how it was being conducted. The contacts made during this period would serve GEMS and the community well. Paul Spraggins, who led the Waukesha NAACP chapter for many years (and whose wife, Beverly, happened to be a GE employee), became an invaluable source of insight and guidance for Trani, Jeff Immelt, and Joe Hogan.

John and his successors also were strong supporters of the African American Forum, a company-wide association of African-American employees dedicated to helping minorities develop and grow their GE careers. With tremendous support from management leaders such as Mike Barber, the Milwaukee chapter was one of the most active and productive in the company. The INROADS program, for example, gave five promising minority college students summer internships working alongside GE professionals. Many joined the company upon graduation.

Diversity efforts also extended to such groups as the Hispanic Professional Association that promoted awareness of Hispanic culture and furthered professional development among its members. ApaF was a networking organization created to promote cultural similarities and professional development among employees from the Asia Pacific and Far East regions. The Women's Network created opportunities for GE professional women to access the information, tools, and contacts that facilitate career growth.

Elfun support for the Clarke Street School was also receiving considerable attention. Whether mentoring the kindergarten through 5th grade students, refurbishing classrooms and school grounds, or helping in countless other ways, the Elfuns had established a close and continuing relationship with their young friends in one of Milwaukee's most distressed neighborhoods. A highlight was the 1988 presentation of a $20,000 GE Foundation grant to establish a science lab at the school. Elfun Craig Saline got this project started through his involvement with the Milwaukee Urban league.

Academic initiatives

Trani launched an educational initiative of a different sort that summer with significant long-term benefits to the business. It was the first meeting of GEMS's Academic Advisory Council (AAC)—a panel of about two dozen top academic radiology chairs from across the U.S. and Canada (and, later, Europe and Asia). It was formed at the urging of Alex Margulis of UCSF to give academia a collaborative role in the technology development process.

"I told John that what he needed was a group of academic leaders to advise the business," Dr. Margulis explained. "My idea was always that industry has to work together with academia, because industry knows what they can afford and we know what is the future."

The first meeting of the AAC was a 2-day session in Chicago that included both customers and several noncustomers, plus key business and technology leaders. It was a revelation for the academicians who had never before gotten such a detailed glimpse into the inner workings of a major supplier. They enthusiastically endorsed John's proposal to make the AAC meeting an annual event. Phil Peck, manager of academic research and organizer of the session, immediately set to work planning the 1989 meeting.

Jim Youker (Medical College of Wisconsin) and Jim Potchen (Michigan State Univer-

sity) attended every Academic Advisory Council meeting over the years. Dr. Potchen explained why it attracted his interest:

> It got the top people in radiology from around the world to sit down together and look at the future of radiology. We would make specific recommendations, and GE would come back the following year and tell us what they had done. We always saw the effect of our contributions and that was very satisfying.

One of those recommendations became reality in 1990–91. At the urging of AAC member Al Moss, radiology chair at the University of Washington and president of the Association of University Radiologists (AUR), Trani agreed to establish and fund the "GE-AUR Radiology Research Academic Fellowship" (GERRAF) program. This was a special effort to encourage young academic radiologists to conduct research in the area of technology assessment. Developed and managed by Phil Peck, with the assistance of Sandra Feil and Gene Medford, GERRAF became a prestigious and much sought-after research award that continues to thrive today.

top to bottom
Most GERRAF Fellows went on to distinguished academic careers. The 1995 class included (l–r) Jeffrey Jarvik, University of Washington; Geoff Rubin, Stanford University; Ella Kazerooni, University of Michigan; Peter Shile, Washington University; and Shannon Swan, University of Wisconsin-Madison.

Al Moss (right), radiology chair at the University of Washington, urged the creation of the GERRAF program and chaired its Board of Review for many years. He is pictured with the 2003 Fellows (l–r): John Carrino, Brigham and Women's Hospital (Harvard); Mukesh Harisinghani, Massachusetts General Hospital (Harvard); Elizabeth Burnside, University of Wisconsin-Madison; and Martina Morrin, Beth Israel Deaconess (Harvard).

Ben Littenberg, long-time member of the GERRAF Board of Review and Professor of Medicine and Nursing at the University of Vermont, mentors several Fellows at an annual Retreat, including (l–r) Annette Johnson, Indiana University; Yoshimi Anzai, University of Washington; and Stephanie Carlson, Mayo Medical School.

GE had long been an active collaborator with academia in more practical ways, such as the product development collaborations with Milwaukee County Medical Complex, Duke University, University of Pennsylvania, Michigan and Michigan State, UCSF, University of Washington, and many others. A particularly productive and mutually beneficial long-term relationship existed with Stanford University that had contributed enormously to GE's digital x-ray development program. GE was also called upon as a key supplier of MR technology when the Richard M. Lucas Center for Imaging was created at Stanford in 1992. During subsequent expansions, Stanford also received the third GE MRT system in North America and launched a collaborative R&D effort in interventional MR. As we shall see, more such programs would mark their future relationships.

Reengineering Sales and Service

A mid-1988 management reshuffle returned Bob Stocking to his long-time role in Sales, while Jim Del Mauro moved over to lead Service. Replacing Stocking atop the Marketing Division was Steve Riedel, who came to Medical Systems from a key marketing position at GE Motors.

Bob's return was marked by a rededication to sales force effectiveness, spearheaded by the newly formed Sales Programs team. It was staffed with high potential, future sales leaders, who were recruited to develop their program, team leadership, and business skills while also building personal credibility in the headquarters environment. The team focused on a range of initiatives, from bringing sales force automation systems and laptop computers to the field sales team, to creating a proprietary deployment and territory analysis system. Other efforts included a broad range of intensive skill development programs such as New Sales Hires, Sales Management Development, and many more. Among the early participants were future sales leaders Scott Mathews, Ted Opie, Peter Arduini, Gail Dewitt, Charlene Grabowski, Brad Lamb, and Tom Prescott. In subsequent years, Sales Programs continued to attract the best and brightest into these special roles.

Del Mauro soon placed his unique stamp on the Service Division as he sought to bring the best people into service management. Jim and his team created the vision for investing in service productivity improvements to better support the huge installed base of high-tech products. In time, remote diagnostics (initially called RACE—Remote Access of Customer Equipment), GE CARES, and other productivity programs would bring an entirely new level of customer-centric support to GE equipment users around the world.

Without doubt, Jim's greatest early win was the August 1988 National Service Management meeting in Kansas City, Missouri, where he laid out a new vision for the organization. This first-ever event for field service managers signaled things were changing, and the field service team now would enjoy the same prestige their field sales counterparts had long taken for granted. Jim laid out an exciting roadmap that would guide the evolution of the Service Division into a truly world-class organization: "The charter for the Service Division going forward will be to fix the customer as well as the equipment. We own customer satisfaction!"

Jim acted at once to begin redeeming his promises by announcing the creation of the "Omega Society" to recognize and reward top service performances just as the "Sigma Society" celebrated outstanding sales achievements. (He also called on Janis Kloeffler, who had arranged the Kansas City meeting and countless customer hospitality and employee recognition events, to apply her exceptional abilities on behalf of future "Omega Society" meetings.) Another pleasant surprise was the announcement of plans to build a new, world-class service training center in Milwaukee. After more than two decades, the old training facilities around town were to be replaced by the largest and most modern institute of its kind anywhere.

John Trani was the featured speaker at that evening's dinner meeting. He praised the Service team for their accomplishments and shared his perspective on their role in helping Medical Systems achieve its goals:

> Since I came to Medical Systems 2 years ago, I have been constantly astonished by the raw power of the field organization, especially Service, to routinely accomplish the impossible. I have referred many times to Sales and Service as 'The Machine'—a massively powerful, yet finely tuned instrument with the speed, precision, and strength to succeed at any task it is given. Our competitors look with envy at GE's field organization and dream of someday having one half as good.

Kudos aside, the real message John had come to deliver was the importance of customer satisfaction and the responsibility of everyone in the business to make it a top priority:

> Can we really be serious about customer satisfaction when the service call rate on MR systems is 8.6 per month? When we are receiving 10 to 15 customer complaints each week? When we are issuing an average of 12 Field Modification Instructions per month? You certainly don't think so and neither do I. And we won't be there until everyone eats, sleeps, and breathes customer satisfaction.

Ken Hickey, area service manager from the San Bernardino (California) and Las Vegas areas, summed up the National Service Management meeting for everyone when he said, "We can do a lot better for our customers if we are given the necessary resources, and that's what this meeting is giving us. We heard the answers to key issues and problems which we have been looking for."

Jim Del Mauro (center), vice president of Service, at a 1988 employee roundtable meeting.

Del Mauro hosted another service management meeting the following May using the latest in communications technology—a GEMS-TV-produced satellite broadcast to field service locations across the U.S. and Canada. He was joined by his key staff, including Jeff Schaper, General Manager, Service Marketing; Tom Franks, Manager, Service Operations; Tom Giordano, Manager, Service Distribution; Mark Bohling, Manager, Service Productivity; and Rick Frowein, Manager, Advanced Service Engineering. Several modality service engineering managers—Chris Fabbri (Ultrasound), David Giessel (Nuclear), and Al DeMars (CT)—also participated.

As at Kansas City, a major emphasis was on customer satisfaction. Especially exciting news was the recent launch of the InSite™ remote service diagnostics system (an outgrowth of the former RACE program). Staffed 24 hours a day by engineers, technicians, and applications specialists, this innovative approach to equipment service allowed the performance of General Electric CT and MR systems to be remotely monitored virtually anywhere in the world. Should problems arise, fixes could often be implemented in minutes with no need to dispatch a service engineer. InSite was a huge win for everyone, since it minimized equipment downtime, reduced patient inconvenience, and improved department efficiency. The benefits of remote service diagnostics were soon extended to other GE digital imaging systems and even certain competitive systems covered by GE service contracts.

Tom Dunham, the manufacturing chief, was on hand to promise viewers no more compliance testing would be done in the field. Rather, this time-consuming work would be brought back into manufacturing where it belonged. "Overall, 50,000 man hours will be taken out of the system with a corresponding improvement in communications between manufacturing and service," he predicted.

Tom also pledged quality would be the top manufacturing priority, closely followed by meeting schedules and controlling costs. "Ultimately, we are responsible for all three but quality comes first," he said. "If anyone knowingly sends a defective product out to the field, it is grounds for dismissal in my book."

Steve Riedel, Marketing vice president, endorsed Dunham's promise to no longer ship problems to the field. "We are making strides in this area," he reported, "such as holding up the next nuclear product launch and the smoother introduction of Signa Advantage. We want to improve further based on these best practices, but it will not be an overnight change."

Though Jim, Tom, and Steve didn't realize it on that May afternoon, their careers were about to take some unexpected turns.

Reorganize, reorganize

The reorganization that had sent Stocking to Sales and Del Mauro to Service was followed by more changes:

- A new Marketing and Engineering Division was established under Riedel, incorporating the former Marketing Division plus all product and service engineering functions.
- Research and engineering associated with new areas of technology and advanced developments for current products became the responsibility of the new Advanced Technology Division headed by Bobby Bowen.
- In the field, the district structure was replaced by nine new sales and service regions. They were subdivided into 19 sales zone offices and 9 service branch offices.
- A new Customer Service Center (CSC) was established for GEMS Americas to centralize order quote and administration, credit and collection, backlog management, and systems support functions.
- Field Applications—the specialists who work with customers on how to use GE imaging equipment—was transferred from Sales to Service. Jack Albertson, an experienced field service management professional, was selected to head up the group.

The CSC ("Service" was later dropped from the title) was a significant innovation. Located in rural Waukesha County, it soon grew to include all the functions directly supporting the field and customers. "Acting as one team in one location allows us to break down barriers between individual organizations, shorten communications lines, and simplify our work to respond faster and more effectively to customer needs," explained CSC manager Frank Fagan.

New leader for Europe

In June 1989, John Trani announced Steve Riedel would lead GE CGR, replacing Vincenzo Morelli who had been named Vice President-Europe for GE International. This leadership change occurred the day before Steve was scheduled to speak in his previous marketing role at the third annual GE CGR Management Meeting in Luxembourg City. His original subject, "Customer Satisfaction in the Americas," was quickly replaced by a message with a Eurocentric focus.

Steve's arrival in Issy-les-Moulineaux followed by just a few months the announcement of plans to close the old, inefficient plant in Stains, a near-north suburb of Paris. The work would be transferred to a new facility to be built in Buc on the southwest side of the city. Also announced were plans to transfer ultrasound engineering to YMS, concentrate central parts warehousing and logistics at La Plaine Saint-Denis, another Paris suburb, and centralize training activities at a new European Service Institute in Slough near London's Heathrow Airport. These and other actions meant the elimination of 450 positions in France.

On the plus side was the new $20 million industrial center for Buc. Built over

top to bottom
Among the many integration issues was cross-training field service technicians in GE and CGR products. GE CGR technicians Jean-Claude Mesleard (left), Claude Maillet (second from left), and Mehdi Smail (right) explain the installation of an Arcomax FMA vascular system to Medical Systems Institute training instructor Rom Braun.

GE Healthcare's Buc headquarters today.

Buc's imposing main entrance.

above, right
The Buc product showroom is an important marketing tool.

the following 18 months next door to the existing research and electronics facility, it allowed GE CGR to concentrate French production, research, marketing, and service engineering on one site. The Buc campus became the home for x-ray and multi-modality research and engineering, CGR MeV (radiotherapy systems), ultrasound manufacturing, x-ray manufacturing, central service, and the Applied Research Center for MR.

During his relatively brief tenure at GE CGR, Riedel built upon the work begun by Morelli to complete the cultural transformation and instill needed processes throughout the organization. Under the banner of "Vision '95," he articulated a 5-year plan to engage the stakeholders in achieving a deeper business transformation. In 1992, he became Chairman and CEO, General Electric Canada, but the initiatives he had set in motion were extremely valuable to his successor in Buc, Arno Bohn, former CEO of Porsche A.G. At this time, the European organization reverted to its former name of GE Medical Systems Europe and Arno's position retitled "President and CEO." The integration of CGR was complete.

After the previous 5 years of intense focus on dealing with the demands of combining two distinct cultures and approaches to business, Arno now called for a refocus on the customer. As in the U.S., customer satisfaction was seen as an urgent issue confronting the Europe team. His response was "Stand Up and Win," a program with a clear and simple premise. Just as excellent processes are needed to run a company, he believed a motivated field team was necessary to keep energized people in front of customers. Many challenges lay ahead, but by the time Arno left several years later to become President and CEO, GE Germany, he had moved GEMS Europe well along the path toward success.

Asian adventures

Chuck Pieper had been leading GE Medical Systems Asia for 3 years and was thinking about his next career move. As it happened, Jack Welch and John Opie, Senior Vice President, GE Lighting, were looking for an experienced international executive to take over the rapidly expanding lighting business in Europe. Chuck's name soon surfaced as the ideal candidate. The issue for Trani was finding a credible replacement for Chuck in Tokyo, a task that proved simpler than one might have supposed.

In the autumn of 1991, Jim Baughman of GE's Crotonville management training center had invited Göran Malm, the number three executive at SKF, the Swedish bearing manufacturer, to speak to an executive development class in Heidelberg, Germany. Two weeks later, on Jim's recommendation, Jack Welch invited Göran to Fairfield for a chat, then sent him to Milwaukee to interview with John, and London for a talk with Paolo Fresco. Göran came aboard in November.

The organizations Göran inherited were strong and growing. In addition to YMS in Japan and Samsung Medical Systems in South Korea, GEMSA now had large presences in China and India. GEMS China, for instance, had grown from a single service engineer working out of a Beijing hotel room to large liaison offices in Beijing and Shanghai, plus a national sales team of 10 representatives. In addition, it had set up a joint venture, GE Hangwei Medical Systems Ltd. (65% GE owned), to assemble CT scanners for the Chinese market and function as a technology center. Similarly, in India, GEMSA had formed a 1990 joint venture with Wipro Ltd. of Bombay to manufacture, sell, and service medical diagnostic imaging and therapy equipment throughout India and South Asia.

A few months after assuming his new position, Göran convened top GEMSA managers in Beijing for a strategy session. Participating were all the JV leaders—Shinichi Kawase of YMS; David Wang of GE Hangwei; C. W. Lee of SMS; and D. A. Prasanna of Wipro-GE—as well as the YMS Sales (Tomoji Okada), Service (Norio Tanaka), Manufacturing (Satoshi Kurata), Engineering (Keiki Yamaguchi), and R&D (Kenjiro Fujita) leaders. Other participants were Keith Williams, head of South East Asia, Pacific Oceania; his deputy, Chih Chen; and Dave Sullivan from Australia/New Zealand. From Göran's personal staff were Nobuhiko Ito (X-ray Game Plan), Larry Bates (Legal), Janet Nelson (Human Resources), and Eric Pillmore (Finance).

Over the course of several days, the group developed a three-part plan to execute Göran's vision of growing sales to $1 billion by 1997. Several immediate steps were renaming YMS "GE Yokogawa Medical Systems," acquiring a majority share in SMS and renaming it Samsung-GE Medical Systems (SGMS), and buying a majority share in Wipro-GE. Taking more time was the construction of the new Service and Repair Center in Hino (completed in June 1994) and the successful deployment of a dedicated "Tiger Team" to help upgrade GE Hangwei, SGMS, and Wipro-GE to world-class status.

The second step of the plan was to expand into new offerings. Tanaka X-ray Company of Japan was soon acquired and renamed GE Tanaka Medical Systems to fill a product gap in low-end x-ray equipment for the Japanese and Chinese markets. Later, the x-ray business of Elpro in Pune, India, was acquired and renamed GE X-ray India. Several new JV companies were set up, including GE Hualun Medical Systems (60% GE owned) in Chengdu, China, to produce "economy" x-ray products; GE Haiying Medical Systems (60% GE owned) in Wuxi, China, to make low-end ultrasound equipment; and GE-Bharat Electronics (75% GE owned) in Bangalore, India, to supply x-ray tubes and transformers.

The third step was a huge build up of GEMSA's sales and service capabilities to support installed base growth. GE China Holding Company was used to facilitate

left to right

During one of his frequent visits to the Far East, John Trani met with his senior Asia staff in Beijing. Pictured during a city tour are (l–r) Savio Kwan, P. S. Sim, Chih Chen, Mei Wei Cheng, Claudia Nelson, John Trani, Göran Malm, Dr. Dai, and Keith Williams.

Göran Malm assembled his executive staff in a Beijing hotel to develop a new strategy to grow GE Medical Systems Asia into a $1 billion enterprise by 1997.

and speed this process. By 1997, a network of some 25 sales and service offices had been established across China. To improve service coverage in other key markets, GE acquired a 75% interest in Mediland, its Taiwanese distributor, and a 75% stake in GE Hospitech Medical Systems of Thailand.

Over the next 5 years, Göran's strategy succeeded brilliantly in making the company a major player throughout the region. External sales reached $968 million in 1997, operating margin $104 million (10.7%), and market share 23%. For a total investment of only $25 million, GEMSA had advanced into new markets and offerings that would help assure its future success.

"It is beyond doubt that Shinichi Kawase was the most significant contributor to our business growth in Japan as well as providing crucial support to our emerging markets," Malm later stated.

Spectacular results also were achieved in China, where sales revenues grew from about $20 million in early 1991 to $800 million by the end of the decade. "Keith Williams and Chih Chen deserve great credit for building a strong sales and service organization across the country," Malm said.

The rapid buildup in India following the Wipro deal brought a credible sales and service organization and a complementary distribution network. Under the leadership of D. A. Prasanna and, later, Vivek Paul, GEMS India became a key supplier of economy ultrasound and x-ray, x-ray tubes, and transformers.

After SGMS was stabilized in 1993, it was decided to transfer mid-tier ultrasound technology there. Under the leadership of C. W. Lee, it became the biggest volume producer of ultrasound products in the world. GEMS acquired 100% ownership during the Asia financial crisis of 1997–98.

In 1997, Malm was appointed President, GE Asia Pacific, with responsibilities for the company's 11 regional business units. Succeeding him in Tokyo was Yoshiaki Fujimori whom Chuck had hired as his business development manager when he was president of GE Japan and later brought to GEMSA in the same role. Fuji-san led Global Nuclear Medicine, Global CT, and Global MR before taking the Asia leadership post.

Field transformers

By the early 1990s, it was apparent the consolidation of the U.S. hospital industry into more and larger for-profit chains would profoundly affect traditional supplier relationships. Whereas GE and its competitors had previously sold their products and services at the department level or, in some instances, to individual hospitals, the emerging multihospital system environment demanded a different approach. What was needed was a new business model that would elevate customer contacts to a higher level.

The idea was simple but profound. By moving the selling process from the imaging department to the executive suite, several good things would likely happen. First, orders for GE equipment, services, and other value-added offerings would increase in scope and volume, since the needs of the entire multihospital system could be

The Hospital Corporation of America (HCA), Nashville, Tennessee, is the largest private operator of health care facilities in the world.

addressed. Second, GE could provide "total solutions," whether imaging equipment and services, lighting, environmental systems, power generation and distribution, financing, and even leadership GE management processes. Third, new relationships would be established at the highest management levels that might lead to exclusive, long-term partnerships, rather than just a series of individual transactions.

To implement this strategy, John needed exactly the right person to create and lead the new customer marketing team he envisioned. He found him sitting just a few offices away—Jim Del Mauro. In coming years, Del Mauro's Corporate Accounts team would score countless competitive victories using the "selling upwards" strategy. Among the more notable early wins were a 5-year, $1.8 *billion,* sole-source agreement with Columbia/HCA for equipment and service; and a $500 million sole-source equipment and service order from Healthmark.

Trani also had recognized the urgent need for greater field service productivity. He chose Tom Dunham, Vice President, Manufacturing and Information Systems, to spearhead this critical strategy. Tom, a Ph.D. metallurgist, had begun his career at GE Lighting in the same area of research that had fascinated Dr. Coolidge—perfecting tungsten wire for incandescent lamp filaments. He joined GE Appliances in 1979, serving in several leadership engineering and manufacturing assignments before coming to Milwaukee in 1986. At the time, Tom recalled, GEMS had a huge parts warehouse in each plant:

> One of first things we did was convert to just-in-time manufacturing by bringing our vendors onto the shop floor and, in effect, making them responsible for managing manufacturing inventory. Next, we outsourced computer processing to GE Appliances, saving us millions. Finally, we moved a good deal of subassembly work to outside vendors, reserving our internal capacity for final assembly and testing.

John was impressed with Tom's wide-ranging changes that had made the manufacturing process more efficient and productive. Now, he was anxious to apply those same kinds of best practices to the service business in order to maximize revenue and enhance customer satisfaction. He commented:

> Long before I arrived, the Continuum strategy had taught us a profitable business could be created by selling upgrades. My thought was that selling equipment was not an end in itself but an opportunity to sell additional upgrades, software applications, financing, parts, and service contracts in the future. That was an entirely different mindset.

John called this new approach the installed base strategy. He wanted Dunham to lead it, because he saw service as the "factory in the field"—a manufacturing-like process with definite inputs and predictable outputs. Nobody knew more about that than Tom.

Teamwork at the customer

The earlier separation of field sales and service into independent organizations was followed by the elimination of the Commercial and Product Sales groups. These changes left the business without many of the functional ties that had promoted strong teamwork and customer satisfaction through the years. To address this problem internally, the Service Division implemented a new cooperative concept that grouped Area Service Managers (ASMs) into larger teams sharing a common set of measurements. This initiative evolved into "Local Customer Teams" (LCTs). As Dunham explained:

It started with the need for Service to do a better job of serving customers. The ASM was the basic organizational entity and was measured on how well their area performed. This created a roadblock to cooperation and led us to regroup several ASMs into teams with shared measurements and shared resources. This fixed the service issues but not the larger boundary/teamwork issues.

Tom Dunham and Bob Stocking, with their key staff members, formed a CAP (Change Acceleration Process) team to work on applying the LCT concept. The hope was to restore and strengthen teamwork between the two field organizations despite the absence of previous resources, organization infrastructure, and reporting lines. The CAP experience helped everyone understand the depth of the cultural change needed and commit the resources to bring about effective change.

LCTs that combined the resources of both Sales and Service were established in each of the 21 geographic areas covered by a sales zone. Their mission was clear and succinct:

> To improve customer satisfaction through focused teamwork between Sales and Service while growing GEMS's market position in a tougher, more competitive environment.

LCT effectiveness was built upon improved speed and responsiveness through greater resource flexibility and local autonomy, plus shared goals and better integration at the customer level. "The concept was very simple," explained Mike Brickey, an early LCT developer "Give the people closest to the customer the resources, knowledge, and decision-making authority they need to present a single 'GE face' to the customer."

The first LCT test was led by Randy Dobbs, Southeast Region service manager, who engaged his region sales counterpart, Lewis Dudley. The concept was soon rolled out across the country. A joint Sales and Service Advisory Council was set up to oversee and facilitate the activities of the LCTs. Process coaches were selected and trained to assist with the training and development of the 200 members in a typical LCT.

The combined leadership set out a new vision for GEMS to become the most effective sales and service organization in the industry through several specific, demonstrated behaviors:

- Put the *Customer First* in everything we do
- Achieve highest *Employee Satisfaction,* individually and as a team
- Make joint decisions that *Optimize Overall Business Results,* not just those of a given function
- Strive to exceed all *Business Measurements*
- Function as a highly *Integrated Team*

Implementation focused on customer satisfaction; joint measurements; teamwork and process skills training; assigning process coaches, including Service in all strategic account management activities; completing an installed base census; and training in hospital economics.

Making the LCTs truly local was important, so flexibility was given for creative approaches. In the Cincinnati LCT, which was ranked just 19 of 21 the previous year, sales manager Ted Opie and his service counterpart created a "Customer Month" during which Sales, Service, and Finance representatives were banned from the local office during regular working hours. Instead, they had to spend all day with customers and each other. In addition, every customer meeting had to have at least one Sales and one Service person in attendance, and letters had to be sent to customers confirming the discussions. The results were so successful, Cincinnati continued thereafter with one "Customer Week" per month using the same rules. This total commitment to being with customers boosted them from #19 to #1 in a single year.

Another creative success was the "West Texas Electric Company," founded by Mark Roberts, full-line sales representative; Ken Keller, ASM; and 19 field engineers. The team committed to regular, disciplined calls to review customer sales and service issues and opportunities. New leads were generated from every call, producing substantial sales and service revenue growth, reduced operating costs, and greatly increased customer satisfaction.

A new cross-compensation system was implemented to reflect the new relationship of Sales and Service. As Scott Mathews, a zone sales manager, described it, "Paying Sales for service contracts was huge. Paying us both on the customer satisfaction number was equally huge. The buzz that cross-compensation created was, to my mind, critical in having the LCTs perceived as 'the real deal'".

Scott went on to say: "Leveraging the team meant Sales should take advantage of long-standing Service relationships. Secondly, Service just plain needed the help of Sales in selling service contracts. Each team brought a big advantage to the other if they cared to use it."

As Dunham later reflected, "Ultimately, the thing that really drove local teamwork was basing attendance at the annual meetings of the Sigma and Omega Societies on joint Sales and Service measurements within each LCT."

Sustained improvement across LCTs was driven by the Trotter Matrix, a tool created by Lloyd Trotter to compare performances among his Electrical Distribution & Control operations and share best practices. It was made famous by Tom Dunham who enthusiastically challenged the lowest performing LCTs in a given metric to seek out the top performing LCT in that metric, learn its best practice, and implement it locally.

Eventually, the LCT approach rolled out to great success in Canada, Mexico, Latin America, and even Europe. A similar process was also used in Japan.

"Multivendor" service

The installed base strategy required a rethinking of GEMS's long-standing philosophy of selling new equipment and, essentially, giving away the service. That attitude had begun to change in the 1970s, when the CT Continuum proved it was possible to generate additional revenue by selling upgrades to users. Could GE's huge installed base be leveraged as a major source of new revenue?

"At that time, our defined service market was $1.6 billion, and we had $1.4 billion of it," Dunham said. "Whereas equipment was growing at 7%, service growth was limited to equipment coming off warranty, or about 2%. That was totally unacceptable to John."

Tom's response was based upon some remarks made by Gary Wendt, then the head of GE Capital Services, at a GE officers' meeting. Though Welch demanded every GE business be #1 or #2 in its market, Gary said he loved being a small part of a very large market, because it meant unlimited opportunity for growth. Tom started thinking about how to redefine the service market to create new growth and decided the best opportunity lay in servicing equipment manufactured by other suppliers—"multivendor service." Now he had to sell the concept to his colleagues.

First on board was Steve Kellett, the entrepreneurial general manager of the Central Service Zone, who immediately volunteered to pilot such a project if Tom could get it okayed. When Trani and Welch proved skeptical, Tom and Steve decided to bootleg a project to find out if the scheme had merit. Dunham recalled:

> We found a hospital that had some GE equipment but much more competitive equipment. We told them we would service all their diagnostic imaging equip-

ment for 10% less than they were currently paying. After 6 months, we were able to show Trani we could service competitive equipment and do so profitably. Welch was also convinced, so Steve launched a zone-wide pilot project.

Though nervous, Tom and Steve had good reasons to anticipate success. First, over 30% of GE's field service engineers had worked for competitors during their careers and, thus, were familiar with other equipment. Second, after tearing down competitive systems, they found many of the same components made by the same suppliers as in GE equipment. The hardest challenge was getting his own field service managers on board. They were worried about such things as taking the focus away from GE products, getting competitive parts, pricing the product, and so on.

Frank Balicki, General Manager, Financial Services, stepped up to address the replacement parts issue. His Gold Seal™ business, under Jim Ficke, remarketed preowned equipment—good equipment customers often traded in on new systems. Since this often included competitive gear, it furnished a ready source of reliable spare parts.

Kellett soon had a number of successes to share with his colleagues and the multivendor service effort gained momentum. Randy Dobbs was next to offer multivendor service, while Tom Franks developed InSite remote monitoring for competitive equipment. In the Global Field Training Operation, Bob Babcock and his team set up competitive equipment at the Education Center to develop training materials and deliver training. Meanwhile, Rick Huber's "distance education" group created electronic performance support tools for on-site repair and skill development.

Kellett was named General Manager, GE HealthCare Services, the new organization charged with marketing and delivering multivendor service. Steve and his chief deputy, Justin Boswell, titled their new one-stop approach to comprehensive service "CompreCare™." It offered guaranteed savings and uptime; program flexibility; service accountability; and consistent service delivery for diagnostic imaging systems, biomedical equipment, and information systems. To obtain the technical expertise needed to service nontraditional technologies, such as biomedical equipment, GE began to acquire small, independent service providers, notably Ray Dalton's National MD. This acquisition was essential in helping Jim Del Mauro land the huge Columbia/HCA sole-source contract, since it included biomedical service in nearly 200 of their hospitals.

General Electric's relationship with Hospital Corporation of America (HCA) had begun back in the early 1970s, when GE Information Services Company began providing IT and information systems for financial reporting and consolidation. In 1989, GE Capital stepped forward with the critical financing for HCA's first major leveraged buy-out at a time when money markets were very tight.

"By the mid 1990s, HCA had built a comprehensive in-house service program for biomedical equipment and diagnostic imaging in all its hospitals," commented Jim Fitzgerald, President and CEO, HealthTrust Purchasing Group, a pooled group purchasing organization that supports over 1,300 not-for-profit and for-profit acute care

hospitals, including the HCA network, plus ambulatory surgery centers, alternative care sites, physician practices, and so forth. "The company had its own personnel in nearly every hospital providing these services."

In 1995, Columbia/HCA completely transitioned its in-house diagnostic imaging service group to GEMS under a major outsourcing agreement. Now, just 1 year later, it transitioned all its biomedical equipment service to GE as well. Fitzgerald explained:

> We moved all in-house services and most of the biomedical engineering personnel to GE. We gave them an exclusive contract for all biomedical engineering services, not only for HCA hospitals but also Humana, HealthTrust, and the other facilities in the network at the time—about 300 hospitals. This was a landmark transaction for GE and, in effect, established a very strategic business line for them.

More than 400,000 pieces of biomedical equipment were covered under the initial contract. For the first time, HCA had a documented inventory of all these devices, plus critical data on each piece of equipment to better inform planning and capital budgeting decisions. For GE, this huge outsourcing agreement meant it could take its proven equipment service practices and pursue increased market share. As the acquisition strategy accelerated, the fragmented and inefficient service industry began to consolidate under GE's nationwide umbrella.

Though we are getting somewhat ahead of our story, HCA would later contract with GE on an exclusive basis for the purchase of major diagnostic imaging equipment. Fitzgerald noted:

> This was a 5-year contract in excess of $1 billion that we negotiated with Jeff Immelt and Jim Del Mauro. A lot of business publications later pointed to this deal as one of the key factors Jack Welch considered in recommending Jeff Immelt as his successor.

Dr. Thomas F. Frist, Jr., HCA's chairman emeritus, agreed:

> Signing this large, multiyear contract was a major coup for Jeff Immelt. Trust and mutual respect grew into relationships that were not just good for us but also good for GE. It's a testament to how the two companies have grown over the past 40 years.

This period also saw a huge spurt in growth for the regular service business. It was driven by the development of flexible, new products and an intensified marketing push, which greatly expanded GE's market footprint. For example, in the fall of 1993, equipment service offerings were regrouped into an expanded series of "tiered" options designed to allow customers to match their financial and coverage needs.

The success of the installed base strategy was illustrated by Service's emergence as the source for one third of GEMS's revenue and two thirds of its profit. "Service is a major contributor to the profitability of the business, so it's important for us to remain #1 on a global basis," Dunham once commented. "Our technology may earn the initial sale, but service is what brings the customer back."

Hi-tech training

Another of Trani's lasting legacies was the creation of the $30 million, 175,000 square foot (16,250 meters²) RiversEdge Global Education Center (now called the GE Healthcare Institute). Opened in late 1994 on a park-like site in rural Pewaukee, it provided ample space for classrooms, conference facilities, offices, a Crotonville-style "pit" (a

left to right

Jim Fitzgerald, President & CEO, HealthTrust Purchasing Group.

Dr. Thomas F. Frist, Jr., Chairman Emeritus, HCA.

top to bottom

The RiversEdge Global Education Center was expanded several times over the years and later renamed the GE Healthcare Institute.

Tom Dunham was honored for his contributions to the global training effort by having a major facility at the GE Healthcare Institute named for him — the Thomas E. Dunham Services Learning Center

The Global Education Solutions team got together for a group photo at RiversEdge in 1998. Pictured are (first row, l-r) Shiro Mori, Mike Teramoto, Sandra Ashwell, Steve Shaw, Marcy Hotz, Bob Babcock, Rick Huber, and Naobumi Ito; (second row, l-r) David Aguilar, Evelyn Peters, John McIntyre, David Brady, Barb Truskoski, and Dave Rose; (third row, l-r) Kimberly Kleiman-Lee, Dave Oreshack, Leon Janssen, Rob Rajala, and Donna Schultz; (back row, l-r) Russ Grothman, Ken Hahn, Saad Iskandarani, Gary Kautzer, and Jill Honerlaw.

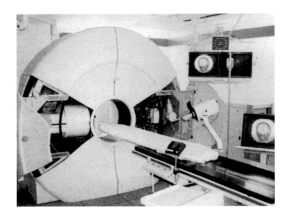

The 3D morphometer, developed at the Buc research center, could make digital images of a 3D volume to assist in various angiographic procedures.

multilevel, semi-circular arrangement of student stations around a small stage), even studios for GEMS-TV. Just across the street, 72 double-occupancy apartments were constructed for students from around the world. "This is a long-term investment in the future," Dunham said at the time, "We need to get ready now to provide training levels equivalent to the worldwide growth we anticipate in the future."

The biggest challenge in creating this remarkable asset was Trani's requirement that it be cost neutral. In other words, no more could spent in building, equipping, and operating it than the cost to provide training at the various locations then in use. "Leon Janssen's role in overcoming this obstacle was huge," Dunham said. "He developed the model that charged all users the same fees they were already paying for less desirable local facilities."

Leon, who had joined Tom's staff as general manager of the Global Field Training Operation in June 1994, was appointed General Manager, Global Education Solutions, when RiversEdge opened in October.

As the need for education and training expanded in step with worldwide business growth, RiversEdge would undergo several expansions. In time, GE's investment there would approach $80 million. In coordination with training centers in Slough, England, and Hino, Japan, it made possible an integrated global education network serving employees and customers alike.

"ORION" rising

Throughout the Trani era, exciting advances were being made in every area of GE imaging technology. An unusual CT variation was the 3D morphometer that was developed by Buc scientists and engineers in collaboration with the French medical community and the national atomic energy authority. Based upon a CT gantry with two x-ray tubes and a 40cm image intensifier, this device allowed the generation of a 3D volume to aid in diagnostic and interventional procedures, surgical planning, and radiation therapy.

Other significant new products included such advances as the: CT HiSpeed Advantage™ system with 1-second scanning; Sytec™ 4000 system; Optima™ multidetector nuclear imaging system; Millennium™ MPS and MPR single-detector scanners; Senographe™ DMR mammography system; Advantx™ DLX digital cardiac/vascular system; Signa® SP open-magnet and Contour™ 0.5 Tesla scanners; Prestige™ VH and Silhouette™ x-ray systems; and Advantx™ Legacy R&F system.

"OPM" program

With the Signa system successfully launched, Morry Blumenfeld and several of his colleagues—Rob Newman, Skip Kerwin, and Bob Coradini—set out to explore new opportunities. Informally known as the "OPM" ("other people's money") program, it raised $36 million from a consortium of 12 research sites to develop a prototype MR interventional system called the Signa MRT (later the SP). Developed in conjunction with the R&D Center and Brigham & Women's Hospital (Boston), its "double doughnut" design gave physicians and surgeons access to the patient during imaging for such MR-guided therapies as interventional procedures. Though it was ultimately not viable as a product due to a combination of cost and technical factors, the MRT was a major step forward in creating the new field of image-guided surgery with real-time feedback to the surgeon.

Under the leadership of Jan Berg and Mel Dean, investments were being made in a technology called "positron emission tomography" (PET), a new way to visualize functional information. In 1989, GE formed an alliance with Scanditronix AB of Sweden, a producer of PET scanners. It also established a development agreement with Hamamatsu Photonics of Japan involving light detection devices for use in PET scanners.

None of these initiatives was more important than the technological revolution that swept through the ultrasound product offering during this period. Ultrasound was the only imaging modality where GE still lacked a complete product line. The RT3200 scanner from YMS was a strong entry in the clinical OB/GYN segment, but there remained a gaping hole in the huge radiology segment,

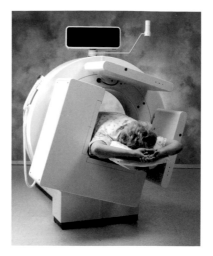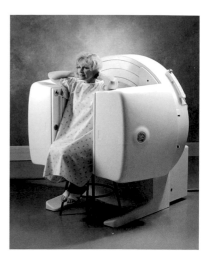

Paul Mirabella had moved to Rancho Cordova in mid-1986 as the Global Ultrasound marketing manager under Ken Leenstra. After a reorganization in early 1987, Paul took over as general manager, assisted by Bob Hubert, Bob Guezenauga, Jay Plugge, Axel Brisken, and Judy Gezon. Three years later, following the consolidation of the business in Milwaukee, Paul became General Manager, Global CT and Radiation Therapy. Mikael Ahlund got the ultrasound assignment and launched a study to determine the feasibility of designing and building a world-class ultrasound scanner. With the strong support of John Trani and Bobby Bowen, the Corporate Executive Council approved the project as one of four major focus areas meant to deliver "GE game changers" (along with AC locomotives, the G-7 washing machine, and the GE-90 jet engine).

This project was named "ORION," and its guiding principal was if ultrasound physics was understood in sufficient depth, smart GE people should be able to build a superior project. With such strong corporate visibility, the ultrasound team was able to hire the best people it could find for the project. Over 80% of the software and design engineers came from outside the business, as did three of the four engineering managers (Jon Snyder, transducers; Ken Kramer, systems; and Tracy Accardi, software; Mike Harsh, hardware, was the sole Milwaukeean).

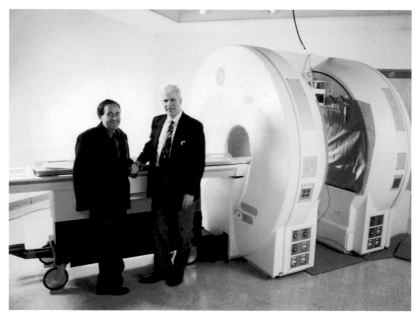

A team at the R&D Center, led by Sharbel Noujaim, soon set out to prove the 128-channel digital beamformer that would be the guts of such a system. Since ORION's software requirements were huge and, in most areas, totally new to the team, Wipro-GE's software group was assigned part of the non-beamformer operating system. Several software engineers from Bangalore were even embedded in the Milwaukee software engineering group so development could continue around the clock.

It was about this time John decided to bring an old friend to Milwaukee to head up the effort. John Kese had worked for him at Audio Electronics as the head of tape recorders and CB radio products, and at Mobile Communications where he ran marketing. "John was probably the best product development guy I have ever known," Trani commented. "Though he wasn't interested in moving again, Jack Welch and I were eventually able to change his mind."

Another important member of the team was Jeff Peiffer who headed the GE YMS ultrasound business in Japan. Thus, he was perfectly positioned to support ORION activities project there while continuing to develop new products for global customers. Also, Joe Tuttle and his manufacturing team were making plans to build ORION in a new way.

The ORION team finally settled on a "narrow-band digital beamformer" design and a distinctive new name—LOGIQ™. The first product was dubbed the LOGIQ 700 and its launch set for RSNA '93 By the time it was released, GEMS had spent more than 3 years and $80 million on the project and the R&D Center almost 2 years. Thanks to good technology and the decision to hire some of the best sales representatives in the industry, the LOGIQ 700 captured $40 million in U.S. sales and $80 million worldwide during its first year. It was joined by the full-featured LOGIQ 500 color Doppler/cardiac system in 1994. Developed by GE YMS to match the best image quality level then available at half the cost, the LOGIQ 500 became GE's top sales volume ultrasound product and really put the company on the ultrasound map.

With these new LOGIQ products successfully launched, John Kese surprised everyone by announcing his retirement! "He told me he had taken the business as far as he was able," Trani recalled, "and we now needed a technology-oriented person to take it to the next level. Not only that, he already had found the perfect guy!"

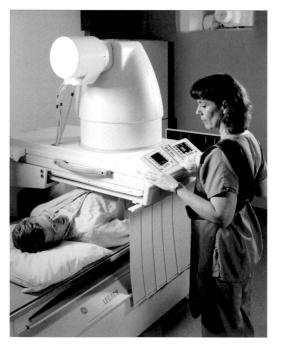

top, left to right
Optima multidetector nuclear imaging system.

Millennium single-detector scanner.

middle
Ferenc Jolesz (left), who established Brigham & Women's image-guided therapy program in 1993, was instrumental in developing the Signa MRT (for "magnetic resonance therapy") system. He and Morry Blumenfeld are shown at the unit's March 1994 dedication in Boston.

bottom
Advantx Legacy R&F system.

Omar Ishrak was Vice President, Engineering & Manufacturing, at Diasonics. Upon his arrival in Milwaukee, he developed the "Breakthrough" business strategy still being followed today. Omar's idea was to introduce at least one significant clinical breakthrough each year, then migrate it to products at all price points. Years later, Kese commented, "Omar was the person who made GE Ultrasound a player. Because of his standing in the ultrasound field, he gave GE recognition and credibility with doctors and ultrasound radiology departments."

Omar would build upon the work begun by Chuck Pieper and Göran Malm to develop multiple low-cost development centers throughout Asia. The result was GE Global Ultrasound—an organization that integrated the company's worldwide resources and aligned its people with the business, rather than individual countries. No other competitor (nor GE modality, for that matter) had such a portfolio of global capabilities.

X-ray tubes...again

The CT x-ray tube crisis that had accompanied the introduction of the high-performance CT 8800 scanner was about to reappear. Though a massive engineering and facilities expansion program had boosted CT tube life from a low of 4,000 to over 25,000 slices, that performance was no longer acceptable for the latest generation of GE scanners. Customers were complaining, and warranty costs were soaring.

Jack Welch personally intervened this time. He remembered a Frenchman who had complained to him years before about poor CT tube life. Trani had recruited Marc Onetto to Milwaukee in mid-1992 to lead Global Information Technology and Process Improvement. Now, at Jack's urging, he was appointed General Manager, Global Tubes & Detectors, a new organization created specifically to solve x-ray tube quality prob-

lems once and for all. Another key move was recruiting Mike Idelchik, from GE Aircraft Engines, to head up x-ray tube engineering.

Onetto recalled the challenge of getting his new organization off the ground:

> The quality of the team was critical to the success of this effort. In addition to the fantastic people in Milwaukee and at the R&D Center, we also had great people in Tokyo and in Paris who contributed. I was also able to leverage the knowledge of some old timers, such as Bill Love and Emile Gabbay, who knew where we came from, what we learned in the past, and helped us avoid making the same mistakes again.

The outcome of this key program will be documented in the next chapter when we cover the Six Sigma initiative.

"Have fun, make a buck, and win!"

After 10-1/2 years of sometimes tumultuous, always transformative leadership, the time had come for Trani to test his management skills in new markets against new competitors. He would never forget his experiences at GE Medical Systems:

> It was the greatest period of my life. We had challenge, change, the laboratory to experiment in, and the best group of people I have ever been associated with. I have an expression everyone who was there will recall: 'Have fun, make a buck, and win!' And that's exactly what we did.

The business Trani left behind had emerged as the largest and most successful company in the diagnostic imaging industry. During his tenure, employment had doubled, sales had grown by a factor of four, and earnings had increased tenfold. Indeed, GE Medical Systems had generated some 75% of total industry profits during this period, some three times the profitability of its next nearest competitor. At the same time, it had matured from an essentially U.S. company with nearly 90% of its sales in North America to a truly global enterprise with more than half of its sales offshore.

John M. Trani

top to bottom
Jack Welch (right), GE chairman, paid a surprise visit to the Electric Avenue x-ray tube manufacturing area in 1993 to see the production process for himself.

"Deep-diving" was Welch's term for talking directly with the people on the production line to find out what was going on. John Trani is at left.

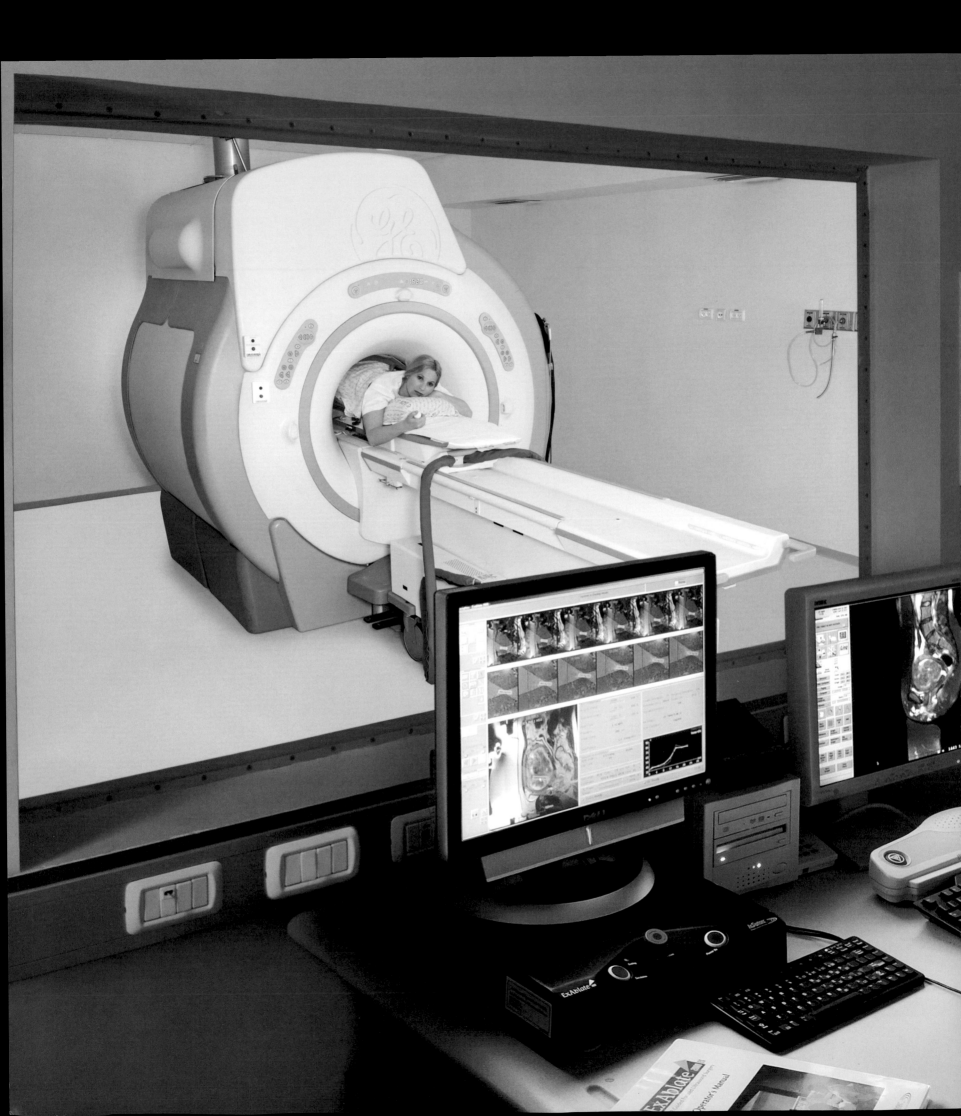

The Immelt Era

1996-2000

As Jack Welch neared GE's retirement age of 65, one of his principal concerns was finding the right person to succeed him as chairman and CEO. He had his eye on several bright, young executives serving in various parts of the company and was giving them challenging assignments to prove their mettle.

Among them was Jeff Immelt, a Dartmouth mathematics graduate, who had spent the bulk of his GE career in the plastics business, primarily in marketing and sales assignments. Most recently, he had been Vice President, GE Plastics-Americas, with responsibilities for business activities and product development in North and South America. When Jack selected him to take over in Milwaukee as President & CEO of GE Medical Systems, Jeff held his future career prospects firmly in his own hands.

Lessons in Leadership

Jeffrey Robert Immelt (b. 1956) holds a B.A. in applied mathematics from Dartmouth College and an M.B.A. from Harvard University. The son of a GE family (his father worked at Aircraft Engines for 38 years), Immelt joined GE Plastics in 1982, where he held various sales and marketing positions. In 1989, he became a GE officer concurrent with his assignment heading up consumer service at GE Appliances. In 1991, he moved to Vice President, Worldwide Marketing and Product Management, before returning to GE Plastics as Vice President, Americas Commercial, in 1992 and becoming Vice President, GE Plastics-Americas, in 1993. Immelt was appointed a GE Senior Vice President and President & CEO of GE Medical Systems in 1996, President & Chairman-elect of General Electric Company in 2000, and Chairman & CEO in 2001. He is a director of the Federal Reserve Bank of New York, a trustee of Dartmouth College, and a member of President Obama's Economic Recovery Advisory Board.

A world to win

Immelt's arrival in Milwaukee coincided with the best year in General Electric's history. Worldwide revenues had grown by 13% to nearly $80 billion, including an unprecedented $33 billion from non-U.S. operations. GE was truly becoming a global enterprise. GEMS's business results were also healthy with all-time record sales and earnings despite increased competition and a continuing slowdown in the worldwide diagnostic imaging equipment market. Orders were strong at $3.9 billion, setting the stage for future growth.

Trani's legacy was having a very positive impact. Due to the rapid pace of technology development during his tenure, more than 80% of equipment sales now were coming from products introduced in just the previous 3 years. Some of the latest examples included such leadership offerings as the Signa® Profile™ 0.2T permanent magnet MRI system, Signa® SP intraoperative surgery scanner, LOGIQ™ 400 MD and 500 MD digital ultrasound platforms, HiSpeed™ CT/i sub-second CT scanner, Advantx® Legacy™ D all-digital R&F system, Advantx® LCA and LCV+ angio/cardio systems, and the Optima™ NX dual-head nuclear imaging system.

Despite these terrific technology successes and excellent business results, Medical Systems was on a relatively slow growth trajectory. With all its eggs in the diagnostic imaging basket, and already holding leadership shares in most product modalities, it was obvious that future growth would largely depend upon overall market expansion. Though opportunities for good gains existed in certain national markets, such as China and India, relatively modest growth was in prospect for as far as the eye could see.

For Immelt, that level of performance simply wasn't good enough for one of GE's marquee businesses. Nor did he view his new role as being merely a caretaker:

> John had done a great job of getting the business through some really tough years, such as when the MR market was cut by half due to reimbursement decreases. When I arrived, this was a $3.5 billion business growing at 10% a year in a $4 *trillion* industry. That was unacceptable from a GE corporate standpoint. The challenge was to find a way to get the level of growth we wanted.

That feeling was reinforced at a GE Corporate Executive Council meeting in early 1997, where one of the Wall Street analysts who covered the company spoke. Jeff recalled:

> She went through the various businesses and didn't even mention Medical Systems as being germane to the way investors looked at GE. Jack Welch and I discussed this problem afterwards and agreed that Medical Systems was way too small and let's use some capital to make it bigger. We decided to look at some adjacencies—related healthcare businesses that we might acquire that would expand our served market and give us the growth we needed.

One of Jeff's first moves in implementing this "inorganic growth" strategy was to hire an expert business development manager with impeccable credentials in high-tech mergers and acquisitions. Mike Jones had spent a dozen years on Wall Street and in San Francisco specializing in M&A activities involving hi-tech firms. When GE invited him to interview with several businesses looking for new business development managers, Mike took the Medical Systems interview first and soon signed aboard:

> Medical Systems is a business with a purpose. I had little appreciation for that going into the interview but soon learned that it is what drives them. The people I met painted a picture of a great business that GE really wanted to expand and that provided a great match for my skill set. It also gave me a great opportunity to have more of an ownership role in helping grow a business.

Resounding successes

Jeff's first acquisition was already being negotiated when Mike arrived. The prize was Diasonics Vingmed Ultrasound, Santa Clara, California, a division of Elbit Medical Imaging of Israel. Elbit had acquired Diasonics and Vingmed, a Norwegian firm, just 3 years before. Not long after, Omar Ishrak, who had been managing engineering and product development for Diasonics while earning a great reputation in the industry as a technology innovator, was recruited by John Trani to come to GE to head up its global ultrasound business. Omar explained:

> My professional goal was to make a difference through innovation in ultrasound. GE gave me the opportunity to do that under the umbrella of a large company but with the operating freedom to do what was necessary to make ultrasound succeed. I was apprehensive about coming to a large company and was worried about moving to Milwaukee from California. But the opportunity to innovate with my own team in complete alignment with management's goals outweighed those concerns.

By late 1996, as Jeff assumed leadership in Milwaukee, Omar was already making a difference at GE Ultrasound. As a former competitor, he was aware of the virtues of the flagship LOGIQ 700 system . . . and its shortcomings. At $140,000 fully equipped, the LOGIQ 700 was simply too expensive for most customers. Omar's solution was to aggressively market the outstanding LOGIQ 500 system around the globe. This full-featured color/Doppler and cardiac system had been developed at GE YMS a couple of years earlier for the general radiology market. Better still, it matched the performance of its key competition at close to half the price. The extra revenue Omar expected it to generate could then be used to cost-reduce the LOGIQ 700. His plan succeeded brilliantly.

GEMS still was a relatively small player in the ultrasound market with less than 10% share (a "startup," as Omar described it). What it needed was strong, innovative offerings in each of the ultrasound market segments. The LOGIQ family and "value" systems from YMS filled several of these niches but serious gaps remained, especially in cardiology. That's where Diasonics Vingmed came in.

On February 13, 1998, Immelt's growth-through-acquisition strategy achieved its first success when a $230 million agreement in principle to acquire Diasonics Vingmed Ultrasound was announced. Through its Vingmed-Sound subsidiary in Horten, Norway, DVU was a world leader in echocardiography and Doppler technology. Its U.S. operation was strong in radiology, while Diasonics Ultrasound Ltd., Haifa, Israel, produced PC-based ultrasound systems for general radiology, as well as cardiology/radiology shared services systems.

The addition of Diasonics Vingmed had an immediate, positive impact by providing a critical mass of world-class people, much needed cardiac ultrasound technology, market experience, a dedicated sales force, and a large footprint in Europe.

"This acquisition allowed GE to better serve cardiac ultrasound customers around the world by dramatically increasing our product offerings and expanding our global reach," Ishrak explained. "It was Jeff's first acquisition—the largest since the CGR deal—and it suddenly doubled our size."

Focused ultrasound

GE's MR-guided focused ultrasound project had been conceived in 1991 as one of Morry Blumenfeld's "OPM" ("other people's money") projects discussed in the Trani chapter. Ultimately, research sites were established at Harvard, Stanford, Mayo Clinic, M. D. Anderson (Houston), and St. Luc (Montreal). When the company decided to abandon therapy delivery, Morry was asked to find a buyer who would continue to support these important customers. Since Diasonsics Vingmed had an ultrasound-guided focused ultrasound development project of its own, it was a natural fit. During the acquisition, the two programs were combined into a JV between GE (20%) and Diasonics Vingmed's parent, Elbit Imaging (80%), called InSightec. It went on to develop a new surgical methodology combining high-intensity, focused ultrasound tissue ablation with MR guidance and control for the noninvasive treatment of benign and malignant tumors, functional neurosurgery, and targeted drug delivery. One key neurosurgeon called it "the most important development in surgery since the invention of the scalpel."

In addition to Jeff and Omar, several other GEMS people played key roles in the acquisition, including Keith Morgan, chief counsel; Keith Sherin, head of finance; and Jack Campo, M&A counsel and de facto business development leader prior to Mike Jones's arrival.

With the DVU win, the LOGIQ 500 marketing success, internal organic growth, and several additional strategic acquisitions, such as Krenzbuehler, Parallel Design, ALI, Kretztechnik, and ViewPoint, GE Ultrasound had become a serious contender. By the close of Immelt's tenure in 2000, it would be the global leader in ultrasound. His growth strategy clearly was succeeding.

left
Jeffrey R. Immelt

middle
Mike Jones, long-time business development manager, who helped strategize and implement the remarkable growth of GE Medical Systems/GE Healthcare.

right
The LOGIQ 700 Expert system—GEMS's second DFSS (Design for Six Sigma) product—was introduced in April 1999 at the Waldorf Astoria Hotel in New York City. Among the attendees were (l–r): Terry Duesterhoeft, Dr. Thomas Stavros, Omar Ishrak, Sharon Banaszewski, Jeff Immelt, Bob Thompson, Dr. Ted Lyons, Peter Pellerito, and Matt Berger.

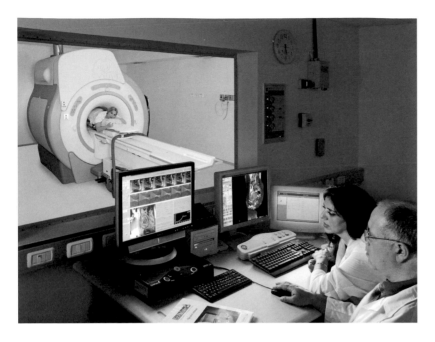

top to bottom

InSightec's ExAblate® 2000 MR-guided focused ultrasound system was cleared for the non-invasive treatment of symptomatic uterine fibroids by the U.S. Food & Drug Administration.

Omar Israk was destined to build GE Ultrasound into a multibillion-dollar enterprise. An exceptional talent, he went on to become President & CEO, Healthcare Systems, with responsibilities for the CT, MR, ultrasound, patient monitoring, molecular imaging, interventional, x-ray, life support, and home health businesses.

Bernd von Pohlheim, former president of Krenzbuehler, was a key contributor to GE Ultrasound's success in Europe.

As Omar explained it:

> The critical early decision was to globalize the LOGIQ 500, which gave us breathing room to fix the LOGIQ 700 product. The Krenzbuehler acquisition helped us to become a big player in Germany. Berndt von Pohlheim, its former president, stayed on after the acquisition and ended up running the European business for us.

Another key development was when Paul Mirabella, Vice President, Americas Sales, agreed to let Omar hire his own dedicated sales team. "We brought Peter Pellerito in to lead the sales effort, and he was an invaluable ally," said Omar. "Peter had important contacts throughout the industry and knew how to hire the best people."

Perhaps Omar's most significant contribution was implementing a new business strategy for GE Ultrasound. It called for introducing at least one significant clinical breakthrough in each segment every year, then migrating them to all price points. With centers of excellence in the U.S., Japan, Israel, South Korea, India, and China sharing technology and quickly leveraging off of each other, GE ultrasound innovations were soon flowing much faster than the competition could ever hope to match. The inevitable result was GE global market leadership.

What wasn't expected was that ultrasound would eventually rival CT and MR as GE's largest imaging modality.

What's IT?

By this time, Medical Systems had been seriously pursuing PACS (picture archiving and communications system) technology for more than 20 years. Joe Marion, Ed Barnes, and a host of marketing and engineering talent had helped evolve early efforts into a multimodality systems business offering "integrated diagnostics" to communicate diagnostic images and related patient information for display, analysis, and archiving purposes. Now, the concept was expanding toward enterprise-wide IT (information technology) systems capable of sharing all types of healthcare data—clinical as well as business management—among all interested parties.

Jeff and Mike Jones soon made several significant investments to strengthen GE's global position in the rapidly expanding medical image information segment. Among them was the acquisition of Lockheed Martin Medical Systems and Innomed of Germany, as well as a 20% stake in ALI, a leader in ultrasound image archiving. The next challenge was to expand beyond image sharing into managing the total workflow surrounding patient care.

In talking with customers, Jeff had learned how important it was for GE to move beyond PACS and become a serious player in the wider arena of healthcare information management. Jeff understood the implications—that as equipment became increasingly commoditized, the game changer would be the digitization of patient information and workflow management. In short, *IT*.

As in ultrasound, Immelt also realized he would have to go to the IT industry itself to find the right person to lead the effort—someone thoroughly immersed in the IT business and fully conversant with the emerging communications needs of healthcare providers. In mid-1997, he found the ideal candidate in the person of Vishal Wanchoo who was heading up Agfa HealthCare's U.S. product management and marketing team. A seasoned IT professional with many years of technical, marketing, and management experience, Vishal had earlier started Agfa's digital radiology PACS business that was now a market leader.

"When Jeff contacted me, I flew in to talk with him," Vishal remembered. "He was very convincing in his willingness to invest to really make IT a big business. So that's how I ended up at GE."

left to right
Vishal Wanchoo took over
GEM's IT business in 1997.

Hedvig Hricak, M.D.

Vishal joined Medical Systems in December 1997 as Global General Manager, Imaging and Information Systems, and immediately launched a detailed assessment of the PACS organization and its products. There were some tough decisions to be made, especially in terms of getting the right global players on board to lead the business—some from the IT industry and some from other GE components. Certain projects and products were also eliminated in order to really focus on the things that had to be done.

The Innomed acquisition that Jeff and Mike had already engineered proved to be an immediate win. This was a $2 million business that Jürgen Reinneger had started several years earlier to develop and market radiology information system software that managed the workflow in the department—scheduling, reporting, and so forth. It proved to be a great fit with GE's PACS technology and both quickly thrived.

"Jürgen is still with the company and leading a $270 million business," Vishal recently said. "Joining GE let him take the product he developed to every part of Europe, Asia, the Far East, Australia, New Zealand, Mexico, Brazil, and the U.S."

Another early move by Wanchoo and his IT team was to set up close clinical relationships with key customers to speed the development and launch of new products. One of the most important was with Northwestern Memorial Hospital, just a 20-minute drive from the IT software engineering facility in Mount Prospect, Illinois. Another was with Memorial Sloan-Kettering Cancer Center (MSKCC) in New York City, one of the world's foremost cancer research and clinical treatment facilities.

Vishal explained:

Northwestern Memorial was our first big PACS customer and we learned a lot working with them. MSKCC worked with us on the contemporary technology that we were bringing out. Our software engineers spent many hours at these sites to understand workflow and clinical requirements. These partnerships were a crucial step in setting the stage for future successes.

The key to developing these customer alliances, however, was flawless execution. For example, MSKCC needed to implement PACS because of a new outpatient imaging center that was due to open in the latter half of 1998. It was located some 40 blocks downtown from the main campus, so a way to efficiently share images was essential. The deadlines were tight, and GE IT was on the hook to perform.

This project coincided with GE's transition from proprietary technology to open system architecture. "We cut the cord to the past to capitalize on future growth," Vishal commented. "We made a huge commitment to overresource the project and got them up and running on time. That was a defining moment for this business."

The challenges in serving MSKCC, which went filmless in 2000, have never slackened. Image storage requirements continued to escalate due to more imaging locations, imaging equipment, patient exams, and slices. They are now entering around 1,500,000 images into PACS *per week!*

Hedvig Hricak, M.D., radiology chair, further explained:

In cancer care, old studies have to be online, because we don't know how many old scans we have to look at. So we have high volume, high demand, and high-profile patients. We are not always patient, but at the end of the day, we all want excellence in patient care and great outcomes. Vishal and his IT team understand that.

Another key breakthrough for the IT team was evolving into the physician office segment with products to manage the revenue cycle. Gary Eyre, who came to GE through one of the smaller acquisitions, brought a new perspective on this formerly taboo business. He analyzed the market and built a strong business case for entering what had always been seen as a high-risk segment. Ultimately, with Corporate's approval, GEMS purchased a small company by the name of Millbrook to establish a solid foundation in the physician office market. From that modest beginning, the stage was set for a new business segment that would eventually grow to nearly *half a billion dollars* in annual sales. Not a bad return on an initial investment of less than $20 million.

The 1998 introduction of the PathSpeed™ workstation was another huge boost to GE's IT credibility. This unique productivity tool provided radiologists with a fast, flexible, integrated system for viewing and archiving a wide range of patient records, diagnostic images, and other critical treatment data. This development was greatly accelerated by a strategic alliance with Cerner Corporation that allowed their radiology information system to be integrated with GE's image archiving system. Within a year, GE could claim the PathSpeed PACS product was the fastest-growing radiology information system in the industry. It would soon be joined by the Catalyst™ cardiovascular information system—the first of its kind to simultaneously capture images and other patient data for cardiologists.

Two key 1999 acquisitions further boosted business prospects, including Applicare, an innovative supplier of web-based archiving and imaging services, and MECON, a leader in healthcare data mining.

Immelt later said:

Hiring Omar Israk and Vishal Wanchoo was one of the defining events of my years at Medical Systems. We had always tried to promote from within but had never gotten any traction. So we finally went out to the industries and hired two talented guys who are still with us today. They both built multibillion-dollar franchises for us and made a massive difference of how we looked at their businesses.

Both went on to stellar careers under Joe Hogan. Omar would become President & CEO, Global Ultrasound & Bone Densitometry and, later, President & CEO, Healthcare Systems, with responsibility for ultrasound, life support, bone densitometry, molecular imaging, patient monitoring, and diagnostic cardiology products. Vishal would become a GE Vice President and General Manager, Clinical Information Technology, a component of Healthcare IT (which included patient monitoring at the time), then President & CEO, GE Healthcare Information Technologies, comprising the digital technologies that blend imaging, clinical, and business information systems to create a complete electronic health record.

Old friend, new relationship

Speaking of patient monitoring, Jeff and Mike's search for new ways to diversify the revenue stream led them to a terrific opportunity in GEMS's own backyard.

GE had entered the electronic patient monitoring business in 1962 (see the "Nelson Era" for details) with a line of bedside modules that detected such vital functions as heart rate, pulse, and blood pressures, then transmitted this data to a central nurse station for display, monitoring, and analysis. Over the next two decades, the product line grew in breadth and sophistication, but competition was fierce and it was decided to concentrate in diagnostic imaging. Consequently, the monitoring business was sold to Marquette Electronics, also in Milwaukee.

Marquette Electronics, as it was then known, was one of the earliest pioneers in biomedical electronics. Michael Cudahy and Warren Cozzens, the cofounders, had met in the early 1950s when they had joined together to represent various manufacturers in electronics. A cardiologist at Northwestern University Medical School called one day looking for an oscilloscope large enough to display electrocardiograms. Cozzens and Cudahy were intrigued and met with him to find out more about the project. From that chance encounter sprang one of the most innovative and successful firms in biomedical electronics.

Marquette's innovation was a bedside device that could detect a patient's heart waveform and transmit it to a central location through the telephone system. There it would be displayed on a large-screen oscilloscope and recorded on microfilm. This eliminated the inefficient, old method of hooking up a small machine to the patient and recording the ECG on a long strip of paper. This would then be cut up into segments and pasted onto large sheets of paper for the cardiologist to read.

After overcoming all the usual birthing pains, Marquette's first system finally went into operation at Northwestern Memorial Hospital to the delight of the cardiologists and hospital administrators. Soon, other luminary institutions, such as Massachusetts General Hospital and The Johns Hopkins Hospital, Baltimore, Maryland, placed orders for central electrocardiograph systems. "We would make about one a month, deliver it, and ask for payment so that we could build the next one," Cudahy recalled. "The situation was that tight."

Marquette's really big break came when Mayo Clinic asked them to build some of their electrocardiographic equipment. The word soon spread, and Marquette was on its way. Competitors such as 3M, Hewlett Packard, and IBM sprang up to challenge them, but Marquette continued to lead the electrocardiography segment of the market.

It was at about this point when Walt Robb approached Mike Cudahy with a proposal to purchase Marquette and add it to GE's monitoring business. Mike declined but made a counterproposal to purchase GE's operation. Walt soon agreed and the deal was done. Now, some 15 years later, the relationship was about to come full circle.

After a long and extremely successful entrepreneurial career, Mike Cudahy was contemplating retirement. Marquette Medical Systems had become the nation's largest maker of electrocardiograph and monitoring equipment—devices used to acquire, record, and monitor cardiology data and vital signs. Its offerings also included exercise stress testing systems; point-of-care monitoring of adult, fetal, and neonatal patients; and clinical information integration products. In its most recent fiscal year, it had reported $578 million in revenues and net income of $26.6 million (4.6%).

"We were working on a system to allow doctors to get medical data, such as electrocardiographs, on a patient from different departments," Cudahy recalled. "I was aware that GE was working on a similar idea, so I called Jeff Immelt and said we should have lunch."

That first discussion soon led to others. Before long, the subject of GE buying Marquette was mentioned. Detailed negotiations followed until the point was reached when Jeff and Mike decided to fly to New York and get CEO Jack Welch's approval. As Mike recalled that meeting:

> Jack said my problem was that I wanted too much for Marquette. I replied that his problem was that he didn't want to pay enough. He told me that he had just come through a board meeting and was authorized to offer up to $45 a share, payable in GE stock. I stuck out my hand and we shook. The deal was done.

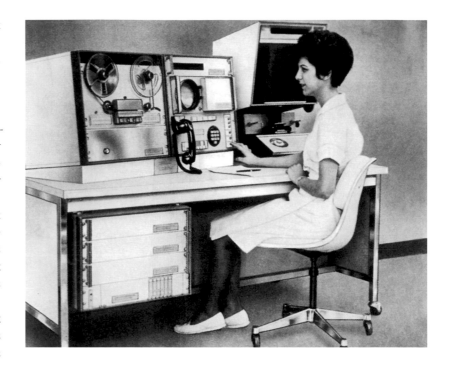

top to bottom

Marquette's first production EKG system. *(Photo courtesy of M. Cudahy)*

Mike Cudahy (left) and Warren Cozzens cofounded Marquette Electronics and developed it into one of the world's leading manufacturers of biomedical electronics. *(Photo courtesy of M. Cudahy)*

This early Marquette EKG system allowed a patient's vital signs to be remotely monitored from a central station. *(Photo courtesy of M. Cudahy)*

The sale of the company to General Electric was a bittersweet moment for the loyal Marquette staff. However, they went on to achieve even greater successes. *(Photo courtesy of M. Cudahy)*

Jeff pointed out the decision to acquire Marquette Medical and reenter the patient monitoring business didn't mean Walt Robb was wrong back in 1982.

I think different things happen in different cycles. In Walt's era, GE was riding a tidal wave of demand in CT and MR. He had all the business he could handle and probably viewed monitoring as a distraction. I came in at a time when ultrasound, CT, and MR were 80% of our profit, so we needed what I call adjacencies—multiple revenue streams—in case those imaging markets went away. Walt saw one side of the mountain, and I saw the other. We were both right in the eras that we ran the business.

Most of the acquisitions that Jeff and Mike Jones had completed or anticipated were related to diagnostic imaging, such as acquiring Elscint's nuclear imaging and MR operations. Though the Diasonics Vingmed Ultrasound deal was really about building GE's cardiology capabilities, it was still an imaging business. Similarly, the growing number of independent service provider acquisitions during this period was made to strengthen and grow the field multivendor DI service force.

"But the Marquette transaction was really different, because it represented an entirely new leg for the business and was a top-down, strategic move into an adjacency," Jones commented.

Besides Jeff, Jack, and Mike, other key players from the GE side who made the Marquette deal such a success were: Keith Sherin, Group Manager of Finance; Keith Morgan, Vice President & Group Counsel; and Tim Kennesy and Adam Miller from the business development staff. Brian Gladden, Finance, and Steve Patscot, Human Resources, played key roles in the integration process following the merger. On the Marquette side, Jeff asked Fred Robertson, Marquette's CEO, to stay on in his previous leadership role to preserve continuity and help ease its transition into the GE culture.

"Six Sigma"

Like many manufacturers, GE had long been dedicated to producing top-quality products and services at the best possible cost. Over the decades, a "quality control" system had developed based upon taking products or components from the production line and testing them to destruction to find out what failed, when, and how. Then the engineers would design a fix to improve the life and reliability of the device.

With the increasing sophistication, cost, and critical nature of many GE products, including medical, a better, more predictive method was needed to help assure performance and reliability. In the early 1990s, some experimentation was done based on the pioneering quality work of W. Edwards Deming, the American professor, statistician, and consultant who was widely credited with helping the Japanese develop their business culture of innovation and quality. GE, however, was seeking a more practical, less theoretical method.

In 1995, Jack Welch invited his former vice chairman, Larry Bossidy, who had become Chairman and CEO of AlliedSignal, to come to Crotonville and address the GE Corporate Executive Council on the subject of a new quality initiative called Six Sigma. Bossidy had become a strong and enthusiastic advocate for this methodology and was happy to oblige his old friend. Though Jack was unable to attend the lecture due to an emergency triple coronary artery bypass operation, Larry carried through and wowed his high-level audience with the potential impact of Six Sigma on virtually any aspect of a product or process.

Six Sigma was first developed by Motorola to measure and eliminate defects. At the One Sigma quality level, about 690,000 defects (defined as anything that might lead to customer dissatisfaction) are generated per million operations in a given manufacturing or service process. But at the Six Sigma quality level, fewer than 3.4

defects are expected. Most U.S. companies were estimated, at that time, to operate in the Three-Four Sigma range—66,807 dpm to 6,210 dpm—at a cost equivalent to some 10–15% of their annual revenues. For GE, in 1996, that penalty could have totaled as much as $12 *billion*.

With such huge numbers in play, Jack became an enthusiastic convert. In the fall of 1995, he launched some 200 Six Sigma projects around the company, along with an intensive training effort to help people use the methodology. The program ballooned to 3,000 projects in 1996 and 6,000 projects in 1997. By its fifth year, Six Sigma had produced more than $2 billion in benefits, and GE had trained more than 100,000 people.

Interestingly, at Medical Systems, Marc Onetto, General Manager, Global Tubes & Detectors, had been employing the Six Sigma technique in redeveloping the x-ray tube line even before it became official GE policy:

When my team began to work on fixing the x-ray tube quality problem in 1993, we quickly saw that applying a very strong scientific approach to find the root causes and resolve them was an absolutely essential element of success. So we looked at various methods, especially Six Sigma, and implemented that technique in 1994, about a year before the corporate effort was launched.

Perhaps because of this, Welch had chosen Medical Systems to prototype Six Sigma for the company. Serge Huot, Vice President & General Manager, Global Sourcing & OTR, was named to lead the implementation effort, assisted by Onetto. To help everyone understand its potential impact, Serge explained:

Six Sigma is a statistical method for describing process variability as the number of defects per million opportunities. At the Three Sigma level, for example, there would be 1.5 misspelled words per page in a book, but at Six Sigma, there would be just one misspelled word in all the books in a small library. That is where we are headed.

Serge and Marc selected the first dozen "Champions" and "Master Black Belts" (training levels) to drive the Six Sigma process. These experts, in turn, trained another

30 "Black Belts" to implement the actual projects. Three illustrate the variety of Six Sigma applications:

"DOA" repair parts: Nothing is more chilling to Service Repair Operations personnel than the term "DOA"—repair parts that are "dead on arrival" when installed on a customer's system. This Six Sigma project examined display monitors for the CT 9800 scanner that were experiencing several dozen unexpected failures per year. Improving the packaging used to ship the monitors eliminated about one quarter of the failures. Identifying and replacing circuit boards that were vulnerable to random age-related failures fixed most of the others. Changing the monitor "burn-in" procedure also helped.

"This project underscores the importance of using statistical analysis and team involvement—the hallmarks of the Six Sigma initiative," explained Black Belt Gary Koth who led the Six Sigma team. "Selecting the correct solutions was easy."

"DOA" x-ray tubes: In a similar case, replacement x-ray tubes were arriving with their anode stems broken. Black Belt Beth Hulse actually traveled with several shipments to find out what was going on. She discovered that when cargo handlers dropped the shipping boxes from the aircraft hold onto the unloader belt, extremely strong (up to 12G) acceleration forces were generated. If the anode axis happened to be perpendicular to the shock axis, the anode stem would break. So the shipping box was redesigned in a pyramid shape to keep the tube positioned vertically. No more breakage occurred and this project alone reduced the DOA rate by over 50%.

"This project was selected to demonstrate the impact of Six Sigma to Jack Welch when he came to Milwaukee for the first Black Belt graduation in March 1996," said Onetto.

CT gantry motors: Motors powering the CT gantry were mysteriously failing. After several years in the field, they simply began to die for what appeared to be a lack of lubrication. When adding more lubricant during the manufacturing process didn't help, the decision was made to use a larger and more expensive motor that wouldn't have to work so hard. Yet the problems continued.

top to bottom
Marc Onetto (left) leading an early Six Sigma report-out session. In the audience was Jeff Immelt (center) and Jim Shepard (next to Jeff).

Jeff Immelt attending a Six Sigma recognition event at the Grand Geneva Resort in Lake Geneva, Wisconsin. Also pictured are Bill Berezowitz (left) and Dan Kerpelman (center).

It was at about this time that Six Sigma arrived on the scene, and this issue was made into a project. The rigorous application of Six Sigma processes—defining, measuring, analyzing, improving, and controlling—soon revealed the source of the problem and its solution. Recalled Tom Dunham, Vice President and General Manager, Americas Service:

What we found was that the grease used to lubricate the motor shaft and other components was in the x-ray field during the scan. This grease was susceptible to degradation due to the radiation and, after a period of time, would turn into glue. So it wasn't the motor that needed replacing but the lubricant. When we made that change, the original motor worked like a charm.

The results achieved by Six Sigma across the company had convinced management it was the key to future competitiveness. Soon, a substantial portion of incentive compensation for managers would be based on their progress in improving quality. And even compensation for senior executives would be heavily weighted toward Six Sigma commitment and success—benefits that GE and its customers could take to the bank!

By the end of its first full year of Six Sigma experience, Medical Systems had trained more than 10,000 people and completed about 75 projects. It was during this period that the leadership change in Milwaukee occurred. Jeff Immelt was fully committed to the program, of course, and one of his first decisions was to ask Onetto to take over as Six Sigma Champion for the entire business. The two oversaw the completion of an additional 950 projects in 1997 that yielded a total of nearly $40 million in cost savings, followed by $92 million in additional benefits in 1998.

By the end of 1999, Jeff could confidently state:

Six Sigma has transformed this business. We introduced seven products in 1999 using Design for Six Sigma (DFSS), with more than 20 to be released in 2000. These products are different; they capture customer and patient needs better and can be brought to market faster than ever before.

DFSS was the commitment to design-in Six Sigma level quality performance from the earliest stages of new product planning and development. The objective was to transform the culture by anticipating quality issues and making designs resistant to defects. Onetto recalled:

Mike Idelchik and I had begun to develop this process in Global Tubes & Detectors. Now the idea was to generalize it across the entire business beginning with engineering. The Engineering Master Black Belt, an energetic change agent named Alex Tokman, and the whole Six Sigma team worked very closely with Scott Donnelly, our engineering manager, and then Gene Saragnese to drive this process. We also got great support from Serge Huot, the head of manufacturing.

Among the first DFSS products to reach the market was the Signa® OpenSpeed™ open magnet MRI system that soon set a new standard for image quality in this technology segment. The following year, 22 additional DFSS products joined the offering, including a new Senographe® digital mammography system and the Innova™ digital interventional cardiac imaging system. Sales of DFSS products exceeded $2 *billion* in 2000 and represented over half of all GEMS equipment sold the following year.

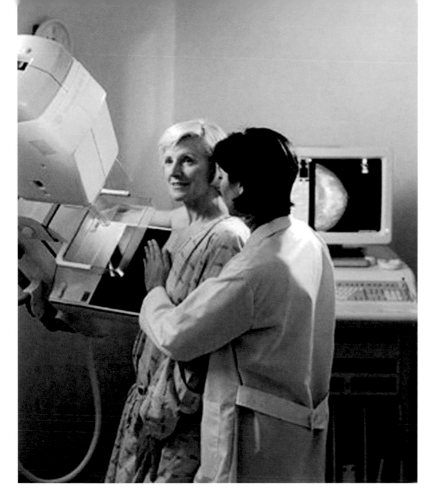

Migrating the quality culture

Six Sigma, which focuses on process defects, was supplemented later by the "Lean" methodology that minimizes the impact of unpredictable errors—usually human mistakes. The Lean quality discipline was developed by Toyota and is based on "jidoka," the fundamental principle that a mistake will not be allowed to go down the production line. Six Sigma and Lean are complementary and, when combined into what GE now calls Lean Six Sigma, are extremely powerful in addressing both technical defects and human errors.

These future achievements aside, perhaps the most significant of the early Six Sigma wins was the transformational role it played in finally overcoming serious CT x-ray tube reliability issues. The new Performix™ 630 x-ray tube that was introduced in 1997, for example, yielded an eight-fold increase in tube life and performance, raising the average life expectancy from 25,000 slices to 200,000 slices. The lessons learned in this project also helped Global Tubes & Detectors to develop the first metal-ceramic frame tube. This remarkable tube, called the Performix™ ADV, ultimately boosted average life expectancy to an incredible *500,000 slices*, establishing a new industry standard and making possible the success of the multislice LightSpeed™ QX/i system, GE's fastest-selling CT scanner ever.

Developing the Performix ADV tube required considerable effort, of course, but Six Sigma came to the rescue. As Onetto remembered:

> The ADV tube issue that we had to solve was Z-axis anode wobble. We were spinning the anode at 10,000 rpm to avoid melting it but that caused a slight vibration. Through Six Sigma analysis, we found that reducing the rotation speed to 8,000 rpm eliminated the problem. This data convinced the system engineers to redesign the image chain algorithm to accommodate the slower speed. As a result, we were able to introduce the LightSpeed QX/i a year-and-a-half ahead of the competition.

Six Sigma was also playing an essential part in other areas for Global Tubes & Detectors. For instance, flat panel detector technology promised to transform the image acquisition process by shifting from analog (x-ray shadows on film) to direct digital detection. That would make it possible to automatically vary image contrast pixel by pixel to better reveal subtle detail—a very important advantage in visualizing tiny lesions in the breast, heart, and vascular system. First, though, manufacturing quality issues had to be solved.

The flat panel detector was made by a partner company in California that was experiencing technical problems. Jim Shepard, who succeeded Onetto at Global Tubes & Detectors, and Marc, dispatched a 60-member Six Sigma commando team to put some order in its manufacturing quality process. Lowry Manson was the Master Black Belt, and Gilles Boisseau came over from Paris to help. The situation was turned around, and the Senographe and Innova digital imaging systems were introduced on time.

Six Sigma was also being applied with great success in such "soft" areas as field sales and service, where process discipline and data-based decision-making improved transactional quality. "With great support from Jeff Immelt and Keith Sherin, our CFO, we made Six Sigma a genuine agent of change at GE Medical Systems," Onetto said.

Jeff Immelt agreed with that assessment:

> The benefit we had inside the company was a very high-tech work force. And Marc was a very good process thinker. We tried to keep Six Sigma very focused on places that could have a big impact and really move the needle

top to bottom

The Senographe 2000D, GE's full field digital mammography system.

The first Gemini CT tube (later renamed the Performix ADV) being delivered to the Ryerson Road CT plant for engineering evaluations. Celebrating the event were (l-r): Quan Lu, Patty Franzel, Marty Plutowski, Tom Tiearney, Attila Meszaros, Dale Chrisien, and Mike Idelchik.

The Performix ADV CT tube won the Dushman Award as the best product codeveloped by a GE business and the Corporate R&D Center (CRD). Attending the award presentation were: (front row, l-r) Charles Baumgartner (CRD), Bijan Dorri (CRD), Kay Schmidt (GEMS), Ray White (CRD), Amy Linsebigler (CRD), Imdad Imam (CRD), and Lonnie Edelheit, Senior Vice President, R&D; (back row, l-r) Tim Sommerer (CRD), Tom Tiearney (GEMS), Lembit Salasoo (CRD), Steve Hansen (GEMS), Brian Graves (GEMS), Mike Idelchik (GEMS), and Mark Vermilyea (CRD).

in terms of product quality. I'd say that even today, GE Healthcare can really be a company leader, because it has so many talented people inside the business who can help drive change."

Quality at LightSpeed

By now, Immelt and Onetto had driven the Six Sigma quality initiative deep within the culture of the business. It had truly become the catalyst energizing GEMS's drive toward total customer satisfaction through technology, new products, and operational excellence. The most spectacular example of its game-changing potential was the LightSpeed QX/i™ CT system that reached the market in 1998. It was the first GEMS product to be completely designed and developed using Six Sigma methodology and raised the quality bar to an unprecedented level. It also provided clear proof of GE's technology leadership to customers and competitors alike. Six Sigma was creating a new paradigm for quality and performance in medical imaging.

During the 25 years or so that had elapsed since the appearance of the EMI Mark I, computed tomography had benefited from a continuing series of technology and software advances. Though the list of credible suppliers by now had been pared down to just a handful, most offered a range of choices to match most applications, from walk-in clinics to cutting-edge academic imaging research centers. No one questioned the efficacy of CT anymore.

The marvelous capabilities of modern CT scanners notwithstanding, there were still opportunities to make a fabulous imaging technology even better. It was a challenge, however, that demanded strong technical capabilities, substantial resources, unflagging management support, and an informed understanding of clinical practice needs. As the worldwide leader in CT, with unmatched experience and expertise, GE Medical Systems was ideally positioned to become a leader in the next big breakthrough—multislice CT.

For as long as there had been CT scanners, all had been designed to scan a single slice of anatomy at a time. Technical advances were concentrated on reducing the scan time, speeding image reconstruction, and developing new software and hardware capabilities to expand clinical utility. One of the most important recent advances was helical scanning in which the x-ray tube and detector array spun continuously around the patient as the moving tabletop slowly indexed a portion of anatomy through the radiation field. Separate, consecutive exposures allowed individual slices to be reconstructed showing adjoining anatomy in a given area.

What's different about multislice CT is that *multiple* images (up to four for the QX/i) are simultaneously acquired during each exposure. This permits exams of a given anatomic region to be conducted more quickly and thoroughly. For example, a trauma patient might be scanned from head to toe to assess internal injuries in as few as 20 seconds—an entirely new level of clinical utility that would launch CT on a different trajectory.

The LightSpeed QX/i was the world's first CT scanner that allowed diagnosticians to capture four simultaneous images of the patient's anatomy. Developed at a cost of more than $60 million, the QX/i provided an elegant solution to the need for more diagnostic information faster. It could acquire four times as much diagnostic information during a single scan as one-slice machines and do so in less than 1 second. Such unprecedented performance was exactly what was needed to save precious time in critical situations. Acquiring multiple slices in a single rotation also eased the burden on the x-ray tube and minimized tube-cooling delays—an essential feature of the LightSpeed QX/i design. (Interestingly, the "LightSpeed" name was coined at a hotel bar in Arizona during a worldwide product planning meeting by Brian Duchinsky, a former CT marketing manager who had moved over to the MR business, Bob Senzig, and Stan Fox. The "Q" signified "quad," of course; "X" suggested a multiplier; and "i" was a family designator used by the Advantage CT/i for "interactive/intuitive.")

Such performance requires remarkable technologies and software, of course. A critical factor, as recounted earlier, was advanced x-ray tube technology, since it must operate for extended scan sequences with little opportunity to dissipate the intense heat that is generated. Heat has always been the major factor limiting tube performance and life expectancy.

According to Ken Denison, Marketing Manager, Americas Premium CT, the LightSpeed QX/i was designed from day one to solve the single biggest customer need with any CT scanner at that time—avoiding tube-cooling delays. "Prior to LightSpeed," he explained, "CT users, no matter how many patients they were trying to scan in a given day, were slowed down by or had to compromise the quality of their studies in order to let the x-ray tube cool."

The Performix™ ADV tube featured lots of advances, such as a metal-ceramic frame for long life, a high-speed bearing for subsecond scanning, and a high-efficiency motor to accelerate its large anode. Its key advantage was an exceptional ability to store and dissipate the huge amount of heat generated during continuous scanning procedures. With a storage capacity of 6.3 million heat units, it virtually eliminated any need to pause during most helical studies to cool the tube—a key contributor to high patient throughput and lower operating costs.

"This was a key breakthrough that meant all of our users would see benefits in image quality and throughput, all from the reduced need for tube cooling," Ken added.

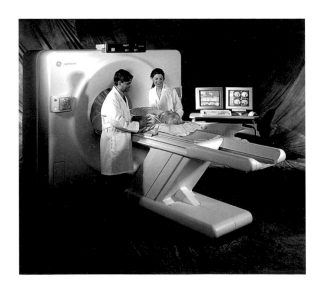

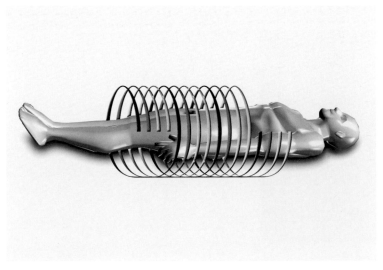

left to right
The LightSpeed QX/i multislice CT system.

LightSpeed QX/i was the first 4-slice CT scanner. By passing the patient through the exposure field as the tube and detector rotated, four slices could be simultaneously obtained over an extended volume in just a few seconds.

Launching the program

A new competitive threat in the early 1990s was the Elscint Twin, a 2-slice CT scanner. There also was reason to think another major vendor was working on its own 2-slice technology. Though GE CT had scored a series of successes in recent years—the 9800 Quick, HiLight, HiLight Advantage helical, HTD, and the HighSpeed CT/i (the first to use the Performix tube)—it now was looking for a "home run" to regain the technological edge.

Stan Fox, the technical guru who was the acknowledged "father" of 4-slice CT, remembered his early interest in the techonology:

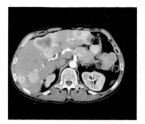
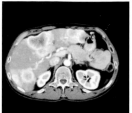
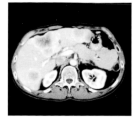

> People from the R&D Center were here with images made by a prototype 16-slice scanner that they were developing for GE Aircraft Engines. They dropped by to ask my opinion if their images were good enough for medical use. I told them they had too many artifacts for soft tissue imaging but that I had done some calculations of how many 5mm-thick slices were needed to image the entire liver in a single breath hold. The magic number was four. I also suggested that a 4-slice scanner would have a small enough cone angle that a cousin of our existing image reconstruction algorithms could be modified to work.

Armin Pfoh, a new member of the Applied Science Lab, became intrigued by Stan's idea and decided to take up the challenge. He, too, calculated a 4-slice solution. Within a few weeks, Stan, Armin, Bob Senzig, and several others were having back-room reviews of possible 4-slice detector designs. "The proposed detector actually had a 16-slice capability, each 1.25mm wide," Stan explained. "But additional slices were added only as needed, and only four were read out at a given time."

These first steps were happening in the early 1990s, when Yoshiaki Fujimori was the CT general manager. The engineers approached him with their calculations and, after considerable discussion, Fuji-san agreed to let them continue their basic research into the technology. Over the next several years, a number of technological concepts were developed, including the detector, data acquisition system (analog-to-digital converter), prepatient collimator, and image reconstruction algorithms. Bob and Armin led these ad hoc efforts.

In 1995, the formal development program called "Helios" was launched to develop all this research work into an actual product. Fuji-san noted:

> This was a big decision, because John Trani was always telling me that I was spending too much money and had to meet my numbers. Knowing that it would be a long time—5 or 6 years—before the multislice detector would be ready to introduce, we had to decide whether to continue multislice, because it took so many resources and so much time. Or should we compromise on a 2-slice scanner.

A huge engineering and marketing debate ensued; Fuji even threatened to cancel the project entirely at one point. He had a big debate with Claude Benchimol, the CT engineering manager; Bob Armstrong; Armin Pfoh; and Bob Senzig. "They pushed back so hard that they convinced me I shouldn't kill their dream," Fuji-san said. "That was a defining moment in the history of GE CT that contributed to the company's future."

Though Fujimori didn't get to enjoy the eventual introduction of the LightSpeed QX/i (he had moved on to the MR business by that time to be replaced by Vivek Paul), his tough decisions to keep the program running despite management pressures and funding issues were vital to its ultimate success.

The Helios development team, led by Claude Benchimol, was now working at full

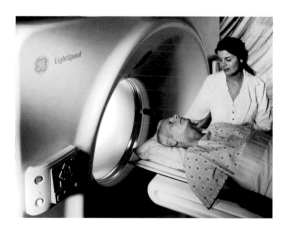

top to bottom
A typical LightSpeed QX/i multislice body series.

The Performix ADV x-ray tube was the heart of the Light-Speed QX/i scanner.

The LightSpeed QX/i 4-slice CT scanner.

Debugging the first 4-slice data acquisition system for the LightSpeed QX/i were (l–r) Jim Anderson, Mark Fries, Jon Strauch-Nelson, and Lee Hao.

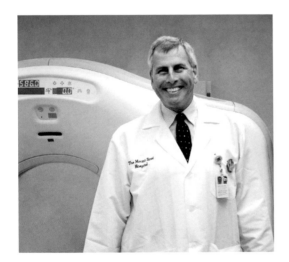

steam. In addition to the original core group, other key personnel were joining the project as it advanced. Bob Senzig was succeeded by Steve Lorenc and then Ben Van Weelden as the engineering program manager. Gary Strong became the lead system designer, Kay Schmidt and Dave Weisz managed detector engineering, David He was overseeing the engineering clinical program, and George Seidenschnur and Tom Toth took on system engineering.

Also playing key roles were: Gene Williams, systems engineering Six Sigma leader; Bob Beckett, system validation lead; and Holly McDaniel, applications specialist. Hui Hu and Guy Besson provided essential support from the Applied Science Lab, as did Jonathan Murray in data acquisition system engineering; and Dave Hoffman, Bob Riedner, Erdogan Gurmen, Paul Massaro, and Laxman Beniwal in detector engineering. Ken Denison and Sholom Ackelsberg soon came aboard as the Americas and Global product marketing managers, respectively.

Over the life of the Helios program, faces continued to change as people moved among other urgent assignments. John Lowry replaced Claude Benchimol as CT engineering GM and was, himself, succeeded by John Chiminski a few months before the 1998 product launch. Gabe Kohanyi, the first lead program integrator (LPI), was replaced by Pete Mauhar and, later, Tim Turco and Joe Block as co-LPIs.

Almost as important was the panel of outside experts that had been assembled to critique every step of the project for clinical utility. GEMS had used "Medical Advisory Boards" (MABs) to great success in a variety of previous projects over many years. MABs, whether ad hoc or semipermanent, usually consisted of a mix of physicians and other health industry experts interested in the project at hand, plus GE technical and marketing people. Discussions were freewheeling and recommendations candid. GE gleaned invaluable insights and guidance from these sessions; the medical community benefited from healthcare technologies more closely aligned with their needs.

Dr. Burt Drayer, radiology chair at Mt. Sinai Medical Center in New York City, who participated on many MABs over the years, said:

> The GE advisory boards were wonderful. About 15 or 20 of us would sit around and exchange ideas in a collegial, serious, yet light-hearted environment. We all had such a nice time and made GE realize what a great job they were really doing and how they should keep on developing.

LightSpeed MAB meetings had started soon after the product concept was first defined and continued at frequent intervals throughout the development program. To solicit the widest range of views possible, multiple sessions were held in various areas of the U.S. with different members participating. The first was held in Boston with radiologists from several prestigious institutions there, followed in time by sessions in New York City, Duke University, Milwaukee, Seattle, and San Francisco. Sessions were also conducted in France and Germany. The feedback they generated had a major impact on the final configuration of the product (such as adding a second board to cut image reconstruction times in half).

Among the scores of participating radiologists were Rendon Nelson from Duke; Dennis Foley, Francisco Quiroz, and Larry Goodman, Medical College of Wisconsin; Geoff Rubin, Stanford; Alec Megibow and David Naidich, New York University; Vasillios Raptopoulos, Beth Israel Boston; Bob Novelline and Sanjay Saini, Massachusetts General Hospital; Tom Lawson, Mary Olson, and Harold Posniak, Loyola University. Chicago; Myron Pozniak, University of Wisconsin Madison; Bill Shuman and Patrick Freeny, University of Washington; Joel Platt and Ella Kazerooni, University of Michigan; and Larry Tanenbaum, Edison Imaging in New Jersey.

Gary Glazer, radiology chair at Stanford University, shared similarly pleasant memories of service on GE MABs:

I remember being at an advisory board meeting where GE asked for opinions about whether to develop MDCT (multidimensional, or helical, CT). Some experts said that scanning a moving human body on a moving table would be like trying to image shaking Jello. I had a very different opinion and thought that the gains in temporal resolution would far outweigh the projected disadvantages. I talked with Stan Fox about it, and it seemed to me like it was going to be something pretty big. I was able to convince Stan that he would put one of the very first units in the world at Stanford.

To facilitate the MAB reviews and increase the value of its inputs, Sholom Ackelsberg, along with Tom Toth, Hui Hu, and David He, developed an Excel spreadsheet they called the "Protocol Simulator." It allowed them to simulate clinical scenarios to assess the potential impact on tube utilization, total scan time, coverage, dose, and so forth. It became a key tool for understanding potential benefits, developing marketing materials, and training customers.

Clinical "trials"

In middevelopment, Immelt arrived on the scene and soon became a huge booster of the LightSpeed QX/i project. Not only did Jeff recognize its importance in both clinical and marketing terms, he also had the chairman's tacit agreement to invest in the medical business. LightSpeed was now on firm financial footing. The only question was if it would meet its technical objectives. Those answers were to come through an extensive in-house evaluation program, plus the "real life" performance of the first two production prototypes—one at Stanford University Medical Center and the second at Duke University Medical Center.

First came tests on the prototype LightSpeed QX/i. A fully operational imaging clinic was constructed at Ryerson Road complete with a separate entrance and waiting room. Volunteer patients came from nearby Froedtert Memorial Lutheran Hospital;

radiologists from the Medical College of Wisconsin, principally Dennis Foley and Francisco Quiroz, oversaw the exams. (A similar, though less elaborate, arrangement had been extremely useful in the early NMR development tests.)

"Each scan of a volunteer patient was treated like a moon shot," Stan Fox remarked. "We were very concerned about image quality and how it was impacted by things we had control over and things we didn't."

Next came actual clinical trials at Froedtert Memorial that soon became the *de facto* "national lab" and hosted a stream of other interested radiologists. What was learned soon found its way into the initial production units that Dr. Gary Glazer at Stanford and Dr. Carl Ravin at Duke were about to receive. These two systems made their first images within hours of each other and were soon generating even more feedback.

The major breakthrough represented by LightSpeed 4-slice CT imaging was its impact in opening the eyes of clinical users to the possibilities of thin-slice and, eventually, isotropic 3D imaging. Before the arrival of 4-slice CT, most body imaging used 10mm slices. Some special applications employed thinner slices, but the routine slice thickness was 1cm.

"With 4-slice imaging," Stan explained, "you got 5mm slices with three times the coverage per rotation than a single-slice scanner doing 10mm slices in the helical mode. Or 2.5mm resolution could be obtained with a little less coverage per rotation."

Both single- and multislice helical mode scanning allowed for continuous overlapping reconstruction. Coupled with real-time image paging display, clinicians now had a new image review tool. The 4-slice, 5mm resolution detector would later lead to 4- and 8-slice, 1.5mm resolution scanners and, eventually, to today's 16-slice, 0.625mm resolution systems.

With 16-slice technology and real-time multiplanar reconstruction, the age of isotropic CT imaging was almost at hand. Stan explained, "Each step enabled wider use of a series of new CT applications—angiography, pulmonary emboli, and cardiac—

The QX/i development team watched as Vivek Paul (sport jacket, front) cut the ribbon to open "Suite 16," the bay at Ryerson Road where the first 10 patients were scanned.

even in community hospitals. They eliminated more costly invasive procedures and reduced hospitalization times."

To appreciate fully the LightSpeed QX/i program, it's important to remember what the CT team had been through over the previous dozen years. The appearance of MRI, coupled with potential reimbursement changes in the U.S. market, had driven the CT market down. As a result, it had lost "share of mind" inside GEMS with negative budgetary consequences. Slowly and painfully, with relatively few resources, the engineering team was rebuilt over the intervening years and kept GE CT atop the market with a series of important technical breakthroughs.

"The CT team is the real story of the QX/i," Stan stated, "We had differences, of course, but they were about how to best serve the interests of the business. Also, our customers never lost faith in us; they sparked and directed the rebirth of GE CT."

The LightSpeed QX/i was officially launched on September 10, 1998, at a huge event in New York City. It was positioned as being indispensable for three types of users: 1) those with the most difficult patients to diagnose where very thin slices were needed; 2) those with the highest patient volumes who needed maximum through-put with no tube cooling delays; and 3) those in very competitive environments who needed the unique capabilities of LightSpeed to capture additional patient volume. (Almost all clinical users consider themselves to be in one or more of these categories!)

As Jeff Immelt later commented about this event:

> We have always had a good CT business and a tradition of getting products out on time. In the case of multislice CT, Vivek Paul was the CT modality leader at that time and had a real flare for technology and for marketing. We had a product launch for the LightSpeed QX/i at the Waldorf Astoria Hotel in New York City and invited Jack and several hundred customers. They all came, and we were sold out from the first minute we launched the product. With this great technology, backed by Paul Mirabella's sales force and Tom Dunham's service organization, we just blew the cover off the ball.

Carl Ravin, the radiology chairman at Duke, also had vivid memories of the Waldorf Astoria launch. Though he wasn't directly involved in the clinical testing of the LightSpeed QX/i—that task was led by Rendon Nelson, his CT director—Jeff invited Carl to attend the New York event and make a few remarks. He recalled:

> In fact, I didn't exactly know what I was going to say. I talked a little about its speed, how fast the studies went, and how the patients were really impressed. I said the most impressive thing was that it worked flawlessly from the moment they set it up. I looked over at Jack Welch and said, "I never really understood how Six Sigma was going to impact us, but if this is an example, we, your customers, thank you, Mr. Welch."

According to Gary Strong, a big challenge for the development team was in the area of software and system reliability:

> The Six Sigma toolbox does not easily or directly translate into the software world. So the team developed a strategy involving automated testing, remote monitoring tools, and defining very detailed reliability metrics. These approaches delivered a huge 10X improvement in system reliability. In fact, Dr. Ravin's early prototype system ran more reliably than our previous production units. I was 'busting my buttons' at his comment!

Stan Fox recounted a humorous anecdote from the launch event:

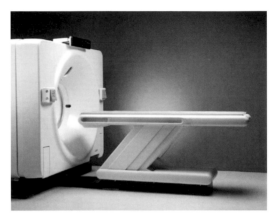

The production LightSpeed QX/i multislice CT system.

Vivek Paul (left), Global CT general manager; Jeff Immelt; and Jack Welch shared a serious moment at the 1998 LightSpeed QX/i introduction event.

Carl Ravin (left), radiology chair at Duke, Gary Glazer (center), radiology chair at Stanford, and Vivek Paul, Global CT general manager, at the LightSpeed QX/i scanner launch. Duke and Stanford hosted the first production systems.

One of our customers asked Jack Welch to autograph a light bulb, so Jack had one of his aides find a maintenance person to take down one of the light bulbs in the hotel hallway where we standing. It was a GE bulb, as Jack must have somehow known it would be. He signed it and gave it to the customer.

The slate of clinical presenters also included Dr. Foley from the Medical College of Wisconsin, Dr. Nelson from Duke, and Dr. Glazer from Stanford, who pointed out:

Multidetector CT was a revolution. Helical or spiral scanning got you a lot of temporal resolution, and multislice got you very high resolution of a volume. It's extremely important in the body where there is so much motion. You now had a method in which you could obtain fine resolution in very short periods of time. So applications like CT angiography became possible.

Even before receiving his LightSpeed, Dr. Glazer thought its potential was so great he would organize an international symposium. Despite the risk (he didn't want to fall on his face, naturally, should the product bomb), he approached Vivek Paul about his plans and secured GE's participation:

We didn't exactly know what the LightSpeed could do, but our intuition was it would be important. I believe this first conference was very important in promoting the responsible development of multidetector CT. Shortly after, it was turned into a major international symposium that most recently attracted over 1,000 attendees from 25 nations on 5 continents.

As mentioned earlier, the LightSpeed QX/i quickly became GE's fastest-selling CT scanner ever. According to Ken Denison, "prelaunch" sales had actually begun the previous January (Food and Drug Administration clearance had come by late 1997), and some 50 orders had already been taken:

We positioned the product at a very high price—$1.25 million—and, for the first time in the history of GE CT, did not allow any discounts. During our prelaunch sales tour, Sholom and I were visiting a major university hospital and after our presentation, the chairman turned to his CT imaging director and asked if they needed this scanner. The response was 'yes' and the chairman said, 'We'll take it.' No questions about price, service support, or anything. He recognized how revolutionary the LightSpeed was and bought it instantly.

Supported by an aggressive marketing and sales effort in the U.S. and around the world, the LightSpeed QX/i had an immediate and dramatic impact. In the following year, GE added some five points to its already high 55% share of the high-end CT segment and increased the price premium over the previous product by 50%.

Today, almost all CT scanners being sold are multislice units; 4-slice machines are now considered the "value tier" products. Indeed, until the global CT market peaked during the general economic slowdown beginning about 2007, each GE CT product following the LightSpeed QX/i—8-slice, 16-slice, 32-slice, and 64-slice models—sold at ever-faster rates. For instance, some 250 orders for the 64-slice LightSpeed VCT™ system had been taken before production actually began.

No matter how you slice it, LightSpeed was, and is, a huge win for GE.

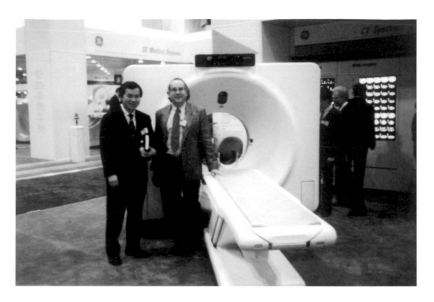

top to bottom

The general introduction of the LightSpeed QX/i multislice CT scanner to the profession came at the RSNA '98 meeting in Chicago.

Gary Glazer (right), Stanford radiology chair, and Nōbuhiko Ito, GE YMS president, established a long-term collaboration between Stanford University and the top Japanese academic imaging departments that developed into an annual conference. This occasion was the 2001 meeting in Palo Alto. Nobuko Schlough (left) from GE interpreted at these events.

Explosion in China

When Jeff Immelt took over at GEMS in late 1996, he set out to visit his far-flung international operations. He began with Europe in January 1997, went to Japan in February, and to India in May. He met Chih Chen for the first time when he stopped by the Singapore headquarters at the conclusion of the latter trip for a business review with all the Asia country managers. After explaining his plans to make India a "center of excellence" for low-end x-ray, Chih immediately objected, pointing out that China had a good organization, an excellent low-end x-ray product, and should be permitted to compete for this special status. Jeff was taken aback—and pleased—by Chih's push-back and agreed to defer his decision until that fall after he had had an opportunity to observe both candidates. When he returned to China in October for a business review, he was convinced of the China team's energy and impressed with Chih's growth plans. China got the "center of excellence" designation.

"After that October meeting, Jeff was able to see China from a different perspective," said Chih. "Without that kind of visionary leadership, we would not have had an opportunity to shine during the coming years."

A native of China, Chih Chen had joined GE Calma, the former CAD/CAM group in Silicon Valley, shortly after completing his Ph.D. in biosciences at Lehigh University (Pennsylvania) in 1983. Five years later, he came to GE Medical Systems as country manager for Taiwan and the Philippines, and then took over Asia service activities in 1990. He added Asia sales not long after. When the Asia organization was later restructured on a country-by-country basis, Chih moved to Beijing as deputy country manager to David Lee. He succeeded David several years later.

At this time, GEMS's major premium market was the U.S., with Milwaukee as the center of excellence for high-end products. Next came Japan as the leading mid tier market with a significant high-end component, many premium products, and great manufacturing technology. China, on the other hand, was still viewed as merely an opportunity to sell a limited number of premium x-ray, CT, and MR systems. Chih had a completely different vision of what China could be—the largest and most competitive marketplace for low-end imaging technology in the world.

"My thought was if we could manufacture in China with GE technology, GE features, and GE performance, we would be able to out-compete the local players," he explained. "Combining American technology with low Chinese engineering and manufacturing costs would allow us to produce a more competitive product than the secondary Japanese players that were the leaders at the time. And if we could win in the most competitive and biggest low-end national market, then there was no reason that we couldn't compete and win in the global low-end market. That was my strategy."

When China was named GE's center of excellence for x-ray, it was still largely a screwdriver operation assembling the CMX battery-powered mobile x-ray unit for the Chinese market and, later, export to the world. What it still lacked was the critical mass of engineers and marketing personnel to become a fully self-sufficient organization capable of designing, manufacturing, and marketing its own line of low-end products. "We felt that China was really a huge opportunity for low-end products made in China, for China," Chih said.

Enter CT/e

The big breakthrough product for China was hardly "low-end" at all—the HiSpeed™ CT/e scanner. Designed and manufactured in Japan, it was a revolutionary combination of features and price. Low siting and operating costs had quickly made it a leader in China and other world markets where price and dependable performance were primary considerations. (The "e", by the way, stood for "everywhere," suggesting its universal appeal.) It was named by Jeff Immelt himself and was still in the product catalog years later. Now, at the urging of Chih Chen, who was in charge of the China JV, the idea was to transfer the entire CT/e program to Beijing, if GE YMS could be persuaded to relinquish it.

Keith Williams, GEMS China president, played a leading role in facilitating the transfer of CT/e manufacturing from Hino to Beijing. Despite this shift of production, however, YMS engineers remained in charge of CT/e design. That was about to change, too, as Chih pressed for the complete transfer. He backed his demands by expanding and training his engineering staff. As their performance capabilities developed, Yoshiaki Fujimori, President & CEO of GE Medical Systems Asia and Chairman & CEO of GE YMS, gave them increasing responsibilities for more and more CT/e subsystems until Beijing eventually owned the complete program. This was a first of its kind event for GE YMS, which never before had given up a product in this way. Fuji-san was greatly assisted by the strong, farsighted support of Shinichi Kawasa, President & COO of GE YMS; Keiki Yamaguchi, GE YMS engineering vice president; and Dow Wilson, Global CT marketing manager.

This spirit of global cooperation involved more than just the transfer of technology. During the ramp-up phase, Chih had sent his young engineers to train with the CT/e design team in Japan and the CT engineering group in Milwaukee. Now, with the CT/e scanner's tremendous success, Japanese engineers started coming to join the design team in China.

The CT/e scanner also led to the rapid expansion of the Chinese distribution network. At a time when many multinational companies were happy with a few sales

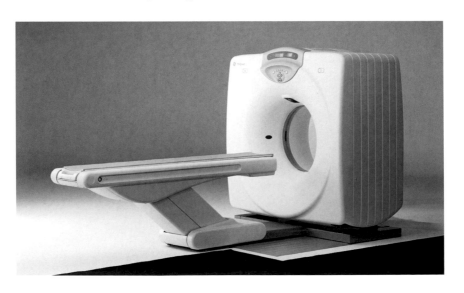

left to right
Chih Chen

The HiSpeed CT/e was a breakthrough product for GEMS's China Operations.

offices around this huge country, GE Medical soon had dozens. Chih recalled:

> When I first arrived in China, a lot of customers told me they were "CT orphans" or "MR orphans". When I asked what they meant, they said as soon as a vendor sold them equipment, they abandoned them. So I started with a total customer focus and trained all of my service technicians and managers to focus on them. I insisted we treat our customers the same as Japanese or European customers were treated. Our infrastructure may not have been the same but our attitude was. That's how we earned the best service reputation in the market from day one.

Jeff and Jack Welch were thrilled with the company's developing position in China and anxious to keep the momentum going. Chih was happy to oblige by developing the extremely popular Proteus general-purpose x-ray system, a low-end product that, like the CT/e scanner before it, soon became a global winner. Jack reciprocated by recommending Chih's election as a GE corporate vice president.

China Operations was embarked upon a new era of growth with an unlimited future. The Chinese economy was booming, especially the healthcare sector where the kinds of affordable, high-performance medical technologies GE supplied were desperately needed. China was en route to becoming the world's second largest healthcare market. It already had 16,000 major hospitals, compared to fewer than 6,000 in the U.S., yet they served only half of its growing population of nearly 1.3 billion.

"GE was the first choice, because our name is known and trusted in China," commented Chih. "We were widely recognized as one of the best Western partners in China, partly because we were a local company—we designed and manufactured there."

Housebreaking PET

Though GE's "positron emission tomography" (PET) section was launched in the 1980s, it found its footing during the Immelt years.

PET is a nuclear medicine technique that generates a 3D image of a functional process. The procedure detects pairs of gamma rays emitted by a special tracer, locates them in a volume, and then reconstructs this distribution information as an image using CT like methods. Various short-lived isotopes may be used depending upon the organ or tissue being studied. Most are injected into the bloodstream, some are inhaled or delivered directly in a cavity (the bladder or eye, for example). The most commonly used PET tracer is fluorodeoxyglucose ^{18}FFDG, a sugar-based compound.

The PET concept has been understood since the 1960s, but it wasn't until the 1970s that scientists at Brookhaven National Laboratory, Upton, New York, first described the synthesis of ^{18}FFDG (FDG). It was administered to human volunteers at the University of Pennsylvania in 1976, and brain scans were performed using specially modified nuclear gamma cameras. Further study into other organs and isotopes followed at various clinical labs.

GE began investing in PET at the urging of Bobby Bowen, who filled a variety of technology and business management positions during his long and productive GE career. Jan Berg and Mel Dean launched the early PET research project that yielded extremely encouraging progress. However, FDG was not an approved agent at that time, so PET exams were ineligible for Medicare reimbursement. Since few hospitals could afford to provide unreimbursed services, PET scanners simply didn't sell. Despite the excellent technology base the PET team had built with the R&D Center's help, continuing reimbursement approval delays finally persuaded management to sell the PET business. Fortunately, the prospective purchaser's financing fell through; 15 months later, reimbursement arrived and PET started to take off.

Convinced things had worked out this way for a reason, Jeff Immelt accelerated PET investments. By 2000, the growing importance of the Functional Imaging business, which included PET and nuclear imaging, led GE to elect its leader—Beth Klein—a corporate officer. Jeff soon appointed her President & Chief Executive Officer, GE Medical Systems Americas.

One of the primary applications of PET is cancer detection and assessment of tumor response to treatment. Since conventional diagnostic techniques can require a month or more to show volume reduction, a way had long been sought to speed the process and make it more specific in terms of the type of cancer detected. PET appeared to offer a possible solution in terms of functional and biological information; its principal shortcoming was low-resolution images. Scintillation detectors needed to measure gamma rays simply couldn't be made small enough to yield high spatial resolution views; doctors were performing "image fusion," superimposing the PET image on the CT image.

GE developed an elegant solution to this problem by combining its leadership CT multislice technology with its PET detector technology. The result was a revolutionary new product that provided a tremendous boost to PET imaging. This breakthrough scanner, called the Discovery™ LS PET/CT system, combined the power of PET and CT in a single, integrated system. It gave doctors an accurate, convenient method to locate tumors, confirm whether they were aggressive based on their glucose metabolism, and determine the best course of treatment. Better yet, it could do all of this in a

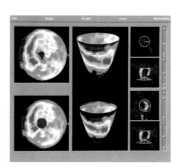

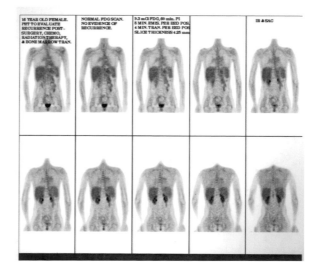

left to right

Solid-state scintillation detectors inside the PET scanner gantry detect the gamma rays emitted by a special radioisotope introduced into the patient.

Using CT-like techniques, PET scanners create a diagnostic image displaying the location and concentration of the radioisotope in the area of interest.

This PET FDG series of a 16-year old female was obtained after surgery, chemo and radiation therapy, and bone marrow transplant. No recurrence was detected.

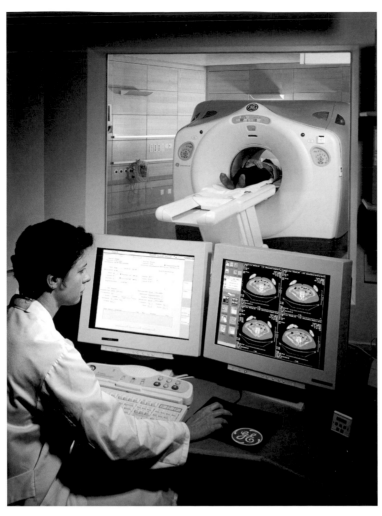

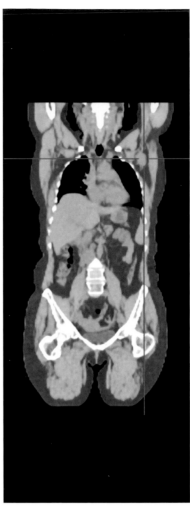

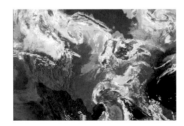

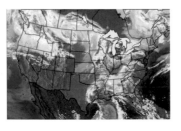

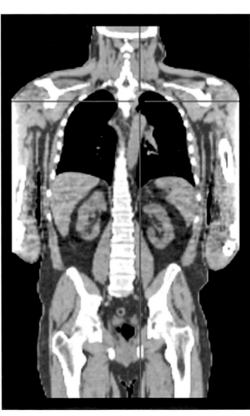

top, left to right
GE's Discovery LS scanner combined the advantages of PET and CT in a single system.

Integrated PET/CT images speeded cancer assessments from days to minutes.

bottom left, top to bottom
PET detects function, much as a satellite image shows the intense activity associated with a hurricane.

CT adds the detailed spatial reference to precisely locate the activity.

The result is a single image displaying the strengths of both techniques.

bottom right
A whole body Discovery LS PET/CT image.

single, integrated, 30-minute scanning procedure that eliminated the previous need for multiple exams spread over many weeks.

Though the Discovery LS system had more lines of computer code than the first mission to the moon, it was launched more than 12 months ahead of schedule.

Because of its unique ability to detect and display 3D functional anatomy quickly and precisely, the Discovery LS system soon became an invaluable clinical tool for nuclear medicine physicians supporting oncologists, neurologists, and cardiologists. Its greatest promise, however, lay several years in the future when it would become GE's preferred platform for molecular imaging and genomics. PET was the technology that had fueled Jeff Immelt's interest in molecular medicine and, ultimately, "personalized healthcare." It was this vision that led him to set a radically new course for GE's healthcare business.

Coming of age in Europe

GE, and Victor X-Ray before it, had been jousting with European competitors virtually since the discovery of the x-ray. Most of these battles had been fought on American soil where the bulk of the global imaging market had always been centered. Beginning in the late 1960s, though, the first inklings of a shift in strategy were signaled by the acquisition of General Medical Balteau in Belgium and the opening of a new competitive front in Europe.

For the next decade and a half, however, the nascent Europe strategy languished despite the efforts of Liege and GE's subsidiary in Spain, several substantial acquisitions, and even the increased entrée that GE's lead in CT technology had provided. Clearly, a more rigorous, structured approach was necessary to compete successfully on the home ground of Philips and Siemens.

Walt Robb had launched the most serious effort yet to become a significant player in Europe with the creation an entirely new marketing, sales, and service organization in 1985. Medical Systems Europe, headquartered in London, provided a new level of focus and dedicated resources to crack through the formidable competitive obstacles it faced.

GE's major offensive in this campaign was the 1987 acquisition of Thomson-CGR, France's premier diagnostic imaging manufacturer. It provided a cadre of talented and dedicated people, a large and loyal customer base, engineering excellence in several key areas of technology, and a well-regarded sales and service organization in Europe. In other words, credibility.

In the ensuing decade, GE CGR had undergone many changes to establish itself as a valuable member of the global GEMS team. It had also lost its separate identity, a sure sign of its assimilation. Unfortunately, despite a parade of first-class business leaders, the European operation had never been able to turn the corner in terms of achieving the financial results that were expected of it. Part of the problem was the mission that it had originally been given—to carry the competitive fight to the home markets of GE's chief European rivals no matter the cost. Top-line growth—orders and sales—was the mantra; profitability was incidental. That was a philosophy begging for change.

One of Jeff's first moves to redress the situation was the 1997 appointment of a new leader for the European team. His choice was startling to some—an executive with whom he had worked half a dozen years before at GE Appliances. Larry Johnston had been the vice president in charge of sales and distribution in Louisville since 1989, and was a master of those essential business skills. What had really impressed Jeff, though, was Larry's leadership ability:

> This was an Appliance guy and everybody looked at us like this is the dumbest thing you could ever do. What does an Appliance guy know about GE Medical?

But he was a good leader—the kind of guy who could motivate a team, keep them focused, and relate well with customers. He did a fantastic job.

As Marc Pelon, who had become the business operation leader for sales and service under Arno Bohn in 1996, explained:

> Larry brought more credibility to the European staff. I was impressed by the friendship he and Jack Welch had together. When Jack came to Europe, he always spent more time with the medical team than any other GE business. So he started to understand that if we were not winning, it was not because we weren't good but because our structure and mission were not the right ones. Larry restored the confidence of the European management in their ability to win.

An incident at the American Hospital in Paris illustrated Larry's leadership style. Reliability issues had developed around an MR system that had been installed there and, despite a long investigation and assistance from the U.S. engineering team, the cause couldn't be found. Though the original installation had required the excavation of a huge hole in the garden, breaking an opening through the basement wall, and removing several internal partitions, Larry demanded that the MR business deinstall the defective unit and replace it with a new one entirely at their own cost.

Fortunately, the technical solution was found before this drastic course action was taken, but the lesson wasn't lost on the Europe team. Larry's aggressive position to protect a customer was something entirely new and gave his staff the sense they were now full and equal partners in the global business. In the future, they would no longer be reluctant to raise their voices to challenge decisions and address specific concerns.

After putting Johnston in charge and redefining the European organization's mission in more practical, achievable terms, Immelt, along with his finance chief, Keith Sherin, took on equally significant action by implementing a different measurement protocol.

Beginning with the 1987 acquisition, when GEMS was learning how to become a global enterprise, new business measurements had been put in place to integrate the Europe operation into GE's financial system. Unfortunately, some had the unintended effect of painting an inaccurate picture of the success of the business. A major problem was the use of statutory measurements to determine the profitability of each transaction. That technique often masked the true variable cost of a product, resulting in a wrong impression of its profitability and, in the worst case, even a mistaken decision to not even sell it because the margin appeared to be too low. Similarly, statutory measurements could also make it difficult to determine which products to market more aggressively due to their higher actual profitability.

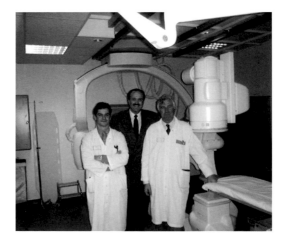

Larry Johnston practiced his customer-centric convictions by calling on customers regularly. This visit was with Prof. Claude Manelfe (right), head of neuroradiology at Centre Hospitalier Universitaire de Purpan in Toulouse, France. (Dr. Manelfe's deputy wasn't identified.)

The new measurement method was called "Global Make" and allowed a much more accurate understanding of the real profitability of the Europe business. It also eliminated many of the rubs that had confused and discouraged the Europe team by providing a much clearer picture of business performance. Now, Larry and his management staff could more intelligently evaluate the business in order to generate the results that were expected of them.

Along with "Global Make" was the shift to a matrix management structure that gave the marketing organization a much greater voice in how products were sold and at what prices. Where marketing had previously reported to the sales vice president, it now was established as a separate function reporting to its own vice president. As a result, the various modality general managers gained considerably more voice in sales decisions, while the sales organization became much more sensitive to pricing, since it now owned a portion of the top-line margin.

"Everybody in Europe was against it at first, because you had a lot of people making a decision and not just one," commented Marc Pelon. "But it definitely changed behavior by bringing margin focus back into the culture."

To help solidify these gains and bring the Europe and global teams closer together, Immelt soon launched a new initiative called the "Modality Swing." He would bring his global modality general managers—MR, CT, ultrasound, and so forth—to Europe at least once a year, usually at the end of the vacation season in August. During these visits, they and Larry's key managers would spend a week traveling around Europe meeting with customers and learning first hand how they viewed GE products and support. Afterwards, they would debrief what they had learned and lay out a common course of action to address problems and opportunities.

Reinaldo Garcia, who would later become the leader of the European organization, recalled:

> It was an amazing dynamic of people working together, listening to the same customers together. This contact between the European team and the global team in a much more real and friendly way worked beautifully. This team, which was thought to be nonperforming, over time began to shine.

With this greater clarity of insight into their operations, everyone began rowing the boat in the same direction. Europe was truly on its way.

Reshaping sales

The Europe field service organization had been split from the sales group about half a dozen years before. It was then drastically reorganized into a single, centralized, pan-European structure that became not only more efficient and responsive but a major source of revenue in its own right.

Now, equally dramatic changes were in store for the Europe sales organization that, in essence, had been a full-line sales organization until 1997. Each individual sales representative was responsible for selling virtually everything in the catalog. But with the ever-increasing number of modalities and sophisticated products, combined with the complexity of new and expanding clinical applications, it had become virtually impossible for one person to be equally effective in all those roles.

It was apparent the European sales force needed to be reshaped in a manner to resemble the U.S. field sales organization—a strong core of full-line sales representatives supported by dedicated specialists responsible for individual modalities and applications. The person chosen to lead this "specialization" transformation was Jean-Yves Burel, whom Larry and Jeff had selected to take over as sales vice president.

Burel's was no small challenge, since the hundreds of field sales representatives who would be affected by this huge change were understandably anxious about having

Reinaldo Garcia

their product portfolio—and, potentially, their incomes—severely slashed. Jean-Yves took on the issue in his straight-ahead style by simply announcing they all were out of their current jobs and had two options: 1) they could reapply for one of a much smaller number of full-line sales positions—in effect, the same jobs they had held before; or 2) they could apply for a specialized sales position representing either CT, MR, ultrasound, vascular x-ray, and so on.

Garcia praised Burel's solution, stating:

> That was, to me, the most important commercial change that we made over the last decade in Europe. Because of that specialization, our sales people were better able to articulate the features, value, and clinical superiority of our products to our customers. That increased our winning capability and enhanced the price and value of the products.

Of course, this specialization transformation took some time to be implemented and mature, but it became the solid basis for the Europe team's subsequent commercial success.

The list of heroes that made the Europe turnaround possible includes names on both sides of the ocean. From the global teams were such people as Yoshiaki Fujimori, Vivek Paul, Omar Ishrak, Vishal Wanchoo, Gene Saragnese, and many others. From the Europe team, in addition to Larry, Reinaldo, and Jean-Yves, were such key contributors as Jean-Michel Malbrancq, CT modality general manager for Europe; Stefano Vagliani, MR modality general manager; and Marc Pelon, Order To Remittance vice president. Noted Garcia:

> Marc Pelon had an amazing impact on predictable execution in Europe. He has been running the fulfillment function for more than a decade and is known as "Mr. Process." He has an amazing institutional knowledge, a great capability to work upstream and downstream, and understands the field extremely well. He brought a lot of good process discipline and reliable execution.

Durable leadership

As events unfolded, Larry Johnston also was destined to lead GE Medical Systems Europe for a relatively brief time. In 1999, Jack Welch called him back to Louisville as President & Chief Executive Officer of GE Appliances, where he served another 2 years before becoming chief executive officer of Albertsons, the huge food retailer. But he had definitely made the most of his years in Paris.

Replacing Johnston was Garcia, who had led the Europe manufacturing organization for about a year, then the Europe service organization for 3 years before returning to the U.S. in 1998 as GM of the multivendor and biomedical services business in Nashville, Tennessee. With his diverse background in global finance, sourcing, manufacturing, and service, he was uniquely qualified for the challenge. He was also to prove a durable leader who would head up the Europe organization throughout the Hogan era and beyond.

Immelt later commented on the changes that had occurred in Europe in the years following his first visit:

> You know, I would say they were just a beaten-down team with no confidence. When I go over there today, I laugh about it, because the same people that we were unsure of 10 years ago are GE officers now. Richard di Benedetto and Reinaldo Garcia have done spectacular, shining jobs, and our business in Europe is almost as profitable as the business in the U.S. We would never have guessed that a decade ago.

Though he had found "a beaten-down team" when he took over in late 1996, Immelt said that attitude began to change as soon as the systemic problems facing the Europe organization were addressed:

> It turned out the people were good, the engineers were very good, and that the customers could actually like us if we were consistent. Sometimes, if you just get one or two people right, you get a tremendous flourish. And that's what happened in Europe.

> Success begets success.

On to the big show

As the new millennium arrived, one of the most important decisions facing Jack Welch was the selection of his successor. He had been wrestling with this issue for several years and, with the help of the Board of Directors and his closest advisors, had finally narrowed the list of prime candidates to three—Bob Nardelli, President & Chief Executive Officer, GE Power Systems; Jim McNerney, President & Chief Executive Officer, GE Aircraft Engines; and, of course, Jeff Immelt. The final selection announcement was scheduled for December 2000.

Early that summer, with the expectation all three would be moving on to other positions regardless of whom his successor would be, Jack had selected young understudies for the three candidates to train as their replacements. Joe Hogan, a 43-year-old star with a background in GE Plastics and GE Fanuc Automation, plus a short tour at GE Corporate, had already arrived in Milwaukee to lead the e-Business initiative. In a short while, he was promoted to the new position of chief operating officer to prepare to step into the GEMS leadership role should Jeff be named GE's new chairman.

As the summer turned to autumn, the urgency to make the final decision was increasing. Finally, at a late-night Board of Directors meeting in Greenville, South Carolina,

following a tour of the turbine plant there, Jack announced his selection—Jeff Immelt. He gave the board several more weeks to consider the matter before calling for a final vote. Their decision was unanimous and the public announcement made at a New York City press conference on November 27.

Jack had expected to retire in April 2001 but plans to acquire Honeywell International, the aerospace and automation giant, had been slowed due to objections on competitive grounds from the European Union (EU). Valued at some $42 billion, this was to have been GE's largest acquisition ever, so he agreed to stay on to complete the deal. In the meantime, Jeff would become President and Chairman-elect.

In a July 2001 vote, however, the 20-member EU Commission fully supported the intransigent position of its competition commissioner, and the proposed merger was soon abandoned. Jack officially retired on September 7, 2001, whereupon Jeff assumed the title of Chairman & CEO.

Chairman Immelt had hardly settled into his new office in Fairfield when the traumatic events of "9/11" unfolded before a stunned nation. Despite this inauspicious start, his leadership of GE in the following years would be marked by challenges overcome and victories achieved. Yet, despite the thrill of playing in a much broader arena at the helm of one of the world's great corporations, he never forgot the people at GE Medical Systems. In an interview for this book, he reminisced:

> I loved all of my jobs and would say that GE people are the best in the world. The people in the medical business were extremely smart and extremely hard working. For instance, when I would have a modality review with the CT team on Ryerson Road, I liked to go down to visit the bench engineers. They were low on ego, high on impact, cared about customers, cared about patients, and cared about the company. It just was an honor to be around these folks. I had confidence in them and could trust what they did. There is something maybe about having a business in a place like Milwaukee where people give you more than a day's work for a day's pay.

The business he left behind was substantially different from the one he found when he arrived some 5 years before. The most remarkable changes were in scale and scope. GEMS had grown from a $3.5 billion business in 1996 to a $5+ billion business in 2000; services alone had reached $3 billion in annual sales. Equally important for the future, the business has expanded far beyond its traditional diagnostic imaging base into such growth technologies as biomedical electronics, IT, cardiovascular information systems, e-Business solutions, women's health, interventional procedures, PET, functional MRI, advanced workstations, and much, much more.

Building upon the model Jeff had established, Joe Hogan was about to create one of the most remarkable chapters of all in GE's more than a century of healthcare technology leadership.

Jeff Immelt became GE Chairman & CEO in September 2001.

The Hogan Era

2000-2008

Joe Hogan was already a familiar figure at GE Medical Systems when he was named President & CEO in the autumn of 2000. He had arrived in Milwaukee the previous spring to lead the e-Business initiative and was appointed chief operating officer that summer. Throughout the following months, he was deeply involved in every aspect of the business and traveled widely to meet the key global business leaders and their customers.

Joe was thrilled by his new post:

> When I worked at Fairfield and saw all the businesses, I used to think that GE Medical is the business I would want to run. I couldn't believe it when Jack called and I had that opportunity. I knew the transition with Jeff would be good, because I had known him for a long time.

Joe had a tough act to follow. Immelt had doubled the size of the business over the previous 5 years through a combination of technology advances, emphasis upon services, and dramatic expansion into new areas of healthcare through an aggressive acquisition strategy. Joe's plan was to continue—even accelerate—that expansion to make GE a much more significant player in the total healthcare industry.

Lessons in Leadership

Joseph Michael Hogan (b. 1957) earned a B.S. in business administration from Geneva College and an M.B.A. from Robert Morris University. He was in field sales for Babcock & Wilcox from 1980–85 then joined GE Plastics, where he served in various sales, marketing, and product development roles over the next 11 years. In 1996, at Jeff Immelt's urging, he accepted a staff executive position at GE headquarters and became President & CEO of GE Fanuc Automation in 1998. Two years later, Jack Welch selected Joe to become Executive VP & COO of GE Medical Systems and appointed him President & CEO on November 25, 2000. He became President & CEO of GE Healthcare in 2005 and was named CEO of ABB Group, a leading international supplier of power and automation technology, in 2008. During his 8 years of leadership, GE's medical business grew by a factor of more than three.

Despite its substantial gains, GEMS primarily was still a U.S. driven diagnostic imaging business dominated by CT and MR. Digital x-ray was growing rapidly, and Positron Emission Tomography was beginning to thrive. Ultrasound, as we've already seen, had entered upon an amazing growth trajectory, and IT was making serious progress toward becoming a key player in patient monitoring and PACS.

In terms of globalization, Joe foresaw both challenges and opportunities:

> I knew that we would have to put more time and effort into China and India, while helping Europe turn the corner to profitability. Something that really surprised me was our wonderful Japanese joint venture. Everybody should be proud of GE Yokogawa, because it is so easy for a Western company to

Joseph M. Hogan

lose in Japan. GE YMS was a real tribute to the people, the partnerships, the sensitivity to the marketplace, and the customer relationships that had been developed over time.

Cultural shifts

Hogan's early assessments of the business soon led him to implement a new strategy based on three primary elements, beginning with a reinvigorated level of sensitivity in all customer relationships—the same formula that had proven so successful in Japan. "There was a certain arrogance in our customer relationships that any successful company goes through," he explained. "I wanted to have much more of a customer mindset—a humbleness in dealing with them and an urgency in responding to their needs."

The second cultural change he set in motion involved GEMS's matrix management structure. Dating back to the Robb years, this organizational approach placed the responsibility for each functional area, such as manufacturing, sourcing, technology, and so forth, into the hands of its own leader. At the time, the only exception was the self-contained ultrasound business; it even had its own sales force. As Joe explained it:

> I came in as someone who really believes in responsibility and accountability, so I wanted to set everything up around contained business units. That was tough to do, because you can't change things in a day. I sheltered Omar's ultrasound business as much as I could and made certain that new acquisitions were holistic profit and loss arrangements. Gradually, we took the U.S. diagnostic imaging businesses and made them more accountable P&L structures, too

His third key initiative was to advance the globalization agenda that Robb had initiated and that both Trani and Immelt had significantly advanced:

> But we were still an international company that primarily manufactured in low-cost countries and shipped products back to developed countries. To become truly globalized, we needed to organize on an "in country for country" basis. That was not a distribution strategy but an opportunity to respond to local demands with local capabilities.

Visioning in Vienna

With those major cultural changes in train, Hogan next turned his attention to the biggest challenge of all—growth.

Mike Jones, who had continued as Hogan's business development manager, said:

> When Joe took over, his mandate was to grow the business by a factor of three. Healthcare was an extremely important industry, and he understood that GE was still underpenetrated. So Joe could take off the gloves in terms of expanding the footprint both globally and from a product offering perspective.

In early 2001, Hogan scheduled an intensive, 3-day brainstorming session with his immediate management team in Vienna, Austria. His objective was to plot the near-term future of GE Medical Systems and agree on new strategies to grow it into a *$15 billion* enterprise by 2005. His staff was startled by this audacious goal, to say the least. After all, based on projected 2001 revenues of $8.5 billion and assuming an average annual growth rate of 8% in the core businesses, a more reasonable 2005 target would have been $12 billion. So the key challenge of this meeting was to identify how and where to find that extra $3 billion in new growth.

Joe framed the discussion by highlighting several potential growth opportunities:

- First, accelerating growth in the core business through digitization, installed base programs, and globalization.
- Second, extending core platforms into new segments (e.g., extension of MR into clinics, new initiatives to attack the competitive installed base, etc.).
- Next, horizontal/vertical expansion (e.g., moving GEMS IT into hospital information system, providing cyclotron services, etc.).
- And, fourth, new platforms to address additional areas of healthcare, such as therapy, oncology, genomics, IVD, and new services.

Joe told the participants that while he didn't expect a finished growth plan at the end of the session, he was counting on a free-wheeling discussion that would help set a directionally correct strategic course for future growth. "No ideas are stupid, though some will be better than others," he promised. "This isn't about titles, egos, or turf; it's about the business."

Over the next couple of days, led by Mike Jones and Gene Saragnese, chief technology officer, the group dissected the business and its capabilities—cold-blooded assessments of what it did well, what it wasn't so good at, and where the best opportunities for new growth were to be found. This visioning process examined an astonishing variety of options. No sacred cows were protected; nothing was off limits.

In looking at the total market for healthcare devices, equipment, and services, Jones had calculated that GEMS was participating in segments (healthcare information technology, diagnostic imaging, and patient monitoring) representing less than $70 billion of a total global opportunity of more than $200 billion. The question was if there were additional segments where the company could leverage its capabilities to create new growth. To stimulate discussion, Mike flagged several of the most promising candidates:

- Minimally invasive surgery ($6 billion): interventional radiology, endoscopes, catheters, etc.
- Cardiology ($12 billion): implantable defibrillators, heart pacers, angioplasty products, stents, valves, electro-physiology devices, etc.
- Orthopedics ($11 billion): artificial implants, such as replacement hip and knee joints, plus devices related to spinal surgeries.
- Analytical instruments ($15 billion): spectroscopy, spectrometry, clinical lab devices.

Among all the possibilities that were suggested, several very promising areas soon emerged, led by molecular imaging, healthcare IT, patient monitoring, and ultrasound. Jones later recalled:

> We really spent 2 days talking about what we should focus on in terms of expanding the footprint. Clearly, we thought that molecular imaging was the next generation for diagnostic imaging, but we looked at it as really being a broad-based diagnostic business, not just a diagnostic imaging business. We identified healthcare IT as an area where we wanted to continue growing beyond what was still primarily a PACS radiology business in the U.S. And we viewed the clinical systems business—ultrasound and patient monitoring—as areas where we could be much bigger.

Of the three, Joe thought molecular imaging would clearly be the greatest stretch:

We decided that we wanted to continue being a diagnostic imaging business but one with a broader diagnostic capability. The life sciences piece was going to define the technology of the future, just as integrated circuitry had defined the past. We were moving from the era of anatomical understanding to one of understanding the chemistry behind the abnormal lesion. So we had to be in life sciences in some way, because of the ability to see things much sooner, much smaller, and in a much more predictive way.

Genomics & Molecular Imaging 101

Genomics is the study of genes and their functions. By understanding an organism's genome—the complete DNA sequence of one set of chromosomes, the potential exists to offer new therapeutic and diagnostic methods. Genomics includes:

- *Functional genomics: the characterization of genes and their mRNA and protein products (proteomics)*
- *Structural genomics: the dissection of the architectural features of genes and chromosomes*
- *Comparative genomics: the evolutionary relationships between the genes and proteins of different species*
- *Epigenomics (or epigenetics): DNA methylation patterns, imprinting, and DNA packaging*
- *Pharmacogenomics: new biological targets and new ways to design drugs and vaccines*

Molecular imaging combines molecular biology with in vivo imaging. Chemical probes, called biomarkers or "signal molecules," are used to help image particular targets or pathways by interacting chemically with their surroundings and altering the image according to molecular changes encountered in the area of interest. This ability to image fine molecular changes opens up many exciting medical applications, such as early detection and treatment of diseases, highly objective quantitative tests, and basic pharmaceutical development.

In retrospect, the speculative discussions Joe and his staff held at the Vienna visioning session proved to be a remarkably accurate harbinger of where the business would soon go. The meeting had refocused everyone's attention on what was important and what wasn't and established an agreed basis for guiding the business in coming years. Joe stated several years later:

If you go back to the Austria meeting in 2001, you can plot out the roadmap that we established and follow it to where the business stands today. We set audacious goals and doubled the business. The real objective was to find ways to expand GE Healthcare in those areas where it really made sense in terms of the future. We hit that almost 100%.

Northern pole

Hogan and Jones wasted no time in implementing the first large acquisition in support of the decisions made in Vienna.

In December 2002, GE Medical Systems announced an agreement to purchase the Finnish medical devices manufacturer, Instrumentarium Corporation, in a $2.3 billion deal. A respected producer and distributor of anesthesia devices, electronic patient monitoring systems, surgical c-arm units, and clinical information systems, Instrumentarium was a significant player in the European market and, through its 2002 Spacelabs acquisition, a factor in the U.S.

GE's interest in Instrumentarium was spurred by the synergies the two firms

would bring to the combined entity. GE was strong in advanced patient monitoring technology through its Marquette Medical acquisition a few years before, mobile surgical c-arms, and healthcare IT. Besides its own strong critical care monitoring and c-arm lines, Instrumentarium also had extremely attractive product offerings in anesthesiology delivery and healthcare information technology. So it was a perfect fit. . . and very much in accord with the new growth plan.

Joe put the proposed acquisition into perspective at the announcement when he observed, "The people and businesses of Instrumentarium are highly regarded and respected at GE Medical Systems, and they will contribute in major ways to the company's future, especially in the areas of product innovation, quality, service, and overall customer commitment."

He went on to announce Instrumentarium would become the European headquarters for GE's $2.6 billion healthcare IT unit and would provide significant support to global business operations, including advanced R&D and manufacturing, among other focus areas.

"Our customers and employees will benefit from the tremendous strengths of GE, especially in the areas of research and development, expansion of our offering, and globally local support," said Olli Riikkala, Instrumentarium's president and CEO, in welcoming the GE offer.

It was GEMS's largest proposed acquisition up until that time and would require months of tough negotiations, and several significant regulatory concessions, to successfully conclude.

Doing the deal

The initial overtures to Instrumentarium were conducted during the bleak days just after "9/11". For the better part of the next year, teams from both firms met regularly to discuss and resolve the many details involved in such a huge transaction. Joe, Mike, and Steve Patscot from human resources personally handled most of the detailed negotiations in Helsinki and London. They were greatly assisted by Kevin King, who was running the patient monitoring business, and Dave Baker from business development. Greg Lucier, President & CEO of GE Medical Systems IT, was involved early on but left the company during the negotiations and was succeeded by Dow Wilson. (Incidentally, Dave Baker was later named the Instrumentarium integration manager, followed by Ralph Strosin.)

Perhaps the greatest challenge confronting the dealmakers was to structure the transaction in a way that would win approvals from the various governmental competition agencies involved. These included the U.S. Department of Justice, naturally, the European Commission, Canada, and the Czech Republic. No one on the GE side was taking the process lightly. The last time the company had brought a proposed deal before the EU's competition panel—the $42 billion bid for Honeywell International in 2001—it had been rejected out of hand.

The competitive aspects of this deal were potentially problematic because of the various overlaps that existed between the two firms. After all, increasing the scale of the combined businesses was the major impetus for the deal in the first place. The proposed purchase would immediately hand GE nearly half of the European market for patient monitoring devices and greatly enhance its positions in the U.S. and Canada. In addition, mobile c-arm imaging devices—large businesses for both GE and Instrumentarium—also presented a "rub."

Instrumentarium's purchase of the U.S. monitoring company, Spacelabs, in the middle of the negotiations created an unexpected complication.

Thus, negotiators on both sides of the table recognized certain regulatory concessions likely would be necessary to preserve the most important aspects of the transaction. So they made their plans and proposals accordingly.

To the surprise of almost everyone, the European Commission was the first to approve the acquisition. In early September 2003, it announced the deal would be allowed to proceed on condition that General Electric sell one unit and pledge not to shut competitors out of a European market, where it would now be the market leader. That disposition target was Spacelabs. Though GE was not happy with this requirement, it immediately launched a search for a buyer. (In 2004, OSI Systems purchased the business and reincorporated it as Spacelabs Healthcare the following year.)

In addition to selling Spacelabs, the EU also required GE to take several related actions. First, they had to complete a supply agreement with the purchaser, OSI Systems, giving it the right to sell Instrumentarium's popular global gas module, a key component in perioperative monitors. Second, GE was required to provide other manufacturers with the necessary technical information to make their patient monitoring equipment compatible with GE surgical and intensive care monitoring systems.

In a statement commenting on its favorable review of the GE-Instrumentarium deal and the conditions attached, the EU's competition regulator noted a significant recent trend toward consolidation in the medical device market:

> The present merger further accentuates this trend by bringing together two of the four leading players in Europe in patient monitors. While the deal would lead to high market shares in a number of countries in the perioperative monitor market, the remedies extracted from GE remove the horizontal overlap between the activities of GE and Instrumentarium in the perioperative monitoring market and will ensure the emergence of an effective competitor to the merged entity.

Before hardly another month elapsed came word the other three regulatory agencies—the U.S. Department of Justice, the Canadian Competition Bureau, and the Czech Republic—also had authorized the acquisition with only a few additional restrictions. The principal requirement was the divestiture of Instrumentarium's Ziehm surgical c-arm business. It soon was sold to ATON, a German asset management company, and remains a vigorous competitor.

The Instrumentarium deal soon would be eclipsed by another European acquisition that would literally transform the nature and identity of GE Medical Systems. Nevertheless, it was a pivotal event.

"The Instrumentarium acquisition was just as important as the later Amersham deal in terms of changing the footprint of the business," Mike Jones stated. "In addition, it gave Marquette global scale and added substantially to what is now the Clinical Systems business."

It was also important in dollars and cents. In 2004, the former Instrumentarium operations contributed well over $1.0 billion in very profitable revenues to GE's bottom line. Joe's $15 billion target by 2005 had moved a giant step closer.

Accounting for Change

In 2003, Joe Hogan recruited Mark Vachon, Executive Vice President & Chief Financial Officer at GE's NBC subsidiary, to help him strengthen the overstressed financial management system of his wildly expanding global business. Mark later became President & CEO, Diagnostic Imaging and, in 2008, President & CEO, Healthcare-Americas.

"In any organization with such a hyper growth trajectory, there is a tradeoff between growth and the underlying infrastructure to support it. We had outrun what I call the plumbing and wiring of the business in terms of the accounting structure, IT capability, and infrastructure compliance.

"When I was asked to come to GE Healthcare as the CFO, my challenge among several was to build the financial control routines. There were a very wide variety of revenue recognition models due to the diversity of the portfolio and the substantial growth of the business. Our goal was to simplify those processes and to create a solid balance sheet.

"My initial assessment was that our people, processes, and systems were not worthy of a business heading toward $20 billion. So we put in place programs to improve in those areas by upgrading and expanding the controllership function, instituting an IT review and management process, and simplifying the complexity of what had been built in prior years.

"In my view, business, like science, has fundamental physics. When you focus on the fundamentals, you get stronger. Whether it's in accounting or other elements of compliance, the foundation must be the #1 priority. And you must build it ahead of the growth trajectory to avoid interrupting the business agenda. Those are the lessons we learned—and what those 'laws of physics' will teach you every time."

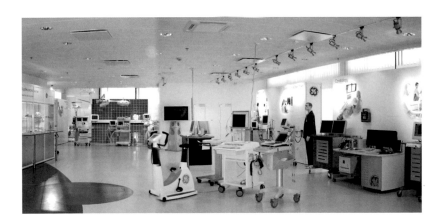

opposite
Instrumentarium's large, modern facilities on Teollisuuskatu in Helsinki continued as a major engineering and production center for patient monitoring and other clinical systems following the acquisition by GE Healthcare

above
Visitors to the Helsinki center are greeted by a comprehensive exhibit of GE clinical monitoring and related products.

Strengthening academic ties

A recurring theme throughout GEMS's history was the special relationships it fostered with leading academic institutions to advance the art and science of imaging. One of the most productive of these collaborations had been with Stanford University, especially after the 1989 arrival of Gary Glazer as radiology chair. During the Immelt years and on into the Hogan era, the two partners found new opportunities to co-operate in various areas of advanced imaging such as interventional and high-field MR techniques, PET, multislice CT, and much more. GE provided 3T and 7T research magnets for the constantly expanding Richard M. Lucas Center for Imaging, Dr. Glazer's brainchild. A 2004 agreement laid out a 5-year collaborative R&D program in which GE scientists would work with Stanford faculty members to develop new techniques and technologies in molecular imaging.

A special relationship also had been developing with the University of Wisconsin (UW), the world-class research university just a few miles down the expressway from GEMS's headquarters. In 2001, Joe Hogan and Paul Mirabella, with Immelt's support, had concluded a 5-year "Image Sciences Alliance Agreement" with the UW Medical School. The Alliance allowed UW access to the latest GE imaging technologies for their research program; GEMS gained access to the competencies and capabilities of one of the world's leading imaging sciences academic institutions in developing next-generation equipment.

At the inaugural dinner in October 2001, Paul Mirabella, then President & CEO, GE Healthcare Services, remarked:

> Certainly, the transactional aspects of the Alliance are attractive to GE, but they aren't the real reason why we have invested in it so generously. Rather, we see this partnership with UW as an unparalleled opportunity to tap into the rich flow of ideas coursing through the intellectual arteries of this great university and to help focus them on areas of mutual interest. Such invest-ments are not new for us. We sponsor research collaborations with scores of leading universities and medical institutions literally around the world. What sets this one apart is the scale of the enterprise and the scope of the tech-nological and operational areas it touches.

The success of this program led to the creation of the UW Image Science Center and, in 2007, the opening of the Wisconsin Institutes for Medical Research building on the Madison campus.

Philip M. Farrell, Dean of the UW Medical School and Vice Chancellor for Medical Affairs at the time of the original agreement, later shared his perspective on the prog-ress and impact of the GE collaboration:

> The UW Image Science Center, occupied in 2007 in the new Wisconsin Institutes for Medical Research building, is providing unique benefits for patients at the adjacent University of Wisconsin Hospital and Clinics in Madi-son. It operates at the interface of translational research and ensures that patients receive the latest innovations in imaging to improve both diagnoses and therapies for life-threatening diseases. Professor Paul DeLuca of the University of Wisconsin and Paul Mirabella of GE Healthcare provided the vision and leadership to create a true center of excellence. The Image Science Center faculty have filed over 50 patents in the last 2 years. The level of NIH funding continues to grow. Dr. Thomas Grist, Chairman of the Department of Radiology, played a key role leading the development of the imaging core facilities. He has frequently commented that the activities of the Center have greatly enhanced the academic mission of the Department of Radiology. Over

top to bottom

Dr. Glazer welcomed visitors attending the 2004 installation of the GE 7 Tesla research magnet in Stanford's Lucas Center. With him was Gary Glover (left), director of the Radiological Sciences Laboratory, and Don Lucas, head of the Richard M. Lucas Cancer Foundation, the principal benefactor of the Lucas Center.

Dr. Glazer invited Jeff Immelt (right), GE chairman, to part-icipate in Stanford University's 2005 radiology centennial celebration as the featured "Fireside Chat Speaker."

The Wisconsin Institutes for Medical Research houses the Image Science Center.

Paul M. DeLuca Jr., Vice Dean, University of Wisconsin School of Medicine, spoke at the opening of the Wisconsin Institutes of Medical Research. He and GE's Paul Mirabella were instrumental in launching the 2001 alliance that led to its creation.

opposite, top

Dr. Thomas Grist, University of Wisconsin radiology chairman.

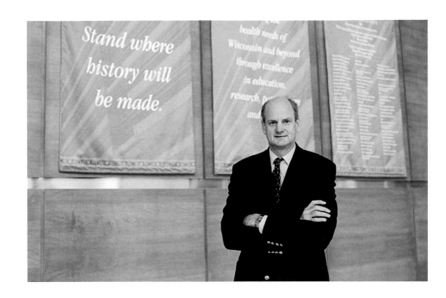

twenty radiology faculty are involved in research projects at the Image Science Center.

Molecular momentum

One of the most stunning developments in the 110-year history of GE's medical equipment business occurred during the early years of Joe's leadership as he sought out new ways to generate additional growth by expanding GE's footprint in health-care technology. Vienna had flagged several key opportunities, including molecular imaging—the ability to personalize patient diagnostic procedures based upon an understanding of molecular processes within the body and specific disease entities—

plus life sciences. Nuclear medicine is the antecedent of molecular imaging in that it also visualizes body functions rather than structural anatomy. Molecular imaging, however, takes it several steps further by actually interrogating these processes at the level of the individual molecule.

As Joe and Mike Jones were casting about for opportunities to act upon their vision to expand beyond nuclear medicine and positron emission tomography (PET) into the wider world of molecular medicine, they were continually communicating upwards to align support in Fairfield for their audacious plans.

"The biggest breakthroughs in science and technology often occur because new partners are able to join together historically isolated capabilities to address new market needs," Joe observed. "In this instance, no one had even combined biochemistry with electrical engineering technology."

That's exactly what he and Mike had in mind now. They were soon evaluating a number of potential partners with skills in the life sciences, such as Beckman Instruments and Roche, the international pharmaceutical giant. None were promising, however, until they discovered Amersham plc, an innovative British firm with expertise in the life sciences and strong nuclear technology that was participating with GE in a Johns Hopkins University lung cancer screening research program. Amersham provided the special diagnostic imaging agents being used and GE the imaging equipment.

Amersham was an appealing acquisition target, because its strong base in biological science provided exactly the expertise GE's growth strategy required.

"Their nuclear component also was important, because you need that to read the small signals that come from cells," Joe explained.

Over the previous two decades, Amersham had built a large and successful business through its demonstrated ability to label life at the cellular level and apply those skills to *in vivo* diagnostics in humans. In the brain, for example, it had developed small chemical molecules that could pass the blood/brain barrier to diagnose and

In 2000, Dr. Jim Potchen and his Michigan State University colleagues began hosting a respected series of GE-sponsored scientific workshops exploring the future of molecular imaging. Among the participants at the 2003 session were: (front, l–r) Eric Stahre, Gene Saragnese, and Steve Bolze from GE; Dr. Potchen; Tom Cooper and Arlene Sierra from MSU; Paul Bottomley, Johns Hopkins; and James Bassingthwaighte, University of Washington; (back, l–r) Mike Klimas, Eric Roman, and Mike Thornton from GE; Norm Beauchamp, University of Washington; Jonathan Rosenthal, GE; Mark Delano, MSU; Dennis Cooke, GE; and Harvey Sparks, MSU.

differentiate various dementias. In the heart, similar compounds were yielding profound gains in physiology and spatial imaging by assessing the blood flow and differentiating ischemia. Its principal products now included diagnostic imaging agents used in medical scanning procedures; protein separation products including chromatography purification systems used in the manufacture of biopharmaceuticals; and high-throughput systems for applications in genomics, proteomics, and bioassays.

Joe and Mike had officially expressed their support for a potential deal with Amersham as early as the 2001 Session One "growth playbook," a well-known GE business planning tool. Joe's convictions had been strengthened by time spent with Sam Gambhir, a leading expert in molecular imaging at the University of California Los Angeles Medical Center, learning about molecular medicine and its implications for personalized healthcare. He became even more insistent in his calls for GE Corporate to closely examine the opportunity he was suggesting.

PET Rules
S. Sam Gambhir, M.D., Ph.D., *was the director of the Crump Institute of Molecular Imaging at the University of California at Los Angeles when he first met Joe Hogan about 2001. Several years later, he became Professor, Radiology and Bio-X Program at Stanford University, head of nuclear medicine, and molecular imaging program director. He and Joe continued their close cooperation there.*

"I remember vividly a meeting where Joe came with a team to learn what molecular imaging was all about. It was an unusual visit, because UCLA had been a Siemens center. We were all very impressed with Joe's ability to quickly understand the massive potential of molecular imaging.

"GE's decision to go back into the PET business was a very aggressive move to not only build better technologies but to invest across the board in PET R&D. Another big moment was when they embraced molecular imaging with PET to bring the next generation of imaging agents beyond FDG (fluorodeoxyglucose).

"GE invested heavily in building our radiochemistry and cyclotron facilities at Stanford, because of the interesting relationship Joe and I had at UCLA and, later, with Gary Glazer here. Thanks to Joe, Jean-Luc Vanderheyden, and Nadeem Ishaque, this cooperation has led to the development of imaging strategies that could lead to many useful new molecular imaging products in the future."

In the summer of 2001, prompted by Joe, GE engaged Goldman Sachs, the global investment banking and securities firm, to evaluate Amersham as a potential acquisition and authorized initial contacts with its leadership to assess their interest in a possible deal. That led to an August 2001 telephone call to Sir William Castell, Amersham's chairman and CEO, who recalled:

> They said that General Electric wanted to have a chat. When the world's biggest company wants to talk to a relatively small company, you get somewhat nervous and twitchy. Jeff Immelt said he would like to meet, and I agreed to see him in New York on October 23.

Their first meeting was merely a get-acquainted session. It went well, so Sir William and Jeff agreed to meet again in the near future. That second meeting didn't occur until August 2002, while Jeff was in Europe on business. When the GE corporate jet touched down at Biggin Hill, a regional airfield in the southeast suburbs of London (and one of the R.A.F. Fighter Command's key bases during the Battle of Britain in World War II), Sir William was on the tarmac to invite him to his nearby home for a relaxed conversation.

Sir William M. Castell

Lessons in Leadership
Sir Willam Martin Castell, LVO* (b. 1947) *was educated at St. Dunstan's College and the City of London College. He spent the early years of his career at Wellcome plc and Wellcome Foundation, rising to Commercial Director in 1986. He was appointed CEO of Amersham International in 1989, overseeing its growth into a global leader in in vivo medical diagnostics and life sciences research technologies. From 1998 to 2003, he was chairman of The Prince's Trust and was knighted in 2000. Following his retirement from GE in 2006, he became Chairman of the Board of Governors of the Wellcome Trust, the world's largest medical research charity. He is an honorary fellow of the University of Cardiff, King's College London, and the Academy of Medical Sciences, and holds honorary degrees from the University of Oxford, Brunei University, and Imperial College London. Sir William is a director of General Electric Company and BP plc.*
(*Lieutenant of the Royal Victorian Order for services to the Royal Family)

Marriage proposal
Sir William was fully aware that if Amersham was to remain a leader in biotechnology, it needed to find a route to either lead the eventual innovation of molecular pathology in clinical diagnostics or expand from its biological base into engineering and digitization. He was talking to several prospective partners, including Beckman Coulter, Roche, and Bayer, to assess their visions of the future and any interest they might share in combining resources to increase market competencies and shareholder value.

"Even as Jeff and I were going through the process of getting to know each other, I was working vigorously to see if there were other routes that would be better for Amersham and its shareholders," explained Sir William. "So that 2-year negotiation process was very useful for me in terms of evaluating all the possibilities and determining a fair price for Amersham."

Meanwhile, GE had given Sir William a concrete offer to acquire Amersham. Having found no route to strike a deal with a biotech firm, Sir William presented this proposal to his board as the most preferable option. After considerable discussion, the board agreed there were enormous potential advantages by combining GE engineering and IT with Amersham's biological expertise. They authorized negotiations with GE, and Sir William relayed the happy news to Jeff and Joe.

The negotiations consumed much of 2003. As the discussions advanced, Joe led a due diligence team to England to examine Amersham's operations. It included Mike Jones; Peter Solmssen, general counsel; Mark Vachon, finance; John Lynch, HR; Keith Sherin, GE's chief financial officer; Scott Donnelly, Global Research; and Steve Bolze, leader of the Nuclear/PET business. Pam Daley, GE Corporate's senior counsel for transactions, was subsequently brought in to negotiate the nonfinancial details of the deal. On the Amersham side were such key people as Peter Löscher, President of Amersham Health; Peter Ehrenheim and Andrew Carr, directors of Amersham's life

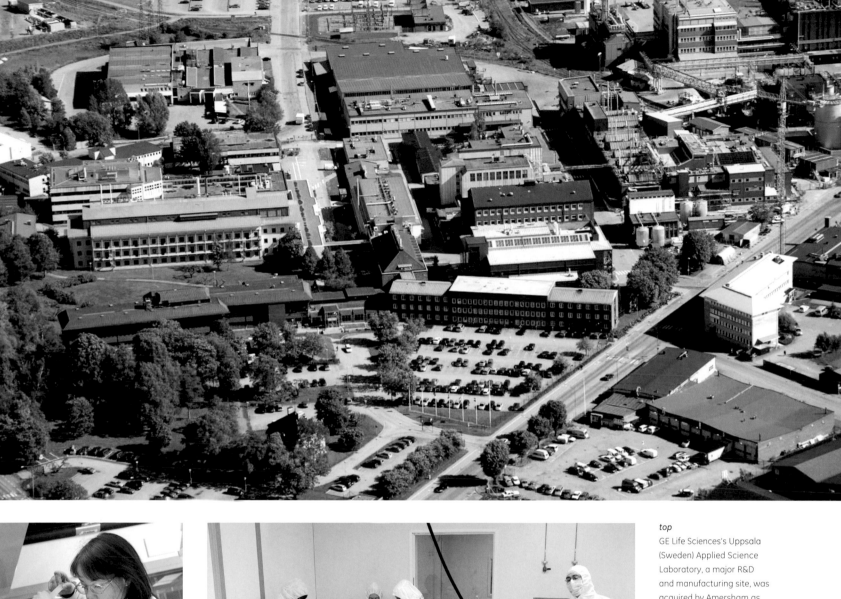

top
GE Life Sciences's Uppsala
(Sweden) Applied Science
Laboratory, a major R&D
and manufacturing site, was
acquired by Amersham as
part of its 1997 purchase of
Pharmacia Biotech.

bottom, left to right
The development of innovative biopharmaceuticals is a
specialty of GE Life Science's
Uppsala center.

The large-scale WAVE Bio-
reactor™ from GE Healthcare's
Ready To Process range of
biopharmaceutical processing
technologies. *(Image courtesy
of Pacific GMP, USA.)*

Chilcote House, Amersham, Bucknghamshire, where Dr. Patrick Grove founded Amersham in 1940. It subsequently grew into one of the world's leading suppliers of diagnostic imaging agents, biopharmaceutical manufacturing products, and related offerings to facilitate molecular medicine.

sciences businesses; Giles Kerr, finance; Mike Steens, corporate development; and several outside advisors, including Bernard Taylor from J.P. Morgan, Michael Tory from Morgan Stanley, and Anthony Salz from Freshfields law firm.

Finally, in October, the $9.5 billion agreement for GE to acquire Amersham was officially announced. The proposed transaction was unusual in that it was based upon an equity swap rather than cash—the largest all-share transaction ever in Britain based on shares (GE) not quoted on the U.K. stock market.

Whence Amersham?

Amersham's name reflects its first home in the market town of Amersham located in the Chiltern Hills district of Buckinghamshire, England, some 30 miles northwest of London. During World War II, Patrick Grove, a British physicist, had located a company there specifically to extract radium from rocks to support the war effort with radioluminescence. It remained in operation following the war, and the British government incorporated it into the Atomic Energy Agency when it became known as the Radiochemical Centre. It specialized in the development and manufacture of radioactive materials for peacetime uses in medicine, scientific research, and industry. In 1982, it became the first company to be fully privatized by the Thatcher government and was renamed Amersham International plc. Following the 1997 acquisition of Pharmacia Biotech of Sweden and merger with Nycomed of Norway, it became Nycomed Amersham plc. In 2001, the company's name again was changed, this time to Amersham plc. Its operations are now known as GE Life Sciences and colocated with GE Healthcare headquarters a few miles from Chalfont St. Giles, Buckinghamshire.

"GE Healthcare"

The prospect of extending GE's business into diagnostic pharmaceuticals and life sciences also provided the ideal opportunity to resolve a related issue. As Mike Jones explained:

> We had been having a discussion about the name "GE Medical Systems" for some time. Given what we had done with the business, everybody felt that it was limiting in terms of describing our activities. So the Amersham transaction gave us the opportunity to change our name to "GE Healthcare."

After clearing U.S. and European Union competition reviews, the deal was completed in April of 2004. Sir William was elected Vice Chairman of the Board and Executive Officer of General Electric Company and concurrently appointed President & CEO of GE Healthcare. Joe Hogan continued as President & CEO of the former GE Medical Systems, now renamed Healthcare Technologies, and Peter Löscher became President & CEO of GE Healthcare Bio-Sciences (he went on to become President of Merck & Company's Global Human Health unit in April of 2006 and President & CEO of Siemens A.G. on July 1, 2007.)

To complete the break with the past for both parties, GE Healthcare's worldwide headquarters were transferred from Milwaukee into a new facility outside the Buckinghamshire village of Chalfont St. Giles. The leadership team included both GE and Amersham executives, the latter relocating from their former headquarters in nearby Little Chalfont.

The acquisition of Amersham was the key event that made Joe's dream—and Jeff's expectation—of a $15 billion medical technology business a reality. To its traditional leadership base in diagnostic imaging, clinical systems, services, and healthcare information technology, it had now added world-class expertise in pharmaceuticals and the life sciences. Supported by an outstanding global leadership team, GE Healthcare was now poised to embark upon an extraordinary new era in healthcare. As the 2004 GE Annual Report predicted:

> The combination of our imaging technology and Amersham's pharmaceutical biomarkers will allow us to uncover genetic tendencies toward diseases such as breast cancer or Alzheimer's; the combination of our high-tech services and Amersham's drug discovery business opens up new ways to support pharmaceutical customers; the combination of our healthcare information technology with Amersham's predictive therapeutic capabilities builds a bridge to personalized medicine. The combination of Medical Systems with Amersham will make GE the most comprehensive diagnostic company in healthcare and create the potential for decades of profitable growth.

But first, the integration of two disparate businesses and business cultures had to be completed. GE had amassed considerable respect for, and expertise in, this process over the previous 25 years through its various acquisitions and joint ventures around the globe. Amersham also had experience thanks to several acquisitions in the U.S. and Scandinavia. A key decision was to assign Steve Bolze, who had been leading the Nuclear/PET business, as the Amersham integration executive and move him to England. Many people from both sides of the Atlantic played important roles to integrate these new partners into a seamless organization. Besides those already mentioned, they included Bill Conaty, Corporate HR; Eric Stahre, who succeeded Steve Bolze in Nuclear/PET; and Dan Tereau, Rafael Torres, and Miguel Blanc, business development,

"It is extraordinary to see a company with the power, the process, and the domain skills that General Electric has," stated Sir William.

One of his earliest lessons was learning about GE's responsiveness:

> My first concern was giving leadership to this beast called GE Healthcare. So I took about 60 of the top people from Milwaukee and Amersham up to Crotonville to spend the day together and develop a mutual vision. About an hour into the meeting, things were going so well that I casually remarked that it was a pity we weren't videotaping the session, because it was so creative. An hour later, an NBC camera crew arrived and began to tape it. I realized then that I should no longer fret about coming to General Electric, because it had the power to deliver.

top, left to right
Joe Hogan and Sir William Castell at the opening ceremonies of GE Healthcare's new worldwide headquarters in Chalfont St. Giles (informally known as Pollards Wood).

GE Healthcare is the only major GE business headquartered outside the U.S.

middle, left to right
GE also was making major investments in Milwaukee. The 2006 dedication of GE Healthcare Research Park was attended by (l–r) Omar Ishrak, President, Clinical Systems; Wauwatosa Mayor Theresa Estness; Joe Hogan; Wisconsin Governor James Doyle; and Mark Irgens, President, Irgens Development Partners.

GE Healthcare Research Park provided a stunning new home for Healthcare Systems, Ultrasound, Diagnostic Cardiology & Interventional Systems and various other functions. Its 500,000 feet^2 (47,000 meters^2) of space included office areas, product development labs, training rooms, customer conference facilities, auditorium, cafeteria, fitness center, medical clinic, and on-site bank. An adjoining building provided another 60,000 feet^2 (5,500 meters^2) of manufacturing and warehousing space.

bottom
When the CT/PET expansion opened on the Waukesha campus in 2002, the Ryerson Road CT engineering and manufacturing center was closed.

Sir William's tenure as GE Healthcare's leader was destined to be rather brief, because of a commitment he had made well before the acquisition to go to the Wellcome Trust as its next chairman. The Trust had agreed to give Sir William up to 4 years to complete the GE transaction before holding him to his pledge. Therefore, in early 2006, he announced his retirement from GE and took up his new leadership role at the Wellcome Trust, the world's largest medical research charity. To the surprise of absolutely no one, Joe Hogan was named to succeed him as President & CEO of GE Healthcare.

The acquisition of Amersham, combined with other key transactions, such as that for Instrumentarium, had now checked off many of the growth boxes that Joe and his team had identified at the "Vienna 2000" visioning session. More remained to be done but a major hurdle had been cleared on the path to GE Healthcare's future.

"Jeff's willingness to accept more risk allowed us to expand into areas that we would never have considered before," Hogan stated. "Before Jeff, the Amersham acquisition would have been impossible because of the potential liability associated with diagnostic pharmaceuticals."

Creating a New Healthcare Paradigm

After the Instrumentarium and Amersham acquisitions, a new name for the business—GE Healthcare—was selected to more accurately reflect its much broader healthcare franchise. A global research effort, led by GE Healthcare Marketing Communications and Corporate GE Marketing, was launched to define a more relevant positioning statement for the expanded enterprise. The result was "Healthcare Re-imagined," a declaration of GE's unique ability to blend technology development, biosciences, and business acumen, and based upon the three core strengths identified by customers around the world as critical to tomorrow's successful healthcare technology suppliers. By leveraging these core strengths, Joe Hogan led GE in promoting "Early Health," a transformational concept to shift the healthcare paradigm from "Late Disease" (intervention after the patient becomes ill) to employing advances in the ability to predict, diagnose, treat, and monitor disease earlier to enable people to live their lives to the fullest. —Brian S. Johnson, Manager, Global Marketing Communications

top to bottom

GE Healthcare was featured at the 2005 "GE Day" event held in London. It gave customers, suppliers, intermediaries, employees, and journalists a fantastic opportunity to meet the 32 entities representing GE's six global businesses.

A famed London double-decker bus, decorated in GE Healthcare livery, was one of the eye-catching sights at the 2005 "GE Day" event.

CT "slice wars"

The debut of the LightSpeed QX/i multislice CT scanner in 1998 had signaled the opening salvo in what soon came to be known as the "slice wars."

The QX/i's success soon compelled the other major CT manufacturers to counter with 4-slice products of their own. GE raised the ante in 2000, introducing the 0.5 second LightSpeed Plus 4-slice system, and again, in 2001, with the LightSpeed Ultra, the world's first 8-slice scanner. Philips, Toshiba, and Siemens trumped this move with 16-slice machines in 2002 but were matched by the LightSpeed[16] a few months later. Meanwhile, GE had further raised the stakes by adding a new ingredient into the competitive mix—cardiac CT software packages for both its 8- and 16-slice models.

While the Milwaukee engineering, manufacturing, and marketing teams were fighting these "slice wars," the Global Research Center (GRC) had already begun working on several core technologies that would be needed for an entirely new generation of multislice CT scanners. This effort, launched in 1999, focused on breakthroughs in analog-to-digital (A/D) converters, solid-state detectors, and related wide-coverage image reconstruction algorithms. The goal was a substantial increase in the number of detector cells and, thus, the number of slices that could be acquired per scan.

Launching VCT

By mid-2002, progress at the GRC was sufficiently encouraging—and the competitive situation at GE Healthcare sufficiently intense—that Joe Hogan decided to formally launch the next-generation CT development effort. Named the VCT ("Volume CT") program, this ambitious project was actually aimed at producing two new CT scanners in parallel—a 32-slice unit and a 64-slice unit. Either would have been a sufficient challenge for most organizations; GE thought it had the technical depth and breadth to accomplish both simultaneously. Time would tell.

Joe conferred with his key staff experts to select the right team to manage the VCT development program. Gary Strong, a 13-year CT engineering veteran, was appointed engineering program manager, and Scott Schubert was appointed marketing program manager. They immediately set to work assembling the team that would plan and execute the VCT design.

By now, the GRC was making excellent progress on two major technical breakthroughs: a miniaturized A/D converter chip called the Volara™ and the Backlit (back-connected) photo diode. The Volara chip, which contained 64 A/D converter channels, promised an unprecedented level of miniaturization. Two of these tiny chips could replace an entire circuit board while reducing power consumption and minimizing "noise." The Backlit photo diode was important because, unlike other CT diodes, it routed detector signal pathways out the back, rather than the sides. This provided the space needed for all the additional signal traces a 64-slice CT scanner would require and allowed the photodiodes to be "tiled" to provide 40mm scan coverage. This great progress notwithstanding, both of these devices still carried tremendous technical risk.

Gary Strong quickly assembled a supporting cast of engineering superstars and set them to work. Included were Gene Williams, lead system designer; Mark Profio, applications lead designer; Duane Filtz and Kevin Korthas, lead program integrators; Jiang Hsieh, Applied Science Laboratory; Evgeny Drapkin, reconstruction lead; Paavana Sainath, image quality lead; Tim Turco, Dave Hoffman, and Mike Hoge, detector engineering; Russ Hum and Brian Breuer, data acquisition system (DAS) engineering; Willi Hampel, Mike Peters, and Brian Graves, DAS and detector hardware engineering managers, respectively. Karen Procknow was recruited as applications specialist. These first-line team members could count on high-level support from people such as Peter Arduini, CT business general manager; Bob Armstrong, CT engineering GM; David Mliner, detector GM; and Jeff Kautzer, detector engineering GM.

The VCT engineering development team spent the second half of 2002 generating design concepts for the proposed scanners. The plan that gained the greatest traction was to double the size of the detector from the then current 20mm to 40mm, and quadruple the number of detector cells from 16 to 64. Not everyone was comfortable with those stretch targets; some felt it would be wise to stick with the 20mm detector to simplify the technical challenge.

As Gary Strong explained it:

Making this jump in performance was not only betting on risky new detectors and A/D converters. It would also require a correspondingly huge development effort in the CT gantry, operator console, patient table, system software, and image reconstruction. This program was arguably larger than the Light-Speed QX/i that had taken 4 years to develop. The difference was that we didn't have that much time given the competitive pressures.

Neither did the Milwaukee CT engineering organization have the resources to complete the product in less than 4 years. Some way had to be found—and found soon—to slash the time to market by half.

Hino to the rescue

For the previous two decades, since it had introduced the CT 8600 scanner, Yokogawa Medical Systems (YMS) had specialized in designing and producing performance-tier CT products, while the Milwaukee team was responsible for premium-tier systems. Some progress had been made in drawing the two groups closer together over the years, but they were still separate teams specializing in different product architectures. Now, the time had arrived to take global teamwork to the next level.

The opportunity came at a VCT "milestone" meeting held at the new CT headquarters building on the Waukesha campus in February of 2003. This session brought together large engineering contingents from Milwaukee and Hino (the Japanese contingent was led by Kazuhiko Sato, engineering general manager; Haruo Kurochi, detector operations general manager; and Mitsuru Yahata, engineering program manager), to settle three fundamental issues: 1) to set the detector and A/D design architecture; 2) explore the best way to use global engineering resources; and, 3) agree on a global organizational strategy in support of the VCT program. Meetings of this sort are usually a challenge, because different groups have different priorities. This was no exception.

"The first day was especially rocky," Gary recalled, "but we got things turned around by having everyone first focus on the technical details. That soon led to consensus on the architecture."

Next, the global team addressed the biggest technical risks of the program by agreeing to develop the 32-slice and 64-slice products concurrently but separately. This was a prudent decision given that the 64-slice machine would be using the risky Backlit photo diode, while the 32-slice version would rely on the conventional Frontlit technology. However, both would "burn the boats" by going to the same 40mm detector. In fact, the two systems would share 98% commonality, the primary difference being the photo diode.

The next issue was how to get the enormous amount of work done fast. Remember, Gary and his colleagues were certain they did not have sufficient resources to invent even one new product on the tight schedule, much less two. The global team discussed all the individuals in the Hino and Milwaukee engineering organizations and assigned each to specific program tasks regardless of location. Another huge breakthrough was assigning responsibility for the 64-slice unit to Milwaukee and the 32-slice version to Hino. This simultaneous combination and separation of responsibili-

top to bottom

The LightSpeed VCT cross-functional team in Milwaukee included: (front row, l–r) John Harold, Yash Shah, Marcella Molezzi, Kevin Korthas, Mark Hammel, Shawn Faessler, Gregg Zeman, Swami Narasimhan, Mike Hoge, and Joe Lacy; (back row, l–r) John Burie, Mary Sue Kulpins, Gene Williams, Santosh Nair, Gary Strong, Duane Filtz, Glenn Korhorn, Tim Turco, Jiang Hsieh, Brian Graves, and Aziz Ikhlef. (Not present were Erwin Sulma, Paavana Sainath, Scott Schubert, Karen Procknow, Mark Profio, Eric Stepanovich, Russ Hum, Evgeny Drapkin, Mike Pinterics, Shawn Ray, and Rich Pennington.)

The Hino development team celebrated the on-time introduction of the 32-slice LightSpeed VCT system.

ties was a brilliant stroke. Both groups felt a shared ownership for the entire product platform, yet each had local responsibility to speed their particular configuration to market. Engineers in yet a third location, Jerry Arenson's group in Haifa, Israel, were also added to the team, providing about one half the resources to support the VCT image reconstruction effort.

"Putting all our global resource together on a single project was a major organizational challenge," Gary said. "It required numerous face-to-face planning meetings, weekly and sometimes daily telephone conferences, and significant personal sacrifices by team members."

None more so than Hino's Koji Bessho. He had volunteered to help the Milwaukee team design the analog-to-digital converter circuit board, one of the most critical elements in the detector. However, since Koji lived in Japan and the detector was being developed in Milwaukee, he and the team had to somehow establish excellent teamwork and trust to execute such a complex design. Both were ultimately achieved largely due to Koji's willingness to fly halfway around the world to Milwaukee six times in a single year and stay there for up to 3 weeks per visit.

"We probably saw Bessho-san more than his family did during that year," chuckled Gary. "I felt so guilty, I would take him shopping for gifts for his family to thank them for their sacrifices. Many other VCT engineers were similarly dedicated."

A good example was collimator engineer, Takashi Yasunaga, who was in the U.S. on an expatriate assignment for the duration of the VCT program. He was invaluable in maintaining a close working relationship between the Milwaukee and Hino detector teams.

Selected to lead the Hino VCT engineering development team was Mitsuru Yahata, who reported to Kazuhiko Sato, engineering general manager. A little over a year later, Mitsuru was succeeded by Makoto Gono, a CT engineer with more than 20 years of experience dating back to the earliest days of YMS. Other key team members included Takashi Hatsukano, lead program integrator; Motoki Watanabe, lead system designer; Masaya Kumazaki, detector program manager; Haruo Kurochi, detector manager; and, of course, Koji Bessho. As Gary recalled:

> Gono-san and I had been working on joint projects for over a decade and had become close friends. I often visited his home when in Japan and was their family tour guide to Disney World when they visited the U.S. Our personal connection enhanced global teamwork by ensuring we had open and honest conversations when issues arose. Everyone had complete confidence that we would always have the best interests of both teams equally in mind.

Hitting its marks

One of the factors behind the decision to separate the two VCT configurations was the expectation their developmental timetables would differ by 9–12 months. In fact, first images from both the 32-slice unit in Hino and the 64-slice unit in Milwaukee were achieved on exactly the same day, April 2, 2004. Even more surprising, the final products were put into production only 3 months apart.

To appreciate the frenetic pace of the VCT program, consider the schedule to get the prototype 64-slice unit up and operating at Froedtert Memorial Lutheran Hospital in Milwaukee, site of the first "beta" unit. At 1:00 p.m. on June 10, 2004, it received engineering signoff at the Waukesha engineering center. By 1:00 a.m. the following morning, it was powered up at Froedtert, passed its image quality tests at 3:00 a.m., a local electrical inspection at 11:00 a.m., and scanned its first clinical patient at 1:00 p.m. It had taken less than 10 weeks for the 64-slice VCT prototype to go from initial test cell images to actual patient scans. That's especially impressive considering it took the LightSpeed QX/i over 11 months to reach that milestone.

This urgency was partly driven by the fact the first of two major CT commercial expositions each year was by now only about 10 days away. The Stanford Multislice Symposium is held in late June under the auspices of Stanford University. Dr. Gary Glazer and his radiology colleagues had launched it in 1998, in anticipation of the arrival of the LightSpeed QX/i prototype. That first symposium had been a big success and subsequently grew into an international event. Hundreds of radiologists from around the world attended each year; CT manufacturers considered it a preferred venue to introduce their latest breakthroughs.

Scott Schubert, VCT marketing program manager, was in charge of the VCT roll-out in Palo Alto, and he and his team laid on an impressive show. The huge GE Healthcare exhibit combined CT products and accessories, plus special contrast media offerings from GE Bio-Sciences. What everyone wanted to hear about, of course, was the rumored GE 64-slice machine. Though no hardware was in evidence, there were impressive clinical images on display and presentations describing the scanner's technical highlights. In the lecture hall, Dr. Dennis Foley from the Medical College of Wisconsin discussed the VCT's clinical benefits, such as faster scanning with high resolution, reduced contrast injection, pure arterial flow, and excellent small vessel visualization.

All the leading competitors were talking about their 64-slice scanner plans, and several claimed to have a number of clinical installations. None, however, had actual hardware on hand. So when GE opened a private tent to visitors that evening, they were surprised to see an actual LightSpeed VCT on display. Not only that, but it was

left
Despite enormous technical challenges, the Milwaukee development team had the 64-slice LightSpeed VCT system ready for production just 11 months after its first image was made. Sales in the first 2 years approached $1.5 *billion*.

opposite
GE purchased Imatron, a manufacturer of "electron beam tomography" scanners, in 2001. Designed for high-speed heart studies, the product was expanded to the dual slice C300 and, later, the eSpeed that brought temporal resolution down to 33 milliseconds. The introduction of 16- and 64-slice cardiac CT scanners eventually led to its withdrawal.

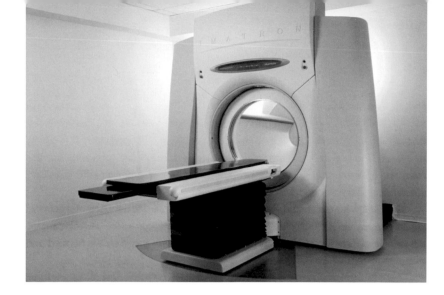

the real thing, as its missing covers clearly proved. It couldn't have been a bigger hit. For the next 2 hours, excited visitors were packed three deep as Scott Schubert, Gary Strong, and Makoto Gono provided a hands-on overview of the exciting new VCT.

Following up on success

During the ensuing months, the Froedtert clinical site hosted customer visits nearly every day. By the time the LightSpeed VCT was introduced at RSNA '04, more than 120 orders had already been received. It also was voted the "2004 Radiology Product of the Year" by *AuntMinnie*, the Internet radiology community. The VCT was also selected by *Popular Science* as "Best of What's New in Technology for 2004."

Even as the orders were flooding in, the Milwaukee team was working tirelessly to complete several aspects of the product, particularly 0.35 second gantry rotation necessary for one of the VCT's most important differential advantages, 5-beat cardiac. Working under intense pressure, the team again came through when it installed the first production prototype at Froedtert on November 22. The first 5-beat examination was obtained just days before the RSNA meeting was set to open, but a selection of great images was completed in time for the show.

5-beat cardiac

A major application of the LightSpeed VCT scanner is 5-beat cardiac. Because of its large (40mm) detector and high scanning speed, it can visualize the human heart within five beats, an important limit since the heartbeat remains constant for only about five beats during a breathhold then begins to accelerate as its tissue consumes the available oxygen. A constant heart rate minimizes image artifacts and enhances diagnostic detail, so it is important to collect the imaging data within the five-beat window. In comparison, 16-slice scanners with a 10mm detector can visualize only about 25% of the heart in 5 beats; a 32-slice scanner with a 20mm detector, about 50%.

The potential market for 5-beat cardiac is enormous. In the U.S. alone, an estimated 70 million people suffer from some level of cardiovascular disease (CVD). One death from this cause occurs every 34 seconds. Highly invasive coronary catheterization currently is the most common method for diagnosing and assessing CVD, but noninvasive coronary CT is gaining increasing popularity due to its greater safety and lower cost. By 2013, experts predict two thirds of all such studies will be conducted via coronary CT.

The honor of being the first 5-beat cardiac patient went to Mark Profio, applications lead system designer, who recalled:

While supporting the VCT 64 at Froedtert, the scheduled patient cancelled. Dr. Foley knew I was interested in cardiac scanning because of a history of heart disease in my family. He asked if I would be interested in becoming the first patient, and the rest is CT history. The scan and the images were flawless, and the results put me and my family at ease.

Production of the VCT started just 11 months after the first image, a full year-and-a-half faster than the LightSpeed QX/i. The original production plan was for $450 million in revenue the first year and $620 million the second. However, with orders flooding in from excited customers around the world, those goals were soon shattered. In the event, first year sales hit $630 million, and second year sales broke through $800 million. Better still, all development expenses were recouped in the first 6 months of production.

This huge upswing in volume put tremendous pressure on the manufacturing team led by Dee Mellor, Vice President, Global Supply Chain, that included Glenn Korhorn, manufacturing general manager; Anne Mahler, manufacturing business team leader; Shawn Faessler and Dick Boettner, manufacturing new product introduction leaders; and Dave Mliner, detector manufacturing manager. Gearing up the production effort to exceed the plan by such a huge margin was no simple task. The total supply chain had to be carefully managed to keep the assembly lines operating and shipments flowing. The team had daily, sometimes hourly, execution control meetings. Thirty extra technicians were added, and engineers were even used to staff the bays. Production ran literally around the clock, 7 days a week.

"I remember we were getting weekly calls from Joe Hogan during the spring and summer of 2005 asking us to give him another X machines," Korhorn laughed.

A key concern was detector reliability due to the tight integration of highly complex electronics, including the untried Volara chip and the new Backlit photodiode. The design incorporated over 250,00 interconnections and more than 10,000 integrated circuits. The detector engineering team, led by Jeff Kautzer and Brian Graves, established a new level of "Design for Reliability" incorporating several defense and automotive industry standards, including environmental stress test equipment. Funding for new test equipment was tight, so a high level delegation approached Paul Mirabella, President & CEO, Global Diagnostic Imaging, with a request for $5 million. "After Peter Arduini explained the request," Gary Strong recalled, "Paul asked Gene Saragnese, Vice President of Technology, if our request was for real. Gene replied that without the funding, Paul didn't have a program." (This special $5 million investment was repaid in just a few day's increased production that it helped make possible.)

The best . . . ever!

Today, almost all CT scanners being sold are multislice units; 4-slice machines are now considered "entry-level" technology. Indeed, until the global CT market peaked during the general economic slowdown of 2007–8, each GE CT product following the LightSpeed QX/i—8-, 16-, 32- and 64-slice models—sold at ever-increasing rates. For example, an unprecedented 250 orders for the LightSpeed VCT system had been taken before production actually began; GE manufactured nearly 300 units during the first 4 months.

The enthusiastic acceptance won by the VCT system around the globe was illustrated by the destinations of the first half-dozen machines to be shipped. Though the first 64-slice unit went to the University of Washington Medical Center in Seattle, the next five systems went to international customers, including the Universität-Klinikum Charite (Berlin); AsiaMedic (Singapore); Handai Fuzoku (Osaka); Städt Kliniken Dortmund-Mitte (Germany); and Toki Shimin (Japan).

At the 2006 GE Corporate Officers' Meeting in Boca Raton, Florida, Jeff Immelt, GE Chairman & CEO, added his own praise to the VCT program when he presented the "Chairman's Leadership Award" to Gene Saragnese, who had now become VP & GM, Global FCT (functional imaging and CT), and Jean-Michel Cossery, VP & Chief Marketing Officer. As Jeff termed it during the award ceremony, the VCT program had been "the most successful product launch in the history of GE Healthcare."

IT adventures

GE's Healthcare IT (information technology) business under Vishal Wanchoo, Vice President, Healthcare Information Technology, had come of age during the 1997–2003 period through a combination of internal developments and strategic acquisitions. By this time, its Centricity® portfolio of image and information management products covered the spectrum from picture archiving and communication systems (PACS), through office-based management systems, to enterprise-wide IT solutions. GE was a strong competitor in all and a leader in many.

According to Wanchoo, Joe Hogan was a strong and extremely knowledgeable advocate of healthcare IT. "Having the attention and support of the CEO, especially when your business is one of the smallest within GE Healthcare, was really a critical aspect of getting the investment required to grow," he said. "Joe was a big asset."

The Healthcare IT Imperative

Jim Potchen, who built the radiology department at Michigan State University literally from a single portable x-ray unit into one of the nation's most respected academic programs, was a valued advisor to GE Medical Systems/Healthcare of long standing. He had been urging the company to take a new view of "information" for many years. So he was especially pleased with the progress made in IT by Immelt and Hogan.

"An issue I've wrestled with the imaging industry about is getting them to understand what their value added really is," he said "They don't just produce equipment but information to guide physician decision-making—the information their equipment brings to patient care. When Jeff Immelt took over, he understood the value of being in the information business right away, as did Joe Hogan after him. When GE bought its first IT company—Logician, Joe and his wife, Lisa, flew to Lansing for a celebration. That set the tone for a series of other IT acquisitions that expanded the information system concept beyond radiology into the electronic medical record. This has led to a whole new business area with a much bigger potential. I believe the necessary components for widespread adoption of real-time decision support tools for diagnostic imaging are already in place. We must simply connect

and use them. The only way we are going to get that information is through the electronic medical record."

Perhaps the most significant IT move during the Hogan era was the 2005 acquisition of IDX Systems Corporation in Burlington, Vermont. IDX, founded in 1969, had emerged as a leading healthcare IT provider with a wide range of highly integrated IT products to improve the quality of care, enhance medical outcomes, and reduce healthcare costs. In September 2005, they jointly announced GE's intention to purchase IDX's outstanding shares for approximately $1.2 billion.

"GE and IDX have a shared vision on how to accelerate the adoption of electronic health records across the globe," Joe explained at the time of the announcement. "We believe our combined offerings are in line with where healthcare is headed and match the needs of our customers."

The transaction was completed in early 2006, when IDX became an integral part of GE Healthcare IT. "GE's acquisition of IDX allows us to provide new and more comprehensive ways for healthcare practitioners to manage the explosion of data," Wanchoo said. " Our IT tools, capabilities, and global scope have the potential to transform the way healthcare is delivered."

The IDX acquisition brought GE approximately 2,000 skilled employees, half a billion dollars in revenue, and a highly complementary product line. Now, GE offered a comprehensive suite of financial and business management solutions for group practices, hospitals, and integrated delivery networks, plus its industry-leading PACS and radiology information systems.

Another farsighted IT initiative during this period was GE's 2005 agreement with Intermountain Healthcare, Salt Lake City, Utah, to conduct a 10-year technology development collaboration. Combining Intermountain's internationally recognized expertise in clinical informatics research with GE Healthcare's advanced clinical software applications and market strength, this agreement was expected to generate substantial advances in a number of important healthcare IT areas—imaging, perioperative, PACS, pharmacy, bio, and ambulatory electronic medical records.

"We colocated 150 GE engineers at the customer's site to work with Intermountain employees as one team codeveloping IT software technology," Wanchoo explained. "This was a first-ever venture for GE Healthcare IT and strongly supported by Joe."

Europe turns the corner

As we have already seen, developing the European business had neither been simple nor swift. From the establishment of GE Medical Systems Europe in 1984, through the CGR acquisition and a series of subsequent leadership changes, nothing had

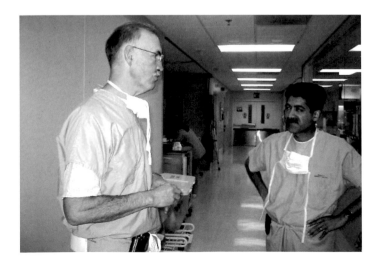

Up Close And Personal: Vishal Wanchoo (right) conferred with Dr. Kevin Tremper after observing procedures at the University of Michigan Medical Center.

seemed to bring the prosperity that was expected. Significant gains had certainly been achieved, but the bottom line was still the wrong color. Jeff Immelt had managed to pare the losses during his tenure, but continuing investments in Europe, combined with disappointing business results, assured tens of millions in negative earnings. However, he had laid the groundwork for a major turnaround, especially with the 1999 appointment of Reinaldo Garcia as President & CEO, GE Medical Systems Europe.

Garcia had first gone to Europe in 1997 on a manufacturing assignment, then moved over to lead the European service organization for three years. After a year and a half back in the U.S., he returned to Europe in 1999 to lead the entire business. "It had been faltering in execution and the delivery of results but I was pleased to have the challenge," he said.

By the time Joe Hogan took over Medical Systems in late 2000, Reinaldo had 2 years of experience in his high-stress position and was achieving double-digit growth rates. The amount of red ink, though still substantial, was declining, and steady progress had been made in restructuring the European operations (see the Immelt chapter for details). Now the time had arrived to find out, once and for all, if the business could turn the corner to profitability.

The nature and scope of GE's healthcare business in Europe—and around the world—had been changing in recent years with the emergence of cardiology, patient monitoring, information technology, and ultrasound, alongside the traditional diagnostic imaging offering. One of the interesting consequences of this wider business scope was GE's growing importance to the overall healthcare community. Not only was the company a major player in the world of diagnostic imaging, but it now was gaining greater credibility with both customers and healthcare policymakers. To borrow a boxing term, GE was beginning to "punch its weight" in Europe.

Among the factors instrumental in making Europe successful, two especially spring to mind. First was the specialization of the sales force that allowed the right level of resources to be focused on each product line and major area of application (cardiology, cancer care, women's health, etc.). Second was the redefinition of service. Not only did it become a separate profit and loss center in its own right but also grew to encompass much more than equipment maintenance. For example, service now included a range of offerings that added customer value, such as programs to help providers understand how their equipment assets were being used and to manage them more effectively.

Undoubtedly, the most remarkable transformation that occurred in Europe during the early years of the Hogan era was in the nature of the organization itself. The acquisitions of Amersham in the U.K. and Instrumentarium in Finland greatly increased the number of GE Healthcare employees outside the U.S. Whereas, 15 years before,

the large majority of employees had been based in the United States, now the majority was in international assignments. The vision of globalization begun under John Trani, and the amazing results Jeff Immelt had created by making the organization work together on a global basis, were now being redeemed as Joe greatly expanded the international footprint of the business. The first phase of globalization was now complete; GE Healthcare had become truly deployed on a global scale.

In China for China

Both John Trani and Jeff Immelt had invested considerably to refashion GE Medical Systems into a truly "globalized" organization. A series of acquisitions had been completed, new joint ventures established, regional sales and service organizations introduced, and special management training initiatives launched. Progress was being made, but GE Medical Systems still remained a largely "U.S.-centric" business, though with a large and growing global presence and a developing global attitude.

Upon his arrival, Joe Hogan immediately recognized the globalization imperative and resolved to apply even more focus on this challenge. Fortunately, he already had strong supporters in key international assignments, such as Reinaldo Garcia in Europe, Naren Gursaheney in Asia, and Chih Chen in China. Joe spent a great amount of his time and energy during the first few months visiting customers around the world and assessing GE's operations in the various regions. It was during one of these stops that he met with Chih Chen, his China Operations president.

"Chih and I were kicking around some ideas when he told me that GE had a terrific opportunity in China but that he couldn't get the engineers in Milwaukee and Buc to respond fast enough or in the right way" Joe remembered, adding:

> Here's a guy who has never gotten his due. Chih built the best sales force in the history of man; a cultured organization of incredible urgency and accountability to customers. He never tried to erect a fence around China but asked people to come and spend time there. He was always with customers and government officials to set the stage somewhere for the deal.

When Joe and Chih met in 2002, GE's medical business in China was growing at an annual rate of 50%. Nonetheless, Chih didn't think he was getting the right level and type of support to take advantage of the opportunities. The China Operation was trying to move beyond the "product assembly" role and wanted to design, engineer, and manufacture more sophisticated x-ray and CT products for both Chinese and global customers. Substantial progress had been made in that direction, as shown by the CT/e and Proteus products, but Chih was impatient for more. That's what had prompted his complaint about Milwaukee and Buc.

above
Reinaldo Garcia addressed his team at the 2000 kickoff meeting, his first as CEO of the Europe organization.

left
Chih Chen

In 2008, Jeff Immelt (center) brought the GE Board of Directors and several senior staff to Beijing to visit the remarkable organization Chih and Joe had created in China.

He had a good point. GE Corporate's strategy for China would demand an even higher level of performance from his team. As Jeff Immelt, now the new GE chairman, stated in the company's 2002 annual report:

> People talk about China as either an opportunity or a threat. The most successful China strategy is to capitalize on its market growth while exporting its deflationary power. We have a vision for China: $5 billion in revenue and $5 billion in sourcing—"5 × 5"—by 2005.

Medical Systems, of course, was expected to contribute a substantial amount toward that goal. Joe and Chih welcomed the challenge, since the strong overall growth of the Chinese healthcare market, compared with GEMS's current share, presented a huge business opportunity. First, though, some way had to be found to address Chih's real and rational concerns.

"You have to remember that we had just come out of the overseas debt crisis that had followed the Russia collapse, so any businessman would have wondered whether the explosion in China was for real," Joe commented. "There was no question by this time that China was a freight train, and we had to get aboard. The challenge was in deciding how much resource, time, and focus to put into China."

Before, the attraction had always been one of taking advantage of the low cost of labor in China, an arbitrage move to manufacture things at a lower cost there. Joe recognized this was ultimately a dead-end road for GEMS, since only about 15% of its costs were in labor. "That's when we realized that in order to satisfy the systemic demand that was developing in China, we were going to have to move a huge amount of resources there," he stated.

The phrase Joe coined to convey this idea was "In China for China." In other words, he and Chih wanted to position all those capabilities in China that were required to serve Chinese customers. That meant local engineering resources to design products for Chinese customers, local marketing resources to sense what the marketplace would want, and local support capabilities to keep everything working.

"It was not a matter of providing better distribution," Joe explained, "but having the capability to respond better and faster to local demand."

His view was completely consistent with GE Corporate's plans for China. With company revenues already approaching $2.6 billion there, significant investments were being made to generate additional growth. For instance, a new Global Research Center facility was being established in Shanghai to develop and expand the capabilities of Chinese suppliers to create technologies GE would be able to use globally. Special programs had also been deployed to train GE's in-country business leaders and their customers in the company's proven management techniques. And, of course, the GE components leading the thrust into China—Medical Systems, Aircraft Engines, Plastics, and Power Systems—were developing local products to solve local needs. In other words, GE was treating China exactly as it did other developed markets, such as the U.S., Japan, and Europe.

From senior government officials to the man on the street, the Chinese noted GE's respect for, and investment in, their country and responded positively. Said Chih:

> Joe formalized the 'In China for China' strategy and made it clear to everyone why it was the right thing to do. He helped us become a self-sufficient organization by building up our local capabilities in terms of facilities and product scope. For example, Joe supported the expansion of the contrast media plant in Shanghai that we had acquired through Amersham. It became the first ever FDA export-certified reagent manufacturer in China.

Perhaps his most far-reaching step in securing the future of the China business was to reorganize it as a separate region reporting directly to him. Chih, naturally, was appointed President & CEO of GE Healthcare China.

Like Jeff Immelt before him, Joe also went to extraordinary lengths to establish close, personal relationships with key Chinese customers. Whenever he was in the country, he always made a point of paying extended calls on key customers to find out what was on their minds and how GE could serve them better. The insights he gained—and shared—during these visits had very positive consequences for business and personal relationships alike.

Another of Joe's legacies that would benefit GE and its Chinese customers for many years to come was the so-called "rural initiative." This was a special effort he initiated and funded to assure the ongoing development of low-end healthcare products to help deliver high-impact care to the 800 million people in rural China who were not being served. "This is a huge opportunity that will help power our continued growth in China for the next 25 years," Chih predicted.

Europe...and beyond

In early 2003, Hogan changed the globalization game by consolidating all of his international operations—GEMS Europe, GEMS Asia, China Operations, etc.—into a single new organization. Reinaldo was appointed President & CEO, International, which he continued to lead from his headquarters in Buc. He explained:

> The creation of International allowed us to take the best practices that were bringing us commercial success in Europe about 10 or 12 time zones east. At that time, Asia meant Japan and China, plus everything else. Nobody wants to be thought of as "everything else," so the first thing we did was to combine Korea, Australia, India, and Southeast Asia into the new Asia Growth Markets region. They were no longer orphans of a larger region but their own region with their own resources and recognition. As a result, their growth in the next few years was three or four times what it had been in the previous 5 or 6 years.

Reinaldo also applied this strategy of finer geographic focus to great advantage in those areas of Europe, the Middle East, and Africa that he also perceived to be underserved. He created the new Eastern and Africa Growth Markets (EAGM) region that included Russia and the Confederation of Independent States, Central Asia, the Middle East, and Africa. These markets had been served by the former Europe, Middle East, and Africa organization with considerable success in the late 1990s and early 2000s but things had changed. As their individual economies expanded at healthy growth rates, it was apparent GE needed to strengthen local marketing and decision-making capabilities in all these areas. So Reinaldo borrowed from himself and duplicated the Asia Growth Markets model here.

"The concept is when something grows, you break it into smaller parts and make each of them grow again into large businesses," he explained. "That was one of the themes under Joe Hogan and a source of constant growth in international markets."

Turkey offered a great example of this strategy at work. For many years, it had been one of numerous countries within the Europe, Middle East, and Africa region. As it began to adjust its economic and political policies with a view toward possible European Union membership, the market began to take on increasing vibrancy. However, as a third-world country within a region reporting into a "pole" of a U.S.-centric organization, it didn't register very high on the visibility scale.

The effect of Reinaldo's new EAGM organization was to make Turkey a discrete region with its own resources, project managers, and markets developers, plus a very short communication channel to the top leadership. Opportunities that previously might have taken some time to bring to the attention of decision-makers could now be shared much faster. Though a thriving healthcare market had been in existence for some time, it now became obvious to everyone. As Reinaldo stated:

> The growth rates we have experienced in Turkey are just phenomenal—30–40% per year. That's because they no longer have to depend on resources sitting in Europe but have the local capabilities to take advantage of the opportunities they find there.

A similar tale was written in Russia that, until the EAGM was created, was treated like a zone within the Eastern Europe region. This was clearly not an appropriate way to approach a proud nation of such enormous size and potential wealth. Now, as a separate region in its own right, Russia was directly in Reinaldo's line of sight through frequent business reviews conducted with his in-country managers:

> A big theme during Joe's leadership was "in country for country." China's needs are somewhat different than India's or Southeast Asia's. It is important to create appropriate capabilities in each country to address their individual needs. Much has been done and more will be done, not only in the Far East but in other international markets. This is extremely important as we continue to globalize the business.

In summing up the accomplishments of his international leadership team, Joe commented:

> Where can you find a better international business person than Reinaldo Garcia? He is an ambassador, speaks several languages, and loves international business. The growth in Europe under his leadership was phenomenal. He and his team, especially Jean Yves Durel, Richard di Benedetto, and Jan DeWitte, got us into the Middle East, Saudi Arabia, the CIS, and Eastern Europe. They also did well in some of the more traditional markets, where it is hard to compete, such as Italy, Spain, France, and the U.K. He planted flags all over the world and ended up with an international business that is one of the stronger and more profitable parts of GE Healthcare today.

Disaster in the desert

As we have seen, the period spanning the Immelt and Hogan years was marked by frenetic growth, especially through acquisitions. In the decade from Immelt's arrival

left to right
The "President's Club Award" was presented annually to the top field performers from the four major international regions. Joe Hogan (left) presented a 2008 award to Wang Le from China, who was accompanied by his wife to the Istanbul event. At the right is Reinaldo Garcia, president and CEO of GE Healthcare International.

The headquarters of OEC Medical Systems in Salt Lake City, Utah.

until the integration of Amersham, GE Medical Systems/Healthcare had grown by a factor of three. Unusual in a company the size and gravitas of General Electric, some thought its healthcare business was acting more like a Silicon Valley start-up during the years of the "dot.com" bubble.

This unprecedented growth was producing stresses and stretch marks on the various business systems and procedures that bonded the worldwide organization together. The demands of integrating all these different organizations into the GE model was causing severe strains, especially on the financial accounting systems and quality processes.

The first visible crack appeared at OEC Medical Systems, Salt Lake City, Utah, a highly regarded manufacturer of surgical mobile c-arm imaging systems that GE had acquired in 1999. OEC enjoyed an outstanding reputation for quality, reliability, and value earned over more than two decades of market leadership in the surgical mobile imaging market. Its capabilities, combined with GE's strengths in state-of-the-art digital x-ray systems, gave the company a highly competitive offering and an extended reach into the fast-growing area of interventional procedures. Things couldn't have been going better in Deseret.

The first intimation of trouble came during a late 2004 inspection of OEC's manufacturing facilities by Food and Drug Administration officials. They had detected a series of seemingly discrete violations that were documented in an FDA-483 Inspectional Observations report. A copy was handed to local managers at the conclusion of the inspection. An official warning letter from FDA headquarters soon followed in early 2005 demanding these lapses be corrected prior to a follow-up inspection.

Meanwhile Hogan had asked Peter McCabe to expand his Lean and Six Sigma management role to include quality. Recognizing the seriousness of the quality issue and its potential impact upon other areas of GE Healthcare, Pete, accompanied by Anita LeFevre from Human Resources, raised the alarm on a global basis. Over a period of several months, the two traveled the world visiting every major GE Healthcare facility to assess local regulatory quality systems, identify deficiencies, share best practices, and do whatever they could to make certain the problems uncovered in the surgery business didn't recur elsewhere.

As Hogan later acknowledged:

> We treated that warning letter like every other warning letter we have ever gotten. We brought consultants in and did all the right things. But when the FDA came back, they didn't look at the FDA-483 deficiencies detected in their first visit; instead, they looked at the systemic quality effort at OEC.

A surprise reinspection in August of 2006 uncovered significant deficiencies in complying with the FDA's Quality System regulation—a system of rules covering the quality assurance program for manufacturing these devices, procedures to prevent and correct problems, product design controls, and procedures to process and analyze complaints. As the FDA has stated, "When a device is designed and manufactured without adequate Quality System regulation controls, the safety and effectiveness of the device cannot be ensured."

Joe immediately sent Pete to Salt Lake City to manage the OEC situation first hand. Diane (Dee) Mellor, Vice President, Global Supply Chain, succeeded him in the new position of Chief Quality Officer.

"We had an opportunity to properly address their original findings and thought we did," Dee stated. "The regulators expect you to take a holistic and systemic approach to fixing your quality system. Clearly, our actions were considered inadequate."

Though OEC had voluntarily stopped shipping its extremely successful OEC 9900 product in September 2006 in hopes of containing the situation, it was too late. The FDA made the seriousness of their concerns clear with a consent decree, signed in January of 2007, that totally shut down the business. OEC could no longer design, manufacture, or market its products. Even its freedom to service c-arms already in the field was greatly limited. A thriving, vital, successful business had suddenly been brought to a total standstill. The shock was profound.

"It showed that FDA enforcement in the device industry was going to become much more active," Joe later said. "It also forced us to create a quality management system for the entire business literally from the ground up."

For many years, FDA inspections of medical device manufacturers had been a routine event, especially so for producers of such relatively "low risk" devices as diagnostic imaging equipment. That had begun to change as the FDA came under increasing Congressional scrutiny and criticism due to several widely publicized lapses involving both pharmaceuticals and medical devices. In response, the agency had stepped up its surveillance and enforcement activities to an unprecedented level.

GE had become especially vulnerable to this increased monitoring for two principal reasons. First, the Amersham acquisition had expanded GE Healthcare's offering far beyond relatively "low risk" DI equipment into the "high risk" world of pharmaceuticals. Second, various other acquisitions had increased its exposure in more sensitive medical device areas such as anesthesiology, maternal/infant care, and surgical support. As a result, FDA regulators had begun to take a much more active interest in what the company was doing.

Thus, the OEC incident was the first symptom of a potentially greater problem that might affect all of GE Healthcare.

Managing the crisis

With its operations now shut down by the FDA's stop-shipment order, OEC was facing a process of third-party certifications and FDA reinspections to be allowed to resume shipping, plus 5 years of third-party audits and FDA reinspections after that to get the consent decree entirely lifted. But that target was tenuous; many of the device and drug manufacturers that previously had found themselves in similar circumstances failed to meet even the 5-year goal for ending the consent decree.

Dee Mellor said GE's initial reaction was shock followed by a demand for action:

> That's when Joe asked me to take over the quality job. We soon agreed that we needed to allocate significant resources to get OEC back into operation and build a new, centralized quality organization for the entire business. It was a test of the leadership team and required their complete commitment, since they would have to give up resources to the quality activity that normally would have gone to new products.

To appreciate the scale of the effort, consider this: in the first year following entry of the consent decree, GE Healthcare invested over $50 million to hire an additional 500 quality experts as new employees. That investment was doubled the following year. Considerable expenditures were also made to retain skilled consultants. These resources were needed to help develop and implement a new quality management system not only at OEC but throughout the organization. To find so many so quickly, GE recruited across the spectrum—from other medical device and pharmaceutical manufacturers, such as Medtronic, Boston Scientific, and Baxter Healthcare, to seasoned former and current staff from the Food and Drug Administration itself.

"In effect, we hired 4,000 years of FDA medical device regulatory experience in just a few months," Joe stated. "We had to, because if they came in and shut us down, we would lose our number one market position in a heartbeat."

The initial focus was to get the right people with the right skills deployed to Salt

Lake City. Joe had already sent Peter McCabe to lead the crippled business, where he soon was joined by Maria Frame, previously the Healthcare IT quality leader. Other volunteers who would prove critical to the turnaround followed, including Carrie Ellington-Manner, service; Bob Hauck, engineering; Greg Henry, finance; and Bridget Bevilacqua, software.

Also "leading from the front" were a number of key people in Milwaukee such as Mark Vachon, President & CEO, Diagnostic Imaging; Mike Barber, Chief Technology Officer; Patti Kaeding, regulatory counsel; and, of course, Joe Hogan. Every member of Joe's staff and all of the P&L leaders also signed up to the new quality strategy.

"There was never anyone who said OEC was just a surgery issue," recalled Mellor. "Instead they all rallied around the cry of 'One GE Healthcare.' It was a test of the leadership team, and the leaders stood up."

The first challenge was to somehow survive through the remainder of 2006. Following the significant deficiencies found during the August OEC inspection, the FDA initiated a series of inspections of other GEHC plants at least every other week during the remainder of the year. The entire business was now under extreme pressure.

Two major deliverables were anticipated in the OEC turnaround effort. First was the creation of a new quality management system, which is where Maria Frame and her team played such an important role. Second was a literal redesign of the products from scratch, beginning with a statement of intended use and continuing through the entire FDA-mandated process of updating designs and creating documentation.

In essence, the FDA expects all medical device manufacturers to understand what their customers want, design and manufacture products that meet those expectations, and service them in the field to assure that long-term performance and reliability meet design standards. As Mike Barber phrased it:

> You have to get the fundamentals right. Joe said that there are islands of excellence everywhere surrounded by a sea of mediocrity. We had to make our quality processes excellent, repeatable, and sustainable. Everyone had to understand the essence of the regulatory requirements and their roles in ensuring patient safety.

Over the coming months, the OEC turnaround team, and all the other Salt Lake City employees, shed blood, sweat, and tears in addressing the thousands of details. Everyone was enthusiastically dedicated to the effort, and progress was surprisingly swift. By late December 2007, the quality management system had been certified by a third-party inspection with very few findings. This was followed by an intensive FDA reinspection that lasted several weeks more.

"The day the FDA lifted the stop-shipment order on the OEC 9900 ESP/GSP in May 2008, there was a loud 'hooray' heard from Salt Lake City," Dee said. "It had taken only a year-and-a-half, but it felt like a lifetime."

A contributing factor to the speedy resolution was an unusual concession in the consent decree that specified three inspections over the course of the corrective process rather than one. This arrangement permitted the stop-shipment order to be lifted for certain product lines without requiring remediation to other product lines. However, a total of 919 days went by before the full 9900 c-arm product could be shipped again.

"OEC must also be credited for building such strong relationships with their customers," Mellor stated. "They waited while the problems were being fixed, and there was a massive backlog of orders when we finally reopened the doors."

Pete McCabe described quality procedures as the hardware and culture as the software:

top to bottom
Reconstructing OEC's quality compliance system required the efforts of hundreds of people over many months.

Every OEC c-arm system was painstakingly tested to assure it met stringent quality and performance standards.

At Last! OEC 9900 ESP/GSP mobile c-arms are readied for shipment after the FDA stop-shipment order was lifted

The quality challenge is not just writing the procedures but how you interpret and execute them when nobody is watching. While procedures provide a directional focus consistent with the regulations, what makes you compliant is the spirit behind how you interpret and execute them over and over again in a consistent manner.

This was the key cultural challenge driving the new way of thinking about quality throughout all of GE Healthcare. "Getting it right" had to trump "meeting the schedule." At OEC, every organization in the business was required to define what "getting it right" meant to their team and make it the backbone of their mission. Now, the same task was being ramped-up into a large-scale effort to create a more robust, comprehensive quality management system for the global business.

With OEC's experience as a guide, great progress was soon made. The focus was on operationalizing and sustaining quality by using Lean and Six Sigma methodology to keep the quality processes simple and help people integrate them into their everyday work. Of course, FDA quality inspections continue to this day and findings are sometimes made. What's different is that quality issues are almost always discovered first through GE's own quality management system, rather than an outside inspection.

Scores of people deserve credit for the OEC turnaround and creation of the new quality management system. Besides those individuals already mentioned, other noteworthy contributors included John Schmeling, Kathy Warren, Jim Dennison, Ron Sullivan, Xiao Zhang, Liz Blackwood, Tracy Zimmerman, Andrea Dircks-Larsen, Jeff Kautzer, and Jon Snyder.

However, the people who really were responsible for the OEC turnaround—and inspiring a new culture of quality within GE Healthcare—were the men and women of OEC. For over 900 consecutive days, they showed up every day to work harder than they could ever have imagined in jobs they weren't hired to fill. Hundreds of thousands of man hours of engineering were applied and tens of thousands of tests run to remedy defects, documentation rewritten, files rebuilt, and all the rest of it. Perhaps their most important accomplishment, however, was to totally rewire OEC's quality culture to make these changes permanent. As McCabe later noted:

> You can only appreciate the situation when you live it yourself, because when you shut down a business nothing works. You spend every day convincing customers the equipment is safe, persuading suppliers to stay with you, giving your fellow employees some hope for the future. We learned that you have to treat regulators with the same respect as customers. It was a tough lesson, but the experience will remain for a lifetime.

Joe Hogan's long-term view of the OEC debacle put it into another perspective:

> People might define the Hogan era in a number of ways—tripling the size of the business, expanding into life sciences, becoming much more global, changing the accountability structure, and so on. But I think our most significant accomplishment was putting a comprehensive quality program into place. It was led by the FDA issue but took advantage of that disaster to persuade the business of the fundamental importance of quality controllership and compliance. That was a tough cultural change, but it's something that everyone can be proud of today.

Ultrasound unleashed

By about 2000, GE Medical Systems had become a serious challenger for the global ultrasound market lead due, in large part, to the management and marketing

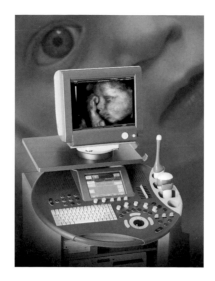
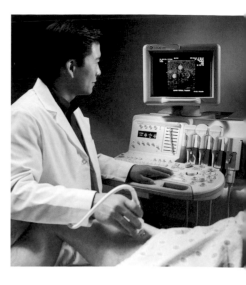

acumen of Omar Ishrak. Joe Hogan stated:

> Omar built an unbelievable strategy. Ultrasound was built through a series of acquisitions around the world—the U.S., Israel, Norway, Germany, India, and so on. As a student of the world, he was the only person who could really orchestrate all these pieces and bring them together in a coherent way to make a product for different world markets. His value strategy recognized we had to have in-country engineers who understood the needs of that country and could design an appropriate answer.

Though it sounds simple in concept, this strategy is incredibly difficult to implement, because traditional interests are reluctant to cede control. John Trani had made certain to set Omar up as an independent business with complete control over all aspects of the ultrasound business around the world, a strategy reinforced by Jeff Immelt and Joe Hogan in their turns. This was an unprecedented organizational innovation for a mainstream business at GE Medical System.

Significant acquisitions late in Immelt's tenure helped keep Ultrasound on its high-growth trajectory, such as the December 2000 deal for Parallel Design, Inc., Phoenix, Arizona, an OEM transducer supplier. This deal substantially reduced GE's need to outsource expensive probes, enhanced its competitive position in this key technology, and helped it meet fast-growing sales volume requirements. Parallel Design, which was designated an Ultrasound Transducer Center of Excellence, would become the largest transducer manufacturer in the world.

The following year, Joe Hogan closed the next major ultrasound deal with the acquisition of Kretztechnik, an Austrian firm that had become a leader in 3D and 4D ultrasound. It had been purchased in 1996 by Medison, a Korean firm with a small line of MRI and x-ray imaging equipment, and went on to introduce its breakthrough "live 3D" (4D) technology. The Kretztechnik Voluson™ 730 system was among the first to offer this capability. Joe and Omar wanted to add advanced 3D and 4D imaging to the GE portfolio, and Kretztechnik was the ideal solution. The GE Voluson 730D, introduced in 2003, became the most successful 3D/4D system ever in terms of share, eventually commanding 60% of the U.S. OB/GYN ultrasound market.

A number of other important ultrasound products were introduced during the early years of the Hogan era, such as the Vivid™ 3, Vivid 5, and LOGIQ 100 systems. They were soon followed by the Vivid 4 cardiovascular, Vivid 7, LOGIQ 3, LOGIQ 5, LOGIQ 7, and LOGIQ 9 systems. The latter featured a significant new software-based design, the first of its kind for a high-end general imaging system and a major advance over

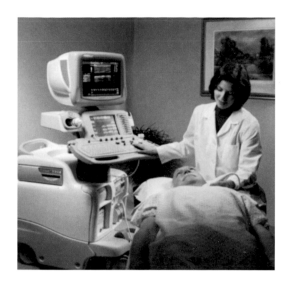

left to right

The Voluson 730 system featured breakthrough "live 3D" imaging.

The LOGIQ 700 Expert Series ultrasound system.

The premium LOGIQ 9 ultrasound system.

the LOGIQ 700 in image quality and performance features. It provided a strong base in the radiology segment and earned GE a new level of respect from luminaries and general clinical practitioners alike.

"From a start-up to a strong contender, GE was now emerging as a market leader," Omar noted. "People were beginning to look to us as the thought leader in terms of defining where the ultrasound industry would progress and driving it in that direction."

This amazing transformation in GE's fortunes wasn't accomplished with just top-end technologies alone. Attention was given to every segment of the ultrasound market. A good example was the remarkable LOGIQ Book, the company's first laptop-sized ultrasound system. Though compact, it offered a remarkable feature set based on the same architecture as the premium LOGIQ 9 system. Its success launched the company into an entirely new ultrasound segment.

GE's worldwide ultrasound sales broke through the $1 billion barrier in 2004, giving it the #1 global position for the first time and making it a strong #2 in the U.S. That same year, two new compact products—the LOGIQ *i* and Vivid *i*—were launched, followed by three more in 2006. The GE family of compact imagers now included:

- Voluson *i*, the first real-time, 4D system for OB/GYN.
- LOGIQ *i*, a premium imager for general radiology, musculoskeletal, neonatal, breast, and vascular applications.
- LOGIQ *c*, especially designed to support real-time clinical decisions in emergency and surgical settings.
- Vivid *i*, high-performance cardiovascular capabilities in a highly portable, wireless design.
- Vivid *e*, a dedicated cardiac ultrasound tool for the physician office.

With these latest additions, GE soon became the world market share leader in this segment in 2006 with a 43% share and total sales of $174 million. This was 74% more than its 2005 segment sales, and well ahead of the overall 41% growth in the compact market. GE further distanced itself from its next nearest rival in 2007 with compact sales reaching $260 million. Joe recalled:

Thanks to Omar, GE was the first of the major competitors to get into portable ultrasound. That business grew to $300 million in 2008, with contribution margins in the 75% range. Amazing! They changed the complexion of this business, because these 7–8 pound units could do everything a LOGIQ 500 did 10 years ago and do it twice as well.

"Leading the way globally shows our commitment to growing compact ultrasound," stated Omar. "By migrating our engineering innovations across multiple ultrasound platforms and customizing ultrasound for specific care areas, we are bringing breakthrough technologies to more patients and clinicians worldwide."

In recognition of Omar's remarkable successes and demonstrated skills, Joe had appointed him President & CEO, Clinical Systems, in 2005. Besides his continuing responsibilities for the global ultrasound business, he now was in charge of patient monitoring, diagnostic ECG, densitometry, respiratory care, anesthesia delivery, and maternal-infant care products as well. He would soon be appointed President & CEO, Healthcare Systems, with responsibilities for the ultrasound, CT, patient monitoring MR, molecular imaging, interventional x-ray, life support, and home health businesses. Enthused Hogan:

Omar built a truly global, diverse business from the highest end product on wheels, to the portable color PC that you can carry around with you, down to the lowest B&W scanner in India. When he arrived, the ultrasound business caught fire and went from #7 in the world to an unequivocal #1 today with sales over $2 billion. And he orchestrated it across all the national boundaries, combining the cardiology capability in Norway with miniaturization capability in Japan, and with packaging capability in Israel. He is the best international business person I know... and the world's nicest human being.

High praise, indeed, from someone who also had carved out a remarkable international business career.

New challenges, new opportunities

In the summer of 2008, with his strategic growth agenda for GE Healthcare largely accomplished, Joe Hogan was seeking another challenge. His search led him to ABB Group, the huge Swiss-Swedish multinational headquartered in Zürich, Switzerland. ABB is one of the largest engineering companies and largest conglomerates in the world with operations in 100 countries and approximately 115,000 employees. On July 17, 2008, ABB's Board of Directors announced Joe's appointment as chief executive officer effective September 1, 2008.

John Dineen was selected to succeed him as President and CEO of GE Healthcare.

Joseph M. Hogan

Looking Forward

Built upon 115 years of transformational advances, GE Healthcare had become a global leader in medical imaging and information technologies, medical diagnostics, patient monitoring systems, drug systems, drug discovery, biopharmaceutical manufacturing technologies, and performance solutions. Now, in concert with the considerable and varied resources of the entire General Electric Company, it was seeking to extend the benefits of modern medical technologies to more people in more places.

GE's healthymagination initiative was launched in mid-2009 to help create a simpler healthcare system delivering better care at lower costs. As a part of its initial commitment, GE pledged to invest $6 billion in technologies and performance tools to reduce, by 2015, the costs of many healthcare procedures and processes by 15%; increase access to essential health services and technologies by 15%; and improve quality and efficiency by 15%.

In support of healthymagination, GE Healthcare announced plans to create simpler, more affordable products matched to the needs of rural and other underserved markets, while putting more innovative technologies into the hands of clinicians around the world. Two excellent examples of such economical new technologies were the Venue 40 compact ultrasound unit and the Brivo DR-F digital x-ray system. They brought an unprecedented level of advanced imaging to many areas where access was previously limited. Imaginative advances in maternal and infant care, breast cancer screening, portable ECG monitoring, home-based health services, rural clinics, prevention programs, and more, would soon join them.

At this stage in its history, the GE Healthcare story had spanned three different centuries and nearly 12 decades. It had reached $17 billion in worldwide sales, employed over 46,000 dedicated people in rewarding jobs around the world, and was the only major General Electric business headquartered outside the U.S. Though its early leaders and employees could hardly have foreseen the size and diversity of today's global enterprise, they all would have been extremely proud of everything GE Healthcare had accomplished and its vision for the future.

Even old Tom Edison, himself, would have been impressed by the imagination on display everyday throughout GE Healthcare.

Sources

In addition to the sources directly credited in the narrative, a variety of others have been researched for the materials used in compiling this work.

Books

Gorowitz, B and G Wise, editors-in-chief, *The General Electric Story 1876–1986*, Hall of History, 1981, 2nd edition (Oct 1989).

Gurda, J, *The Making of Milwaukee*, Milwaukee County Historical Society, 1999.

Liebhafsky, HA, *William David Coolidge, A Centenarian and His Work*, John Wiley & Sons, 1974.

Linton, OW, *The World of Stanford Radiology, 1902–2006*, Board of Trustees of the Leland Stanford Junior University, 2006.

Welch, Jack, with John A. Byrne, *JACK: Straight from the Gut*, Warner Business Books, 2001.

Journal articles

Angus, WM, A commentary on the development of diagnostic imaging technology, RadioGraphics, Vol. 9, No. 6, 1225–1244, November, 1989

Boesch, C, Nobel prizes for nuclear magnetic resonance: 2003 and historical perspectives, Journal of Magnetic Resonance Imaging, Vol. 20, No. 2, 1177–1179), May, 2004

Bottomley, PA, The development of high-field NMR imaging: 0.12 T to 1.5 T. In: Grant DM, Harris RK, eds. Encyclopedia of NMR. Chichester: Wiley, 1995.

Bradley, WG, The Nobel prize: Three investigators allowed but two were chosen, Journal of Magnetic Resonance Imaging, Vol. 20, No. 2, 180, May, 2004

DiSantis, DJ and DM DiSantis, Radiologic History Exhibit. Wrong turns on radiology's road of progress, RadioGraphics, Vol. 11, No. 6, 1121–1138, November, 1991

Dümmling, K, 10 years computed tomography—a retrospective view, Electromedica, 13–27, 52 (1984) No. 1

Feldman, AA, Sketch of the technical history of radiology from 1896 to 1920, RadioGraphics, Vol. 9, No. 6, 1113–1128, November, 1989

Friedland, GW and BD Thurber, The birth of CT, American Journal of Roentgenology, Vol. 167, 1365–1370, December, 1996

Graham, LS, JG Kereiakes, C Harris, and MB Cohen, Nuclear medicine from Becquerel to the present, RadioGraphics, Vol. 9, No. 6, 1189–1202, November, 1989

Hendee, WR, Cross sectional medical imaging: A history, RadioGraphics, Vol. 9, No. 6, 1155–1180, November, 1989

Knight, N, Seventy-five years of the RSNA, approaching a century of radiology: Museum and information resources, RadioGraphics, Vol. 9, No. 6, 1101–1111, November, 1989

Krohmer. JS, Radiography and fluoroscopy, 1920 to the present, RadioGraphics, Vol. 9, No. 6, 1129–1153, November, 1989

Partain, CL, The 2003 Nobel prize for MRI: Significance and impact, Journal of Magnetic Resonance Imaging, Vol. 20, No. 2, 173–174, May, 2004

Patton, DD, Roentgen and the "new light"—Roentgen's moment of discovery. Part 2: The first glimmer of the "new light," Investigative Radiology, Vol. 28, No. 1, 51–58, January, 1993

Robb, WL, Revolution in diagnostic imaging technology is expected to continue unabated in 1980s, FAH Review, 24–26, September/October, 1980

Young, IR, Significant events in the development of MRI, Journal of Magnetic Resonance Imaging, Vol. 20, No. 2, 183–186, May, 2004

GE and predecessor organization publications

IDEAS (monthly publication for employees, distributors, and dealers of the Victor X-Ray Corporation Export Department/General Electric X-Ray Corporation Export Department/General Electric

Medical Products Company), various editions

VICTOR X-Ogram (Victor X-ray Corporation employee publication), various editions

GEXCO NEWS (in-house employee publication of GE X-Ray Corporation), various editions

GEXTRA NEWS (employee publication of GE X-Ray Department), various editions

MEDICAL SYSTEMS NEWS (employee publication of GE Medical Systems), various editions

GEMS WORLD (quarterly newspaper for international employees of GE Medical Systems), various editions

Various GE Medical Systems/GE Healthcare marketing communications materials, executive presentations, etc.

General Electric Company Annual Reports (1976–2008)

Formal, recorded interviews

Michael J. Barber, Waukesha, Wisconsin, March 17, 2009
S. Morry Blumenfeld, Milwaukee, Wisconsin, June 14, 2002
Sir William M. Castell, via telephone, December 18, 2008
Ram Charan, via telephone, August 3, 2008
Chih Chen, Crotonville, New York, October 16, 2008
Michael J. Cudahy, Milwaukee, Wisconsin, October 22, 2008
Richard di Benedetto, via telephone, May 15, 2009
Burton P. Drayer, M.D., via telephone, April 6, 2009
Thomas E. Dunham, via telephone, October 2, 2008
Lewis S. Edelheit, Milwaukee, Wisconsin, June 14, 2002
Thomas F. Frist, Jr., via telephone, May 13, 2009
Yoshiaki Fujimori, Crotonville, New York, October 15, 2008
S. Sam Gambhir, M.D., Ph.D., via telephone, April 13, 2009
Reinaldo A. Garcia, Crotonville, New York, October 16, 2008
Gary M. Glazer, M.D., via telephone, April 7, 2009
L.B. "Buzz" Hardy, Waukesha, Wisconsin, August 9, 2007
Joseph M. Hogan, Waukesha, Wisconsin, August 23, 2008
Hedvig Hricak, M.D., via telephone, March 18, 2009

Jeffrey R. Immelt, New York, New York, August 12, 2008
S. Omar Ishrak, Wauwatosa, Wisconsin, September 25, 2008
Michael A. Jones, Crotonville, New York, October 16, 2008
Alfred S. LeBlang, Milwaukee, Wisconsin, June 14, 2002
Alexander R. Margulis, M.D., via telephone, May 11, 2009
Diane P. Mellor, Waukesha, Wisconsin, October 22, 2008
James W. Nelson, Jr., Milwaukee, Wisconsin, June 14, 2002
Marc Onetto, via telephone, November 26, 2008
Vivek Paul, via telephone, May 8, 2008
Marc Pelon, Villers sur Mer, France, September 5, 2008
E. James Potchen, M.D., via telephone, April 2, 2009
Carl E. Ravin, M.D., via telephone, April 22, 2009
Walter L. Robb, Milwaukee, Wisconsin, June 14, 2002
Noel M. Tichy, via telephone, May 7, 2009
John M. Trani, Farmington, Connecticut, July 14, 2008
Mark L. Vachon, Waukesha, Wisconsin, October 21, 2008
Edward F. Voboril, via telephone, December 2, 2008
Vishal K. Wanchoo, Crotonville, New York, October 15, 2008

Other
Photographs were generously provided in conjunction with many of these formal interviews.

Personal reminisces and materials from dozens of people who participated directly in the events described.

Waukesha Freeman for permission to use copyrighted material.

Scores of on-line sources accessed through the worldwide web.

Additional photo captions
page 2: GE Healthcare's Research Park facility in Wauwatosa, Wisconsin. Ultrasound, Diagnostic Cardiology & Interventional Systems, plus the headquarters of Healthcare Systems are located here.
page 6: A GE R&F table from the 1960's. Radiologists viewed the fluoroscopic image via mirror optics.
page 8: A technician assembling the electronics for an implantable General Electric cardiac pacemaker inside a sterile cabinet.
page 10: GE magnetic resonance imaging products cover the full range of technologies and clinical applications.
page 196: General Electric's innovative Vscan portable ultrasound scanner—an ultrasmart, ultra-small imager for primary care physicians.
page 200: Victor X-Ray's remarkably varied line of healthcare products included Type "DRX" quartz lamps used to treat certain skin disorders.

Index